MODERN THEORIES OF
INTEGRATION

Craig Benham

MODERN THEORIES OF
INTEGRATION

BY

H. KESTELMAN, M.Sc.

READER IN MATHEMATICS
UNIVERSITY COLLEGE
LONDON

SECOND REVISED EDITION

DOVER PUBLICATIONS, INC.

NEW YORK

Manufactured in the United States of America

Dover Publications, Inc.
180 Varick Street
New York 14, N.Y.

PREFACE TO DOVER EDITION

THE Dover edition of *Modern Theories of Integration* differs from the original edition in having added to it

(1) a chapter on Riemann-Stieltjes Integration, and
(2) a substantial collection of exercises for the reader covering most of the topics dealt with in the text.

The treatment of (1) is deliberately elementary. Riemann-Stieltjes integration has elementary and basic applications in analysis which are not illuminated by a generalised treatment. There are indeed many books now available in which integration and measure are, with advantage, treated in great generality; but the present text retains its elementary and concrete character.

The exercises are in approximately the same order as the subject matter in the text. It is hoped that these exercises will enhance the value of the book both to students and to instructors. Whereas some of the exercises are theorems intended to supplement the text, most of them are questions of a straightforward character which have been set at London University B.Sc. degree examinations. For permission to reproduce these we are indebted to the Senate of the University of London.

It has not been practicable to alter the set-theoretic notation of the original edition to make it accord with current usage; the principal differences are noted on page x.

OCTOBER, 1959   H. K.

UNIVERSITY COLLEGE, LONDON

PREFACE TO FIRST EDITION

ALTHOUGH Lebesgue integration is now well established as an indispensable part of the theory of functions, its treatment in English text-books remains unsatisfactory and apparently uninfluenced by the simplifications due to the work of C. Carathéodory. The account of the Lebesgue integral which is developed in this book follows the lines of C. Carathéodory's *Vorlesungen über reelle Funktionen*, being based on the geometric approach which identifies the problem of integration with that of measuring sets of points. An important advantage of this method is that it makes the discussion of integrals of functions of several variables no more difficult than that for functions of a single variable. The chapter on Riemann integration has two main aims: to establish conditions in which the Riemann integral exists, and to discuss its relation to standard problems such as the integration of derivatives and the integration of limit functions in general. For many purposes of analysis the Cauchy-Riemann integral is quite sufficient; but to appreciate the circumstances in which it is not sufficient is to understand more clearly the peculiar achievement of the Lebesgue integral. The geometric aspect of Riemann integration is discussed in the last section of Chapter II (appeals to geometric *intuition* have been carefully avoided in all the proofs), and the few theorems on Jordan content which are given there will enable the reader to compare Riemann and Lebesgue integrals from the measure-theory point of view; many of the characteristic differences between the two integrals are best understood by this comparison. In Chapter IX we consider some extensions of the Lebesgue integral, these being restricted to the single line of development from the Cauchy-Lebesgue to the general Denjoy integral. The account given of the Denjoy integral is derived from a recent paper of P. Romanovski in which the usual rather complicated treatment of the integral is replaced by something altogether simpler, and the need for transfinite numbers is at the same time avoided. The Perron integral, which is a development of integration theory regarded as the inverse to differentiation, is not discussed at all, and the reader may be referred to S. Saks's *Théorie de l'intégrale* for a thorough treatment of this as well as of other modern problems of integration. Chapter X, on Fourier series, has been included largely in order to illustrate the application of Lebesgue theory to a branch of analysis where it has proved to be of the greatest importance; the reader who is interested in a systematic study of the subject may regard this chapter as an introduction to A. Zygmund's *Trigonometrical Series*.

The book is intended primarily for students who have covered the ground of G. H. Hardy's *Pure Mathematics*, and no other special knowledge is assumed. The text has been written so as to be of service to readers who are not following courses of lectures on the subject, and it is hoped that the numerous cross-references in the proofs will be of special assistance to such readers.

In addition to the works of G. H. Hardy, C. Carathéodory, and S. Saks already mentioned, the volumes of *Fundamenta Mathematicae* have been an invaluable source of information and of simplification: in particular, the contributions of S. Banach, S. Saks, and W. Sierpiński.

Finally I must express the greatest debt of all to my teacher and colleague Dr. T. Estermann. My own labours in the production of this book have been a continuation of his original plan to present a concise and accurate introduction to the theory of Lebesgue integration based on post-graduate lectures which he had given at University College, London. The notes of these lectures, which Dr. Estermann has so generously placed at my disposal, have been incorporated in this book and form its essential nucleus. More than this, Dr. Estermann has read the manuscript of the book, criticized it, and collaborated with me at every stage for its improvement. For his unstinted personal assistance and for his constant encouragement I wish here to thank him and to express my indebtedness. I am also grateful to Professor E. C. Titchmarsh for reading the manuscript and for his suggestions.

H. K.

UNIVERSITY COLLEGE, LONDON

CONTENTS

I. SETS OF POINTS 1
   § 1. Real numbers 1
   § 2. Sets of points 2
   § 3. Equivalence of aggregates 8
   § 4. Metrical properties of R_n 13
   § 5. The Selection Axiom 28
   § 6. General Principle of Convergence in R_n . . . 29

II. RIEMANN INTEGRATION 30
   § 1. Functions defined in a set of points . . . 30
   § 2. Definition of Riemann integral 32
   § 3. Conditions for a function to be integrable-R . . 36
   § 4. Properties of the Riemann integral . . . 42
   § 5. Riemann integration of derivatives . . . 46
   § 6. Riemann integration of limit functions . . . 50
   § 7. Cauchy-Riemann integral 54
   § 8. Geometric interpretation of Riemann integration . . 55

III. LEBESGUE MEASURE 67
   § 1. Exterior Lebesgue measure 67
   § 2. Measurable sets 70
   § 3. Interior Lebesgue measure 80
   § 4. Linear transformations 87
   § 5. Non-measurable sets 89

IV. SETS OF ORDINATES AND MEASURABLE FUNCTIONS 92
   § 1. Sets of ordinates 92
   § 2. Cylinder sets 94
   § 3. Measurable functions 96
   § 4. Lusin's theorem 109

V. LEBESGUE INTEGRAL OF A NON-NEGATIVE FUNCTION 113

VI. LEBESGUE INTEGRALS OF FUNCTIONS WHICH ARE
   SOMETIMES NEGATIVE 128
   § 1. Real functions 128
   § 2. Complex functions 156

VII. FUNCTIONS OF A SINGLE VARIABLE . . . 161
   § 1. Miscellaneous theorems: integration by parts, second mean-value theorem, differentiation under the integral sign . 161
   § 2. Derivative of a Lebesgue integral . . . 172
   § 3. Summability of derivatives 174
   § 4. Bounded variation and absolute continuity . . 184
   § 5. Integration by substitution 192
   § 6. Appendix to § 3 199

VIII. EVALUATION OF DOUBLE INTEGRALS . . . 202

IX. EXTENSIONS OF THE LEBESGUE INTEGRAL . . 213
 § 1. Holder-Lebesgue integral 213
 § 2. General Denjoy integral 217

X. FOURIER SERIES 228
 § 1. Introduction 228
 § 2. Convergence tests 232
 § 3. Summability $(C, 1)$ of Fourier series . . . 240
 § 4. Integration of Fourier series 241
 § 5. Trigonometric and Fourier series. . . . 243

XI. RIEMANN-STIELTJES INTEGRATION . . . 247
 § 1. Introduction 247
 § 2. The Riemann-Stieltjes integral 248
 § 3. Properties of the Riemann-Stieltjes integral . . 251
 § 4. Applications of Stieltjes integration . . . 262
 § 5. Riesz's theorem 265

EXERCISES 270
BIBLIOGRAPHY 303
INDEX OF DEFINITIONS AND SYMBOLS . . . 304
GENERAL INDEX 306
INDEX TO THE EXERCISES 309

SET-THEORY NOTATION

The principal differences between the notation in the text and that in current use are noted below. The intersection AB is now usually denoted by $A \cap B$ and ΠA_r by $\bigcap_r A_r$. Similarly $A + B$ and $A + B$ may be denoted by $A \cup B$ and $\sum_r A_r$ by $\bigcup_r A_r$. The symbol $\overline{A}$ is now generally used to denote the closure of A, i.e. $A \cup A'$ (denoted in the text by A^c [def.20]); the complement of A (denoted in the text by $\overline{A}$) is then denoted by $C(A)$.

I

SETS OF POINTS

§ 1. Real numbers

THE real numbers, as defined in Hardy, Chapter I, have the property that, if x is any real number, then there are others, say y and z, such that $y < x < z$. We shall call such numbers *finite real numbers* to distinguish them from the numbers ∞ and $-\infty$ which we now introduce; the term 'real number' will then be used in an extended sense so that it may also denote ∞ or $-\infty$. The introduction of these symbols as real numbers, and the conventions which are chosen to govern their relations with other real numbers, are justified largely on the grounds of expediency. There are certain propositions, for example

(A) a_n tends to infinity as n tends to infinity,

and

(B) $\sum\limits_{r=1}^{\infty} b_r$ diverges to plus infinity,

which continually occur in the analysis of finite real numbers and whose meaning may be made precise in terms of such numbers; thus (A) means that to every integer s there is a positive integer $r(s)$ such that $a_n > s$ whenever $n > r(s)$, while (B) means that, if $S_n = \sum\limits_{r=1}^{n} b_r$, then S_n tends to infinity as n tends to infinity. It is convenient to replace (A) by the equation

(A') $\lim\limits_{n\to\infty} a_n = \infty$,

and (B) by the equation

(B') $\sum\limits_{r=1}^{\infty} b_r = \infty$;

for, in addition to the economy of the notation, this convention permits considerable formal simplification when enunciating general theorems. Thus, when (A') and (B') are admitted, we may say that every increasing sequence of finite real numbers tends to a limit, and that every infinite series of positive terms has a sum. Similar and obvious definitions will give the meaning of

$$\lim\limits_{n\to\infty} a_n = -\infty \quad \text{and} \quad \sum\limits_{r=1}^{\infty} b_r = -\infty.$$

It is also convenient to say that the upper bound of an aggregate of real numbers unbounded above is ∞, and that the lower bound of an aggregate of real numbers unbounded below is $-\infty$. The conventions defining the use of ∞ and $-\infty$ in combination with real numbers by the symbols

$$+, \ -, \ \times, \ \div, \ <, \ >$$

are as follows:

If a is any finite real number, then

$$-\infty < a < \infty, \qquad \infty > a > -\infty,$$

$$a+\infty = \infty+a = a-(-\infty) = \infty-a = \infty,$$

$$a-\infty = a+(-\infty) = -\infty+a = -\infty-a = -\infty,$$

$$\frac{a}{\infty} = 0,$$

$$\frac{\infty}{a} = \infty \times a = a \times \infty = \begin{cases} \infty & \text{if } a > 0 \\ -\infty & \text{if } a < 0; \end{cases}$$

further,

$$\infty \times \infty = (-\infty) \times (-\infty) = \infty+\infty = \infty-(-\infty) = \infty,$$

$$\infty \times (-\infty) = (-\infty) \times (\infty) = -\infty-\infty = -\infty.$$

The following combinations remain meaningless, and are therefore not admissible:

$$\infty+(-\infty), \quad -\infty+\infty, \quad \infty-\infty, \quad (-\infty)-(-\infty), \quad 0\times\infty, \quad \infty\times 0,$$

$$\frac{a}{0}, \ \frac{\infty}{0}, \ \frac{-\infty}{0}, \ \frac{\infty}{\infty}, \ \frac{-\infty}{\infty}, \ \frac{\infty}{-\infty}, \ \frac{-\infty}{-\infty}.$$

We could of course assign meanings to these symbols, but, for the general purposes of analysis, no convenience would result; thus $\dfrac{\infty}{\infty}$ is declared meaningless, because statements about finite real numbers which such a combination might reasonably be expected to represent may have several meanings; for example, each of the functions

$$2n/n, \quad n/n^2, \quad n^2/n$$

tends to a different limit as n tends to infinity, and hence no economy would result from expressing their limits by the symbol $\dfrac{\infty}{\infty}$.

Use of ϵ, δ, x, and y: *Whenever ϵ, δ, x, or y (with or without a suffix) is used to denote a real number, the following convention is to be observed:*

x and y stand for finite numbers;

ϵ and δ stand for positive finite numbers.

§ 2. Sets of points

This chapter is mainly concerned with some of the definitions and elementary theorems of the theory of aggregates: more particularly with the theory of sets of points in so far as it is needed for a study of the Lebesgue integral. To present the foundations of the theory of aggregates in a rigorous manner is beyond the scope of this book; the reader who is interested in the basic concepts of this theory is referred to *Einleitung in die Mengenlehre* by A. Fraenkel, where the difficulties of this branch of mathematics and the controversies to which they have given rise are discussed in detail. The difficulties which appear when the concept of 'set' is examined critically belong properly to the study of the foundations of mathematics, and, for the purpose of this book, the reader need not probe them too deeply. (See also § 5 of this chapter.)

Roughly speaking, an aggregate α consists of certain objects, and corresponds to our ordinary notion of a collection; α is defined when we have indicated, by some formula, or by some distinguishing property, which objects are included in α and which are not. Thus, we speak of the aggregate of all even integers, or of the aggregate of all rational numbers, or of the aggregate of the pairs of real numbers (x, y) which satisfy $x^2 + y^2 = 1$.

Definition 1. If α is an aggregate and P is a member, or *element*, of α, we say P *belongs* to α, and write $P \in \alpha$; if P is an object which is not an element of α, we write $P \bar{\in} \alpha$.

There is a point of distinction between the ordinary use of the word '*collection*' and our use of the word '*aggregate*' which the reader should note carefully: we might say, for example, that the letters which spell the word 'noon' form a collection which has four members, namely the letters n and o each taken twice; however, the *aggregate* of the letters in the word '*noon*' has just two members, the letters n and o. Thus 'multiplicity' is not a character of the elements of an aggregate: for our purpose we need only know of any given object whether it belongs to the aggregate in question, or not.

Definition 2. An *n-dimensional point* is given by n finite real numbers $x_1, x_2, ..., x_n$ (its *coordinates*), and is denoted by $(x_1, x_2, ..., x_n)$. The integer n being fixed, the aggregate of all n-dimensional points is called the *n-dimensional space* and is denoted by R_n. A point is called *rational* if *all* its coordinates are rational; the point with all its coordinates zero is called the *origin*. If P is the point $(x_1, x_2, ..., x_{n-1})$, then (P, x_n) denotes the point $(x_1, x_2, ..., x_n)$.

Definition 3. We shall often use the symbol '&' to combine propositions as an abbreviation for the word 'and': thus if A and B

are propositions, then to assert A & B is to assert both A and B, while to deny A & B is to deny either A, or B, or both.

'A *implies* B' means 'If A is true, then so is B'; for example, the proposition

$$'x^2+y^2 < 1 \ \& \ y > 0 \quad \text{implies} \quad f(x,y) > 0'$$

means that, if $x^2+y^2 < 1$ and $y > 0$, then $f(x,y) > 0$. It will be noticed that the symbol '&' binds propositions more closely than does 'implies'.

Definition 4. An aggregate whose members are points of R_n is called a *set of points in* R_n, and may consist of all, or some, or none of the points of R_n. In the last case, the set is said to be *empty*, and is denoted by 0 (confusion of this symbol 0 with the number 0 will be excluded by the context). Similarly any aggregate which has no members, for example the aggregate of the integers n satisfying $n^2 = 2$, is said to be empty. The set of all the points of R_n which satisfy a given condition C is denoted by

$$\mathscr{S}(P; \ P \text{ satisfies } C),$$

the integer n being implied in the context. Thus

$$\mathscr{S}((x,y); \ y > 0)$$

denotes the set of all points (x,y) for which $y > 0$, and similarly, $\mathscr{S}((P,y); \ y > 0)$, where P denotes a typical point of R_n, denotes the set of all points $(x_1, x_2, ..., x_{n+1})$ for which $x_{n+1} > 0$.

Unless otherwise stated, the word 'set' will be used to denote a set of points in R_n for some positive integer n. Sets in R_1 are called *linear* sets, and sets in R_2 are called *plane* sets. It is convenient, in practice, to denote the point (x) of R_1 by the real number x; on the other hand, an aggregate of finite real numbers is often identified with the linear set of points having those numbers for coordinates. It is also convenient to represent the points of R_1 by the geometrical points of a straight line, and those of R_2 by the geometrical points of a plane. To represent the points of R_1, a directed straight line is chosen, one of its points is taken for origin, and then, a unit of measurement having been chosen, we assign to the point x of R_1 the geometrical point of the line whose 'algebraic distance' from the origin is x. Similarly, to represent the points of R_2, a plane is chosen and in it a set of rectangular Cartesian axes; the point (x_1, x_2) of R_2 is then represented by the geometrical point of the plane whose coordinates are (x_1, x_2) in the usual notation of analytical geometry.

This physical representation is very useful; it often happens, especially with general theorems on sets in R_n, that the idea behind a proof is simple and is easily grasped by the imagination in terms of visual images, whereas to express it accurately requires so many symbols as to end by obscuring itself; in such cases, the language of analytical geometry may be best suited to suggest economies in the form of proof. Naturally, suggestions from these sources must be tested to ensure that they can be transformed into logical statements derivable from the system of axioms proper to the subject. The reader should note that sets which can be represented by the same set of geometrical points are not necessarily identical; for example, $\mathscr{S}((x_1, x_2); x_2 = 0)$ is not identical with R_1, although both sets may be represented on the x-axis in a Cartesian plane.

Definition 5. If $a_1 < b_1$, $a_2 < b_2$,..., $a_n < b_n$, and the numbers a_1, b_1,..., a_n, b_n are *all finite*, the set of all those points $(x_1, x_2,..., x_n)$ for which
$$a_r < x_r < b_r \quad (r = 1, 2,..., n)$$
is called an *interval*, and the set of those for which
$$a_r \leqslant x_r \leqslant b_r \quad (r = 1, 2,..., n)$$
is called a *closed interval*. (The term 'closed' is later used in a more precise sense (def. 21), but there is no inconsistency (th. 21).) The point
$$\left(\frac{a_1+b_1}{2}, \frac{a_2+b_2}{2},..., \frac{a_n+b_n}{2}\right)$$
is said to be the *centre* of both the interval and the closed interval. The interval is said to be *rational* if all the numbers a_1, b_1,..., a_n, b_n are rational. If $n \geqslant 2$ and
$$b_1 - a_1 = b_2 - a_2 = ... = b_n - a_n = \sigma,$$
the interval is said to be a *cube* of side σ. If a and b are real numbers and $a < b$, then

(a, b) denotes the linear set $\mathscr{S}(x; a < x < b)$;

if a and b are both finite and $a < b$, then clearly (a, b) is an interval, and in this case

$[a, b]$ denotes the closed interval $\mathscr{S}(x; a \leqslant x \leqslant b)$;

a and b are called the *end-points* of (a, b) and of $[a, b]$.

The reader will easily see that intervals in R_1 are represented by segments of a straight line, and those in R_2 by rectangles whose sides are parallel to the axes of coordinates.

Definition 6. If α and β are aggregates and

$$P \in \alpha \quad \text{implies} \quad P \in \beta,$$

we say that α is a *sub-aggregate* of β, or α is *contained* in β, $(\alpha \subset \beta)$, or β contains α, $(\beta \supset \alpha)$. If $\alpha \subset \beta$ & $\beta \subset \alpha$, α and β are said to be *equal* $(\alpha = \beta)$; otherwise the aggregates are unequal $(\alpha \neq \beta)$. When the aggregates are sets, the sub-aggregates are called *subsets*; clearly, for every set S, $0 \subset S$ & $S \subset S$.

Definition 7. The aggregate of the elements common to two aggregates α and β is denoted by $\alpha\beta$; if $\alpha\beta = 0$, α and β are said to be *mutually exclusive*. If A and B are sets in the same space, AB denotes the set of all the points common to A and B: in symbols,

$$AB = \mathscr{S}(P;\ P \in A\ \&\ P \in B);$$

AB is called the *intersection* of A and B. If k is a positive integer and $A_1, A_2, ..., A_k$ are sets in the same space, we write

$$A_1 A_2 ... A_k, \text{ or } \prod_{r=1}^{k} A_r, \text{ for the set } \mathscr{S}(P;\ P \in A_r \quad (r = 1, 2, ..., k)).$$

Again, if to every positive integer r there is a set A_r in R_n, the intersection of the sets A_r is defined as

$$\mathscr{S}(P;\ P \in A_r \quad (r = 1, 2, ...)), \text{ denoted by } \prod_{r=1}^{\infty} A_r \text{ or by } A_1 A_2 ....$$

More generally, if α is an aggregate of sets of points in R_n, the set of the points common to all the members of α is called the intersection of the members of α.

Examples.

(i) If $A_r = \mathscr{S}\left((x_1, x_2);\ 0 < x_1^2 + x_2^2 < \dfrac{1}{r}\right)$, then $\prod_{r=1}^{\infty} A_r = 0$.

(ii) If $A_r = \mathscr{S}((x_1, x_2);\ 0 \leqslant x_1^2 + x_2^2 \leqslant r)$, then $\prod_{r=1}^{\infty} A_r$ consists of the 'circle' $x_1^2 + x_2^2 = 1$ together with its interior, i.e.

$$\mathscr{S}((x_1, x_2);\ 0 \leqslant x_1^2 + x_2^2 \leqslant 1).$$

Definition 8. If k is a positive integer and $S_1, S_2, ..., S_k$ are sets in the same space, their *union* is defined as the set of all points which belong to *at least one* of the sets $S_1, S_2, ..., S_k$, and is denoted by

$$S_1 \dotplus S_2 \dotplus ... \dotplus S_k \quad \text{or by} \quad \sum_{r=1}^{k}{}^* S_r;$$

if and only if the sets are mutually exclusive, their union may be called their *sum*, which may then be denoted by

$$S_1 + S_2 + ... + S_k \quad \text{or by} \quad \sum_{r=1}^{k} S_r.$$

Again, if to every positive integer r there is a set S_r in R_n, the union of the sets S_r is defined as the set of all the points P which satisfy the relation $P \in S_r$ for *at least one* positive integer r; the union is denoted by

$$S_1 \dot{+} S_2 \dot{+} \ldots \quad \text{or by} \quad \sum_{r=1}^{\infty *} S_r;$$

if and only if the sets S_r are mutually exclusive, their union may be called their sum, denoted by

$$S_1 + S_2 + \ldots \quad \text{or by} \quad \sum_{r=1}^{\infty} S_r.$$

Similar conventions define the meanings of

$$\sum_{r=1}^{k *} \alpha_r, \quad \sum_{r=1}^{k} \alpha_r, \quad \sum_{r=1}^{\infty *} \alpha_r, \quad \text{and} \quad \sum_{r=1}^{\infty} \alpha_r,$$

when the α_r are aggregates which are not sets of points. Also, if α is an aggregate of aggregates, then the *union of the members of* α is defined as the aggregate of all objects which belong to at least one of the members of α; as before, the term 'sum' may replace 'union' if and only if the aggregates are mutually exclusive.

Examples.

(i) If α consists of the numbers 1, 2, 3, 4, and β consists of the numbers 3, 4, 5, 6, then $\alpha \dot{+} \beta$ consists of the numbers 1, 2, 3, 4, 5, 6; thus, to form $\alpha \dot{+} \beta$ we add to β only those elements of α which are not already in β.

(ii) If α_r is the aggregate of all the positive rational numbers $\dfrac{m}{n}$ (where m and n are integers having no common divisor) such that $m + n = r$, then $\sum_{r=2}^{\infty} \alpha_r$ is the aggregate of all positive rational numbers.

(iii) If $S_r = \mathscr{S}((x_1, x_2); r-1 \leqslant x_1^2 + x_2^2 \leqslant r)$, then $\sum_{r=1}^{\infty *} S_r = R_2$; note that $\sum_{r=1}^{\infty} S_r$ is not defined.

(iv) If $S_r = \mathscr{S}(x; r-1 \leqslant |x| < r)$, then $\sum_{r=1}^{\infty} S_r = R_1$.

Definition 9. If $\beta \subset \alpha$, the *difference* $\alpha - \beta$ is defined as the aggregate of those elements of α which do not belong to β. Thus if A and B are sets and $A \supset B$, then

$$A - B = \mathscr{S}(P; P \in A \ \& \ P \bar{\in} B).$$

If $A \subset R_n$, then

$R_n - A$ is called the *complement* of A, and is denoted by $\bar{A}$.

Theorem 1 summarizes a number of formulae which are constantly being used to manipulate equations relating sets in the same space; they are immediate consequences of the definitions, and their proof is left to the reader.

Theorem 1.

(i) *If* $A = \bar{B}$, *then* $\bar{A} = B$;

(ii) $A - AB = A\bar{B}$;

(iii) $A \dotplus B = A + B\bar{A}$;

(iv) *if* $C \subset B$, *then* $A(B-C) = AB - AC$;

(v) $A \sum\limits_{r=1}^{k}{}^{*} B_r = \sum\limits_{r=1}^{k}{}^{*} AB_r$; $A \sum\limits_{r=1}^{\infty}{}^{*} B_r = \sum\limits_{r=1}^{\infty}{}^{*} AB_r$;

(vi) *if* $A = \prod\limits_{r=1}^{k} B_r$, *then* $\bar{A} = \sum\limits_{r=1}^{k}{}^{*} \bar{B}_r$; *if* $A = \prod\limits_{r=1}^{\infty} B_r$, *then* $\bar{A} = \sum\limits_{r=1}^{\infty}{}^{*} \bar{B}_r$;

(vii) *if* $A = \sum\limits_{r=1}^{k}{}^{*} B_r$, *then* $\bar{A} = \prod\limits_{r=1}^{k} \bar{B}_r$; *if* $A = \sum\limits_{r=1}^{\infty}{}^{*} B_r$, *then* $\bar{A} = \prod\limits_{r=1}^{\infty} \bar{B}_r$.

(In (v), (vi), and (vii), k denotes a positive integer.)

§ 3. Equivalence of Aggregates

Given two collections of physical objects, we can always find out whether they have an equal number of members; broadly speaking, there are two methods: the usual one of counting, and the more primitive one of pairing off the members of the two collections with a view to exhausting them simultaneously. For example, to discover whether there are as many persons as chairs in a room, we may count the number of persons and then the number of chairs; alternatively, we may invite the persons to sit down, one in a chair; if no person is left standing and no chair is left empty, we conclude that there are as many persons as chairs. Thus, to deduce the equality, we need not know how many members there are in each collection: in fact the conclusion does not depend on counting. The same two methods are, of course, available for the comparison of any two aggregates of mathematical objects which are finite in number, but what is their application to aggregates which are not finite? Will they enable us to compare the aggregate of all positive integers with the aggregate of all rational numbers, or with the aggregate of all real numbers? The theorems which follow will make it clear that merely to characterize all such aggregates as 'infinite' is to overlook essential distinctions among them. Now counting, as we ordinarily know it, is clearly not applicable to 'infinite' aggregates, and so we turn to the notion of pairing, or, more technically, to the notion of one–one correspondence. This idea, as we shall see, not only enables the problem of the comparison of aggregates to be clearly formulated, but also suggests simple arguments which reveal important differences among infinite aggregates.

Definition 10. Two aggregates α and β are said to be *equivalent* $(\alpha \sim \beta)$ if a one–one correspondence between their members is possible; more precisely, if there exists a function $F(x)$, defined for every element x of β, such that

   (i) if $b \in \beta$, then $F(b) \in \alpha$,

and

   (ii) if $a \in \alpha$, then there is one and only one member b of β, such that $F(b) = a$.

(The term 'function' is here used in a generalized sense, in which neither the independent nor the dependent variable need be a number.)

For example, if β is the interval $(0, 1)$ and α the interval $(0, 2)$, the function $F(x) = 2x$ effects a correspondence which shows that $\alpha \sim \beta$.

We first classify aggregates according to their relation to the aggregate of all positive integers.

Definition 11. If m is a non-negative integer, the aggregate of all positive integers not exceeding m is said to be a *section* of the positive integers.

Definition 12. An aggregate is called *finite* if it is equivalent to a section of the positive integers; otherwise it is called *infinite*.

Definition 13. An aggregate which is equivalent to the aggregate of all positive integers is said to be *enumerable*; more precisely, 'α is enumerable' means that there exists a function $F(n)$, defined for *every* positive integer n, such that

   (i) if n is a positive integer, then $F(n) \in \alpha$,

and

   (ii) if $a \in \alpha$, then there is *just one* positive integer n, such that $F(n) = a$.

For example, the aggregate of all even positive integers is enumerable ($F(n) = 2n$); the aggregate of all odd positive integers is enumerable ($F(n) = 2n-1$). There are, however, infinite aggregates which are not enumerable; in particular, the set of the points of a closed interval is non-enumerable (ths. 21 and 37.1).

Definition 14. If a_n is defined, not necessarily as a number, for *every* positive integer n, we speak of the *sequence* a_1, a_2,... and denote it by $\{a_n\}$. The objects a_n are not necessarily different for different values of n, but it is essential in our definition that a_n should be defined for *every* positive integer n. For example, if $a_n = (-1)^n$, the *aggregate* of all the terms of the sequence $\{a_n\}$ consists of two members, viz. 1 and -1. If m_1, m_2,... is an increasing sequence of positive integers, then

$$a_{m_1}, a_{m_2},... \text{ is said to be a } \textit{sub-sequence} \text{ of } \{a_n\}.$$

In ths. 2 and 6 we state two of the most important properties of enumerable aggregates.

Theorem 2. *Any sub-aggregate of an enumerable aggregate is finite or enumerable.*

Proof. If α is an enumerable aggregate and $\beta \subset \alpha$, then α is equivalent to the aggregate of all positive integers, and β is therefore equivalent to *an* aggregate of positive integers. Hence it is sufficient to prove that any infinite aggregate of positive integers is enumerable. Let γ be such an aggregate, and define $f(n)$ for every member n of γ as the number of members of γ which do not exceed n. If n_1 and n_2 belong to γ and $n_1 < n_2$, then clearly

$$(1) \qquad 0 < f(n_2)-f(n_1) = \sigma(n_1, n_2),$$

where $\sigma(n_1, n_2)$ is the number of members n of γ such that $n_1 < n \leqslant n_2$. So, to prove that γ is enumerable, we have only to show that, as n runs through γ, $f(n)$ runs through all positive integers. Suppose, if possible, that m is the least positive integer not assumed by $f(n)$. If ν is the least member of γ, then $f(\nu) = 1$; hence

$$m > 1, \text{ and } m-1 = f(n_1) \text{ say};$$

since γ is infinite, it will have members which exceed n_1: let n_2 be the least of these; then

$$n_1 < n_2 \quad \& \quad \sigma(n_1, n_2) = 1,$$

and so, by (1),

$$f(n_2) = \sigma(n_1, n_2)+f(n_1) = m,$$

which contradicts the definition of m. Hence $f(n)$ runs through all positive integers, and this completes the proof.

Theorem 3. *If α is an enumerable aggregate and β is equivalent to a sub-aggregate of α, then β is finite or enumerable.*

Proof. By th. 2 and def. 13.

Theorem 4. *Let α be the aggregate of all the terms of a sequence $\{a_n\}$; then α is enumerable or finite.*

Proof. Assign to each member P of α the least integer n for which $a_n = P$; then α is equivalent to the aggregate β consisting of the integers assigned to members of α. By th. 2, β is finite or enumerable, and so, by th. 3, α is finite or enumerable.

Theorem 5. *The aggregate π of all pairs of positive integers is enumerable.*

Proof. (The idea of the proof is to represent the members of π as the terms of a sequence. The first step is to express π as a sum of finite aggregates: let π_2 consist of $(1,1)$ alone, π_3 of $(1,2)$ and $(2,1)$, π_4 of $(1,3)$, $(2,2)$, $(3,1)$, and, more generally, let π_n be the aggregate of the members (m,r) of π for which $m+r = n$, arranged so that (m,r) is the mth member of π_{m+r}. If the sub-aggregates π_r are then arranged so that all the members of π_r precede all those of π_{r+1}, an arrangement of all the members of π is thereby effected so that they form a sequence of which (m,r) is the

$$\left\{m + \sum_{s=2}^{m+r-1} (s-1)\right\}\text{th, i.e. the } \{\tfrac{1}{2}(m+r-2)(m+r-1)+m\}\text{th}$$

term. This suggests a precise function with which to show that π is equivalent to the aggregate of all positive integers.)

Let

(1) $\qquad F(m,r) = \tfrac{1}{2}(m+r-2)(m+r-1)+m.$

Clearly

$\qquad$ if $(m,r) \in \pi$, then $F(m,r)$ is a positive integer.

Now let n be any chosen positive integer; we have to show that there is *just one* member (m,r) of π such that

(2) $\qquad n = \tfrac{1}{2}(m+r-1)(m+r-2)+m.$

If m and r are positive integers satisfying (2), then

$\tfrac{1}{2}(m+r-1)(m+r-2) < n \leqslant \tfrac{1}{2}(m+r-1)(m+r-2)+m+r-1$
$\qquad = \tfrac{1}{2}(m+r-1)(m+r),$

which means that $m+r$ is the unique integer p such that

$$\tfrac{1}{2}(p-1)(p-2) < n \leqslant \tfrac{1}{2}p(p-1) \quad \& \quad p \geqslant 2;$$

hence, if we put

$$m = n - \tfrac{1}{2}(p-1)(p-2) \quad \& \quad r = p-m,$$

it follows that m and r are positive integers and are unique in satisfying (2).

Theorem 6. *Let α be a finite or an enumerable aggregate whose members are themselves finite or enumerable aggregates; then the union of the members of α is finite or enumerable.*

Proof. The idea of the proof is to set up a 1–1 correspondence between the union in question and a certain aggregate of pairs of positive integers.

The members of α may be denoted by α_r, where r runs through all positive integers or through a section; put $\beta_1 = \alpha_1$, and for each of the remaining aggregates α_r let

$$\beta_r = \alpha_r - \alpha_r \sum_{s=1}^{r-1}{}^* \alpha_s.$$

Then γ, the *union* of the members of α, is the *sum* of the aggregates β_r; hence, if P is any chosen member of γ, there is a unique positive integer r for which $P \in \beta_r$. Now, by th. 2, β_r is finite or enumerable, and so there is a 1–1 correspondence, say Γ_r, between the members of β_r and a certain aggregate of positive integers; suppose m is the positive integer assigned to P by Γ_r, and let us now assign to the member P of γ the pair of positive integers (m, r). Since to different members of γ are assigned different pairs of positive integers, this effects a 1–1 correspondence between the members of γ and a certain aggregate of pairs of positive integers; hence, by ths. 5 and 3, γ is finite or enumerable.

Theorem 7. *The aggregate of all rational numbers is enumerable.*

Proof. Let α_1 be the aggregate of all positive, α_2 that of all negative rational numbers, and let α_3 consist of the number 0 alone. Since every member of α_1 can be expressed in one and only one way in the form r/m, where r and m are positive integers prime to one another, α_1 is equivalent to the aggregate of all pairs of positive integers (m, r) for which m and r are prime to each other. Hence, by ths. 5 and 3, α_1 is enumerable, as it is obviously not finite. Similarly α_2 is enumerable, and α_3 is finite. Hence, by th. 6, $\alpha_1 + \alpha_2 + \alpha_3$ is enumerable.

Theorem 8. *The set of all the rational points of R_n is enumerable.*

Proof. The case $n = 1$ is equivalent to th. 7; hence, by the principle of induction, it is sufficient to prove the theorem for every n greater than 1 for which the set of the rational points of R_{n-1} is enumerable. Now, in this case, there is a 1–1 correspondence between the rational points P of R_{n-1} and the positive integers m; also, by th. 7, there is a 1–1 correspondence between the rational numbers x_n and the positive integers r. Hence there is a 1–1 correspondence between the pairs (P, x_n) and the pairs (m, r), and so (ths. 5 and 3) the aggregate of the pairs (P, x_n) is enumerable, which gives the required result by def. 2.

Theorem 9. *Every aggregate of rational points of R_n is finite or enumerable.*

Proof. By ths. 8 and 2.

Theorem 10. *The aggregate of all rational intervals in R_n is enumerable.*

Proof. The correspondence between the interval given by

$$a_r < x_r < b_r \quad (r = 1, 2, ..., n)$$

and the point $(a_1, b_1, a_2, b_2, ..., a_n, b_n)$ of R_{2n}

shows that the aggregate in question is equivalent to a set of rational points of R_{2n}, and hence (ths. 9 and 3) it is enumerable since it is obviously not finite.

Theorem 11. *Let α be an aggregate of mutually exclusive intervals in R_n; then α is finite or enumerable.*

Proof. By th. 8 there is a sequence $P_1, P_2, ...$ consisting of all the rational points of R_n. Assign to every member U of α the least integer m for which $P_m \in U$. Since the members of α are mutually exclusive intervals, this defines a 1–1 correspondence between α and an aggregate of positive integers, and hence (th. 3) α is finite or enumerable.

§ 4. Metrical Properties of R_n

We now consider what may be called the metrical properties of the space R_n.

Definition 15. If P and Q are the points

$$(x_1, x_2, ..., x_n), \qquad (y_1, y_2, ..., y_n),$$

the *distance* between P and Q, denoted by dist(P, Q), is defined as

$$\sqrt{\left\{\sum_{r=1}^{n}(x_r-y_r)^2\right\}}.$$

The next theorem is the analogue, in R_n, of the well-known theorem of plane geometry that two sides of a triangle are together greater than the third.

Theorem 12. *Let A, B, C, be any points of R_n; then*

$$\text{dist}(A, B)+\text{dist}(B, C) \geqslant \text{dist}(A, C).$$

Proof. Let $(a_1, a_2,..., a_n)$, $(b_1, b_2,..., b_n)$, $(c_1, c_2,..., c_n)$ be the points A, B, C respectively; if we put

$$\xi_r = b_r-a_r \quad \text{and} \quad \eta_r = c_r-b_r,$$

we have to show

(1) $$\sqrt{\left(\sum_r \xi_r^2\right)}+\sqrt{\left(\sum_r \eta_r^2\right)} \geqslant \sqrt{\left\{\sum_r (\xi_r+\eta_r)^2\right\}},$$

where r runs from 1 to n.

Now

$$\left\{\sqrt{\left(\sum_r \xi_r^2\right)}+\sqrt{\left(\sum_r \eta_r^2\right)}\right\}^2 = \sum_r \xi_r^2+ \sum_r \eta_r^2+2\sqrt{\left(\sum_r \xi_r^2 \sum_r \eta_r^2\right)};$$

hence, if s runs from 1 to n, we may replace

$$\sum_r \xi_r^2 \sum_r \eta_r^2 \quad \text{by} \quad \sum_{r,s} \xi_r^2 \eta_s^2,$$

and obtain

(2) $$\left\{\sqrt{\left(\sum_r \xi_r^2\right)}+\sqrt{\left(\sum_r \eta_r^2\right)}\right\}^2 = \sum_r (\xi_r+\eta_r)^2+2\left\{\sqrt{\left(\sum_{r,s} \xi_r^2 \eta_s^2\right)}- \sum_r \xi_r \eta_r\right\}.$$

Now

$$2\sum_{r,s} \xi_r^2 \eta_s^2 = \sum_{r,s} (\xi_r^2 \eta_s^2+\xi_s^2 \eta_r^2) = \sum_{r,s} (\xi_r \eta_s-\xi_s \eta_r)^2+2\sum_{r,s} \xi_r \eta_r \xi_s \eta_s$$

$$= \sum_{r,s} (\xi_r \eta_s-\xi_s \eta_r)^2+2\left\{\sum_r \xi_r \eta_r\right\}^2;$$

hence $$\sqrt{\left(\sum_{r,s} \xi_r^2 \eta_s^2\right)} \geqslant \sum_r \xi_r \eta_r,$$

which, by (2), gives (1).

Definition 16. If $Q \in R_n$ and ρ is any finite positive number, the set

$$\mathscr{S}(P; \text{dist}(P, Q) < \rho)$$

is called the *sphere* about Q of radius ρ, and Q is called the *centre* of the sphere.

A set is said to be *bounded* if there is a sphere which contains it, and a sequence of points of R_n is said to be bounded if the set of its points is bounded.

Theorem 13. *Let P be a point of R_n; then*

(i) *every sphere about P contains a rational interval including P;*

(ii) *every sphere about P contains a closed interval centre P (a cube centre P if $n \geqslant 2$);*

(iii) *every interval including P contains a sphere about P;*

(iv) *every sphere including P contains a sphere about P.*

Proof. Suppose $P = (\xi_1, \xi_2, ..., \xi_n)$ and let U denote a sphere about P of radius ρ. To every integer r from 1 to n choose numbers a_r and b_r, such that

$$a_r \text{ and } b_r \text{ are rational} \quad \& \quad \xi_n - \frac{\rho}{\sqrt{n}} < a_r < \xi_r < b_r < \xi_r + \frac{\rho}{\sqrt{n}},$$

and let I be the rational interval given by

$$a_r < x_r < b_r \qquad (r = 1, 2, ..., n);$$

then $\qquad\qquad Q \in I \quad$ implies $\quad \mathrm{dist}(P, Q) < \rho$,

and hence $I \subset U$, proving (i).

Similarly, the closed interval (a cube if $n \geqslant 2$) given by

$$\xi_r - \frac{\rho}{2\sqrt{n}} \leqslant x_r \leqslant \xi_r + \frac{\rho}{2\sqrt{n}} \quad (r = 1, 2, ..., n)$$

is contained in U and has its centre at P. To prove (iii), let I be any interval including P and suppose I is given by

$$a_r < x_r < b_r \qquad (r = 1, 2, ..., n).$$

Let ρ be the least of the $2n$ numbers

$$\xi_1 - a_1, \xi_2 - a_2, ..., \xi_n - a_n, \qquad b_1 - \xi_1, b_2 - \xi_2, ..., b_n - \xi_n,$$

which are all positive, and let U be the sphere about P of radius ρ. Let Q be any point of U; if $Q = (x_1, x_2, ..., x_n)$, then

$$\sum_{r=1}^{n} (x_r - \xi_r)^2 < \rho^2, \quad \text{which implies} \quad |x_r - \xi_r| < \rho \quad (r = 1, 2, ..., n).$$

Hence, by the definition of ρ, it follows that

$$x_r > a_r \quad \& \quad x_r < b_r \quad (r = 1, 2, ..., n),$$

which means that $Q \in I$; hence $U \subset I$, proving (iii). Finally, to prove (iv), let A be the centre of a sphere U of radius ρ which includes P.

By th. 12, if Q is any point such that

$$\text{dist}(Q, P) < \rho - \text{dist}(P, A),$$

then $\text{dist}(Q, A) \leqslant \text{dist}(Q, P) + \text{dist}(P, A) < \rho,$

which means that $Q \in U$; hence the sphere about P of radius $\{\rho - \text{dist}(P, A)\}$ is contained in U.

Definition 17. The point P is said to be *interior* to the set S if there is a sphere about P every point of which belongs to S. The set of all the points interior to S is called *the interior* of S and is denoted by S^o.

Definition 18. If all the points of a set are interior to it, the set is called *open*; the empty set is also called open.

Theorem 14. *Every interval in R_n is open, and every sphere in R_n is open.*

Proof. By th. 13 (iii) and (iv) and def. 17.

Theorem 15. *The interior of any set S is open.*

Proof. Let P be any point of S^o (def. 17); then S contains a sphere U about P. U being open (th. 14), every point of U is interior to U and therefore to S which contains U. Hence $U \subset S^o$, which means that P is an interior point of S^o, and so S^o is open.

Theorem 16. *Any union of open sets is open.*

Proof. Let α be an aggregate of open sets and U the union of the members of α. If $P \in U$, there is a member S of α which includes P; since S is open, it contains a sphere about P, and this sphere must be contained in U; hence P is interior to U.

Theorem 17. *The intersection of a* finite *number of open sets is open.*

Proof. Let A_1, $A_2,..., A_k$ be open sets and let $A = \prod_{r=1}^{k} A_r$; the theorem being trivial if $A = 0$, suppose $P \in A$. Then to every integer r from 1 to k there is a sphere U_r about P contained in A_r. Let ρ_r be the radius of U_r, and let ρ be the least of the numbers $\rho_1, \rho_2,..., \rho_k$; then U, the sphere about P of radius ρ, is contained in U_r and therefore in A_r for $r = 1, 2,..., k$. Hence $U \subset A$ and so $P \in A^o$.

The word 'finite' is essential in th. 17; for suppose A_r is the interval $\left(-\dfrac{1}{r}, \dfrac{1}{r}\right)$; then A_r is open for every positive integer r, but $\prod_{r=1}^{\infty} A_r$ consists of the origin alone and is therefore not open.

Theorem 18. *Let S be a non-empty open set; then there is a sequence $\{I_r\}$, consisting of all the rational intervals contained in S, such that*
$$S = \sum_{r=1}^{\infty}{}^* I_r.$$

Proof. By ths. 10 and 2, the aggregate of the rational intervals contained in S is enumerable, for it is obviously not finite, and so these intervals can be arranged in a sequence $\{I_r\}$. Clearly $S \supset \sum_{r=1}^{\infty}{}^* I_r$; on the other hand, if $P \in S$, there is a sphere about P contained in S, and therefore (th. 13 (i)) a rational interval including P and contained in S, which implies $S \subset \sum_{r=1}^{\infty}{}^* I_r$; hence $S = \sum_{r=1}^{\infty}{}^* I_r$.

Theorem 19. *Let U be a bounded open linear set; then U is the sum of the members of a finite or enumerable aggregate of intervals, the end points of which belong to $\bar{U}$.*

Proof. Let α be the aggregate of all intervals (λ, μ) such that

(1) $\qquad\qquad (\lambda, \mu) \subset U \quad \& \quad \lambda \in \bar{U} \quad \& \quad \mu \in \bar{U}.$

By (1) the members of α are mutually exclusive, and so (th. 11) α is finite or enumerable. Since every member of α is contained in U, it remains only to show that if $\xi \in U$, then there is a member of α which includes ξ. Let m be the upper bound of the aggregate β which consists of all numbers x such that

$$x < \xi \quad \& \quad x \in \bar{U},$$

and let M be the lower bound of the aggregate of all numbers y such that
$$y > \xi \quad \& \quad y \in \bar{U}.$$

Since U is bounded, β is not empty, and since U is open, it follows that $m \in \bar{U}$ & $m < \xi$; hence $(m, \xi) \subset U$ & $m \in \bar{U}$, and, similarly, $(\xi, M) \subset U$ & $M \in \bar{U}$. Since $\xi \in U$, this means that (m, M) is a member of α which includes ξ.

The restriction of th. 19 to linear sets is essential; the reader will readily see, for example, that the plane set consisting of the interior of a circle cannot be expressed as the sum of a finite number, or of a sequence, of intervals.

Definition 19. A point P is called a *limiting point* of the set S if every sphere about P includes a point of S other than P. (A limiting point is also sometimes called a *point of accumulation*, Hardy, § 18.)

Example. If S is the linear set consisting of the points $1/r$, where r runs through all positive integers, then the origin is a limiting point of S. Note that a limiting point of S is not necessarily a point of S.

Theorem 20. *Suppose P is a limiting point of S and U is any sphere about P; then the set US is infinite.*

Proof. If possible, suppose U contains only a finite number of points of S other than P, and let ρ be the least of the distances of these points from P; then the sphere about P of radius ρ includes no point of S other than P, which contradicts the definition of P. Hence US is infinite.

Definition 20. The set of all the limiting points of a set S is denoted by S' and is sometimes called the *derived set* of S. The set $S \dotplus S'$, denoted by S^c, is called the *closed envelope* of S.

Definition 21. A set S is said to be

(i)　　　*closed* if $S' \subset S$
　　　　(i.e. a closed set either has no limiting points or includes all its limiting points),

(ii)　　　*dense in itself* if $S \subset S'$ & $S \neq 0$
　　　　(i.e. S is dense in itself if every point of S is a limiting point of S),

(iii)　　　*perfect* if $S = S' \neq 0$
　　　　(i.e. S is perfect if S is closed and dense in itself).

Examples.

(i) If S is finite, then $S' = 0$ (th. 20), and so S is closed but not dense in itself.

(ii) The set E, consisting of all rational numbers, is dense in itself, but is not closed since every irrational number belongs to E'. It should be noted that E is not open either, since every interval contains points which are not rational; thus a set may be neither open nor closed. The empty set and the set R_n are both open and closed.

Theorem 21. *Every closed interval is perfect.*

Proof. Suppose J is a closed interval given by
$$a_r \leqslant x_r \leqslant b_r \quad (r = 1, 2, ..., n);$$
if possible, suppose $P \in \bar{J}J'$; then, if $P = (\xi_1, \xi_2, ..., \xi_n)$, there is an

integer k among $1, 2, ..., n$ such that

$$\xi_k < a_k \quad \text{or} \quad \xi_k > b_k.$$

Suppose the former is true and put $\epsilon = a_k - \xi_k$; let U be the sphere about P of radius ϵ, and let Q, the point $(x_1, x_2, ..., x_n)$, belong to U; since $\text{dist}(P, Q) < \epsilon$, i.e. $\sum_{r=1}^{n} (x_r - \xi_r)^2 < \epsilon^2$, we have $x_k - \xi_k < \epsilon$, which implies $Q \bar\in J$; but this is impossible, since every sphere about P includes points of J. Similarly, the assumption $\xi_k > b_k$ leads to a contradiction, and so it appears that

$$P \in J' \quad \text{implies} \quad P \in J, \quad \text{i.e. } J \text{ is closed.}$$

To prove $J \subset J'$, let P be any point of J, $P = (\xi_1, \xi_2, ..., \xi_n)$. Let δ be freely chosen; then, since $\xi_1 < b_1$ or $\xi_1 > a_1$, it follows that there is a number ξ_1' such that

$$a_1 \leqslant \xi_1' \leqslant b_1 \quad \& \quad 0 < |\xi_1 - \xi_1'| < \delta.$$

Hence $(\xi_1', \xi_2, ..., \xi_n)$ belongs to J, and its distance from P, being $|\xi_1 - \xi_1'|$, is less than δ. Hence every sphere about P includes a point of J other than P, i.e. $P \in J'$.

Theorem 22. *If S is any set, then S' is closed.*

Proof. Suppose P is a limiting point of S' and let U be any sphere about P; then U includes a point of S', say Q, and so (th. 13 (iv)) U contains a sphere U_1 about Q; since $Q \in S'$, SU_1 is infinite (th. 20), and hence U, which contains U_1, includes points of S other than P, which means $P \in S'$.

Theorem 23. *Let C be a closed set and P a point such that every sphere about P includes at least one point of C; then $P \in C$.*

Proof. Suppose $P \bar\in C$; then, by hypothesis, every sphere about P includes a point of C other than P, which means $P \in C'$. Since C is closed, this implies $P \in C$, which contradicts the assumption $P \bar\in C$.

Theorem 24. *Let S be any set; then S^c, i.e. $S \dotplus S'$, is closed.*

Proof. Suppose P is a limiting point of S^c. If every sphere about P includes points of S, then $P \in S$ and/or $P \in S'$, i.e. $P \in S^c$; otherwise there is a sphere U about P such that $SU = 0$, and so, since every sphere about P includes points of S^c, it follows that every sphere about P includes points of S', and this, by ths. 22 and 23, means that $P \in S'$

Theorem 24.1. *Let S be any set; then*

(i) *S^o contains every open subset of S;*

(ii) *every closed set containing S also contains S^c.*

Proof. Suppose U is an open subset of S; if $P \in U$, then P is the centre of a sphere which is contained in U and therefore in S, and hence $P \in S^o$; this proves (i).

Suppose F is a closed set which contains S; then we have

$$S \subset F \quad \& \quad S' \subset F' \subset F,$$

from which $\qquad\qquad S^c = S \dotplus S' \subset F,$

and this proves (ii).

Theorem 25. *Let C be a closed set; then $\bar{C}$ is open.*

Proof. Suppose $P \in \bar{C}$; we have to show that there is a sphere about P which is contained in $\bar{C}$. Now if this is not so, every sphere about P includes a point of C, and this, by th. 23, implies $P \in C$, contrary to hypothesis.

Definition 22. Let C be a closed *linear* set contained in I, an interval (a,b), or in $[a,b]$, and such that $I\bar{C} \neq 0$; then $I\bar{C}$ is a bounded, non-empty, open linear set (ths. 25 and 17), and can therefore be expressed as the sum of the members of a finite or enumerable aggregate of intervals whose end points (with the possible exceptions of a and b) belong to C (th. 19); this aggregate of intervals is sometimes known as the aggregate of the *intervals of I contiguous to C.*

Theorem 26. *Let U be an open set; then $\bar{U}$ is closed.*

Proof. Suppose P is a limiting point of $\bar{U}$; then every sphere about P includes a point of $\bar{U}$, and hence P is not interior to U. Since U is open, this implies $P \,\bar{\in}\, U$, i.e. $P \in \bar{U}$.

Theorem 27. *Any intersection of closed sets is closed.*

Proof. Let β be an aggregate of closed sets, C their intersection, and U the union of their complements. Since U is open (ths. 25 and 16), $\bar{U}$ is closed (th. 26); it remains to show that $C = \bar{U}$. If $P \in \bar{U}$, then P belongs to every member of β, and so $P \in C$; on the other hand, if $P \in C$, then P does not belong to any of the sets which are complements of members of β, which means $P \,\bar{\in}\, U$, i.e. $P \in \bar{U}$.

Theorem 28. *The union of a finite number of closed sets is closed.*

Proof. Let $C_1, C_2,..., C_k$ be closed sets and put $C = \sum_{r=1}^{k}* C_r$; by th. 1

$$\bar{C} = \prod_{r=1}^{k} \bar{C}_r,$$

and so, by ths. 25 and 17, $\bar{C}$ is open; hence C is closed (th. 26).

The word 'finite' is essential to th. 28, just as it is to th. 17, of which it is obviously a dual; for example, if

$$C_r \text{ is the closed interval} \left[\frac{1}{r+1}, 1\right],$$

then $\quad \sum_{r=1}^{\infty}* C_r \text{ is } \mathscr{S}(x; 0 < x \leqslant 1),$

which is not closed, since the origin is one of its limiting points.

Definition 23. The sequence $\{P_r\}$, where P_r is the point

$$(x_{1,r}, x_{2,r},..., x_{n,r}),$$

is said to be *convergent* if each of the n sequences

$$x_{s,1}, x_{s,2},... \quad (s = 1, 2,..., n)$$

is convergent; if

$$x_s = \lim_{r\to\infty} x_{s,r} \quad (s = 1, 2,..., n) \quad \& \quad P = (x_1, x_2,..., x_n),$$

then P is called the *limit* of the sequence $\{P_r\}$, and is written

$$P = \lim_{r\to\infty} P_r.$$

Theorem 29. $P = \lim_{r\to\infty} P_r$ *if and only if* $\lim_{r\to\infty} \text{dist}(P, P_r) = 0.$

Proof. Let $\{P_r\}$ be a sequence of points of R_n, and suppose

$$P_r = (x_{1,r}, x_{2,r},..., x_{n,r}) \quad (r = 1, 2,...).$$

To prove the condition necessary, suppose

$$P = \lim_{r\to\infty} P_r \quad \& \quad P = (x_1, x_2,..., x_n), \quad \text{i.e.}$$

(1) $\qquad x_s = \lim_{r\to\infty} x_{s,r} \quad (s = 1, 2,..., n).$

Choose ϵ freely; by (1) there are numbers $\mu_1, \mu_2,..., \mu_n$ such that

$$r > \mu_s \text{ implies } |x_s - x_{s,r}| < \frac{\epsilon}{\sqrt{n}} \quad (s = 1, 2,..., n);$$

hence, if $\qquad \mu = \max(\mu_1, \mu_2,..., \mu_n),$

then $r > \mu$ implies $|x_s - x_{s,r}| < \dfrac{\epsilon}{\sqrt{n}}$ $(s = 1, 2, ..., n);$

hence $r > \mu$ implies $\mathrm{dist}(P, P_r) < \epsilon,$

and this, since ϵ is arbitrary, means $\lim\limits_{r\to\infty} \mathrm{dist}(P, P_r) = 0.$

     Conversely, suppose only that

$$\lim_{r\to\infty} \mathrm{dist}(P, P_r) = 0;$$

choose ϵ freely, and then a number μ such that

$$r > \mu \quad \text{implies} \quad \mathrm{dist}(P, P_r) < \epsilon;$$

by def. 15, it then follows that

$$r > \mu \quad \text{implies} \quad |x_s - x_{s,r}| < \epsilon \quad (s = 1, 2, ..., n),$$

which, since ϵ is arbitrary, means

$$x_s = \lim_{r\to\infty} x_{s,r} \quad (s = 1, 2, ..., n), \quad \text{i.e.} \quad P = \lim_{r\to\infty} P_r.$$

Theorem 30. *Suppose* $\lim\limits_{r\to\infty} P_r = P$ *and* $\{m_s\}$ *is an increasing sequence of positive integers; then* $\lim\limits_{s\to\infty} P_{m_s} = P.$

Proof. Choose ϵ freely; by hypothesis and th. 29, μ exists so that

$$r > \mu \quad \text{implies} \quad \mathrm{dist}(P, P_r) < \epsilon,$$

and since obviously $m_s \geqslant s$, it follows that

$$s > \mu \quad \text{implies} \quad \mathrm{dist}(P, P_{m_s}) < \epsilon;$$

ϵ being arbitrary, this means

$$\lim_{s\to\infty} \mathrm{dist}(P, P_{m_s}) = 0,$$

and so (th. 29) $\lim\limits_{s\to\infty} P_{m_s} = P.$

Theorem 31. *Let* $\{a_r\}$ *be a bounded sequence of real numbers; then* $\{a_r\}$ *contains a convergent sub-sequence.*

Proof. Let α_1 be the aggregate of the numbers $a_1, a_2, ...,$ and g_1 its upper bound; let n_1 be the least integer n satisfying

$$0 \leqslant g_1 - a_n < 1.$$

Let α_2 be the aggregate of the numbers a_r having $r > n_1$, and let g_2 be the upper bound of α_2; let n_2 be the least integer n satisfying

$$0 \leqslant g_2 - a_n < \tfrac{1}{2} \quad \& \quad n > n_1.$$

More generally, suppose $a_{n_1}, a_{n_2}, ..., a_{n_{k-1}}$ are defined and let α_k be the aggregate of the numbers a_r having $r > n_{k-1}$; let g_k be the upper bound of α_k, and n_k the least integer n satisfying

(1)
$$0 \leqslant g_k - a_n < \frac{1}{k} \quad \& \quad n > n_{k-1}.$$

Clearly $\quad \alpha_1 \supset \alpha_2 \supset ...,\quad$ and so $\quad g_1 \geqslant g_2 \geqslant ...;$

the sequence of numbers g_n being bounded and non-increasing tends to a finite limit, say g, and by (1)

$$n_1 < n_2 < ... \quad \& \quad \lim_{k \to \infty} a_{n_k} = g;$$

hence the sequence $a_{n_1}, a_{n_2},...$ satisfies the conditions of the theorem.

Theorem 32. *Any bounded sequence of points of R_n contains a convergent sub-sequence.*

Proof. The case $n = 1$ is equivalent to th. 31; hence, by the principle of induction, it is sufficient to prove the result for every n greater than 1 for which the corresponding result holds with $n-1$ instead of n. Suppose n is such a number and $\{P_r\}$ is a bounded sequence of points of R_n. Let

$$P_r = (x_{1,r}, x_{2,r},...,x_{n,r}) \quad \& \quad P'_r = (x_{1,r}, x_{2,r},...,x_{n-1,r});$$

then $\{P'_r\}$ is a bounded sequence of points of R_{n-1} and must therefore contain a convergent sub-sequence $P'_{m_1}, P'_{m_2},...$. Put

$$P'_{m_r} = Q_r \quad \text{and} \quad x_{n,m_r} = \xi_r;$$

then $\{\xi_r\}$ is a bounded sequence, and so, by th. 31, contains a convergent sub-sequence $\xi_{r_1}, \xi_{r_2},...$; also, by th. 30, the sequence $Q_{r_1}, Q_{r_2},...$ converges. Put $m_{r_s} = h_s$; then

$$\xi_{r_s} = x_{n,h_s} \quad \& \quad Q_{r_s} = P'_{h_s}$$

Hence the sequences $P'_{h_1}, P'_{h_2},...$ and $x_{n,h_1}, x_{n,h_2},...$ converge, which means that the sequence $P_{h_1}, P_{h_2},...$ converges.

Theorem 33. *The limit of a convergent sequence of distinct points is a limiting point of their set.*

Proof. Let $\{P_r\}$ be a sequence of distinct points and S their set. Suppose

$$P = \lim_{r \to \infty} P_r, \quad \text{i.e. (th. 29)} \quad \lim_{r \to \infty} \text{dist}(P, P_r) = 0;$$

choose ϵ freely and then a number μ such that

$$\text{dist}(P, P_r) < \epsilon \quad (r = \mu, \mu+1).$$

Since at least one of the points P_μ, $P_{\mu+1}$ differs from P, this means that the sphere about P of radius ϵ includes a point of S other than P; ϵ being arbitrary, this implies $P \in S'$.

Theorem 34 (WEIERSTRASS). *Let S be a bounded infinite set of points; then $S' \neq 0$.*

Proof. Since S is infinite, it follows (see also § 5) that S contains a sequence of distinct points, and this sequence, being bounded, contains a convergent sub-sequence (th. 32); the limit of the latter is, by th. 33, a limiting point of a subset of S and therefore belongs to S'.

The word 'bounded' is essential to th. 34, for if S is the set of all integers, then S is infinite, but $S' = 0$.

Theorem 35. *Suppose $P = \lim\limits_{r \to \infty} P_r$ and C is a closed set such that $P_r \in C$ for infinitely many values of r; then $P \in C$.*

Proof. Choose ϵ freely and let U be the sphere about P of radius ϵ; by th. 29, m exists such that

$$n > m \quad \text{implies} \quad P_n \in U,$$

and since $P_r \in C$ for values of r exceeding m, it follows that U includes points of C. Since ϵ is arbitrary and C is closed, it follows from th. 23 that $P \in C$.

Theorem 36 (CANTOR). *Let $\{C_r\}$ be a sequence of bounded non-empty closed sets such that $C_1 \supset C_2 \supset \ldots$; then $\prod\limits_{r=1}^{\infty} C_r \neq 0$.*

Proof. For every positive integer r let P_r be a point chosen from C_r (since C_r is closed and bounded, it is easily seen that P_r may be precisely defined in terms of C_r: for example, if C_r is linear, we may (by th. 35) take P_r to be the number ξ_r which is the upper bound of the numbers x belonging to C_r). Since $\{P_r\}$ is contained in C_1, it is bounded; hence, by th. 32, there is an increasing sequence of positive integers $\{r_n\}$ such that the sequence $P_{r_1}, P_{r_2}, \ldots$ converges to some limit P. Let m be any chosen positive integer; then

$$r \geqslant m \quad \text{implies} \quad P_r \in C_m,$$

and, since $r_s \geqslant s$,

$$s \geqslant m \quad \text{implies} \quad P_{r_s} \in C_m;$$

hence, by th. 35, $P \in C_m$. This being true for every positive integer m, we have

$$P \in \prod_{r=1}^{\infty} C_r.$$

The words 'closed' and 'bounded' are both essential to th. 36, as the following examples show.

(i) Let $C_r = \mathscr{S}(x; x \geqslant r)$; C_r is closed and $C_1 \supset C_2 \supset C_3 \supset \dots$, but

$$\prod_{r=1}^{\infty} C_r = 0.$$

(ii) Let $S_r = (0, 1/r)$; then $S_1 \supset S_2 \dots$ and the intervals S_r are bounded, but

$$\prod_{r=1}^{\infty} S_r = 0.$$

Theorem 37 (BAIRE). *Let C be a non-empty closed set which is the union of a sequence of closed sets $\{C_n\}$; then there is a closed cube K (a closed interval if $C \subset R_1$) whose centre belongs to C, and a positive integer n such that $CK \subset C_n$.*

Proof. Suppose the theorem is false; to prove the truth of the theorem it will be sufficient to show that this assumption implies the existence of a sequence of closed intervals $\{J_r\}$ such that

(1) $J_{n+1} \subset J_n$ & $CJ_n \neq 0$ & $J_n C_n = 0$ $(n = 1, 2,\dots)$,

for, if (1) holds and we put $S = \prod_{n=1}^{\infty} CJ_n$, it follows from ths. 27 and 36 that $0 \neq S \subset C$, and at the same time $SC_n = 0$ $(n = 1, 2,\dots)$, which contradicts the hypothesis $C = C_1 + C_2 + \dots$.

To define $\{J_r\}$, let α be the aggregate of closed rational intervals J such that $CJ^o \neq 0$. By ths. 10 and 2, α is enumerable and its members may be arranged in a sequence σ: $\Delta_1, \Delta_2,\dots$. If J is a member of σ and n is any positive integer, it follows easily (since the theorem is assumed false) that J^o includes at least one point of $C - C_n$, say P. Since C_n is closed, J^o contains a sphere in $\bar{C}_n$ centre P, and consequently J^o contains members of σ in $\bar{C}_n$; these form a sub-sequence of σ, and we shall denote the first member of this sub-sequence by $f_n(J)$. We now put

$$J_1 = f_1(\Delta_1) \quad \text{and} \quad J_{n+1} = f_{n+1}(J_n) \quad (n = 1, 2,\dots);$$

the sequence $\{J_r\}$ clearly satisfies (1).

Theorem 37.1. *Let E be an enumerable closed set; then E is not perfect.*

Proof. Let $P_1, P_2,\dots$, denote the members of E and let C_r be the set whose only member is P_r. By th. 37 there is a closed cube K, whose centre belongs to E, and a positive integer n such that $KE \subset C_n$; this means that P_n is the centre of K and is the only point of E which belongs to K; hence (th. 13 (iii)) P_n is the centre of a sphere which includes just one point of E. This means that P_n is a point of E which is not a limiting point of E, and hence E is not perfect.

Theorem 38. *Let C be a closed bounded set, and let $\{U_r\}$ be a sequence of open sets such that $C \subset \sum\limits_{r=1}^{\infty}* U_r$; then there is an integer k such that $C \subset \sum\limits_{r=1}^{k}* U_r$.*

Proof. For every positive integer r, let $B_r = \sum\limits_{s=1}^{r}* U_s$; then B_r is open and $\bar{B}_r$ closed (ths. 16 and 26). Put $C_r = C\bar{B}_r$; then C_r is closed (th. 27) and bounded (like C), and $C_1 \supset C_2 \supset \dots$. Hence, by th. 36, if $C_r \neq 0$ for every positive integer r, then $\prod\limits_{r=1}^{\infty} C_r \neq 0$. But, by th. 1, $\prod\limits_{r=1}^{\infty} C_r$ is the intersection of C and the complement of $\sum\limits_{r=1}^{\infty}* B_r$, and this intersection must be empty since $C \subset \sum\limits_{r=1}^{\infty}* U_r$. Hence there is an integer k such that $C_k = 0$, which means that

$$C \subset B_k = \sum\limits_{r=1}^{k}* U_r.$$

Definition 24. An aggregate α of sets of points is said to *cover* a set S, if S is contained in the union of the members of α.

Theorem 39 (LINDELÖF). *Let α be a non-empty aggregate of open sets covering a set S; then there is a sequence, $\{U_r\}$, of members of α, such that $S \subset \sum\limits_{r=1}^{\infty}* U_r$.*

Proof. Let β be the aggregate of all rational intervals contained in members of α; by th. 18, β covers S, and, by ths. 10 and 2, β is finite or enumerable. Let us consider the non-trivial case, $S \neq 0$; then β cannot be finite, and so we may suppose that $I_1, I_2, \dots$ are the members of β. Now I_1 is contained in a member of α, say U_1; I_2 is contained in a member of α, say U_2, and so on. Since β covers S, this means $S \subset \sum\limits_{r=1}^{\infty}* U_r$. (See also § 5, where a similar application of the 'Selection Axiom' is explained in detail.)

Theorem 40 (HEINE-BOREL). *If an aggregate α of open sets covers a closed bounded set C, then there is a finite sub-aggregate of α which* *covers C; i.e. there are sets* U_1, U_2,..., U_k *belonging to* α *such that*

$$C \subset \sum_{r=1}^{k} * \ U_r.$$

Proof. By ths. 39 and 38.

The words 'closed' and 'bounded' are both essential to th. 40, and it is essential that the covering sets should be open; these facts are emphasized by the following examples:

Examples.

(i) Let S be the linear interval $(0, 1)$ and let α be the aggregate of all intervals $(x, 1)$ for which $0 < x < 1$. The members of α are open sets, α covers S, and S is bounded. Since the union of any finite number of intervals $(a_1, 1)$, $(a_2, 1)$,..., $(a_k, 1)$, with $0 < a_r < 1$ $(r = 1, 2,..., k)$, is the interval $(a, 1)$, where a is the least of the numbers a_1, a_2,..., a_k, it follows that no finite sub-aggregate of α covers S.

(ii) Let $S = R_1$ and let α be the aggregate of all linear intervals; then S is closed and is covered by α, which is an aggregate of open sets, but no finite sub-aggregate of α covers S.

(iii) Let S be the linear set of the points x for which

$$x = 0 \quad \text{or} \quad x = \frac{1}{r} \quad (r = 1, 2,...),$$

and let α be the aggregate whose members are the sets $A(x)$, where $x \in S$ and $A(x)$ consists of the point x alone. Then S is closed and bounded, and α covers S, but no finite sub-aggregate of α covers S.

Definition 25. A point P is said to be a *point of condensation* of a set S if every sphere about P contains a non-enumerable subset of S.

Corollary. Every point of condensation of S belongs to S'.

Theorem 40.1. *Let S be a non-enumerable set; then S includes at least one point of condensation of S.*

Proof. Let α be the aggregate of spheres U whose centres belong to S and which are such that US is finite or enumerable. If the theorem is false, it follows from th. 39 that S is covered by a sequence of members of α and consequently that S is the union of a sequence of sets each of which is finite or enumerable; but this implies (th. 6) that S is finite or enumerable and contradicts an assumption of the theorem. Hence the theorem cannot be false.

Corollary. If S is any set, then the set of the points of S which are not limiting points of S is finite or enumerable.

Theorem 40.2 (CANTOR-BENDIXSON). *Every non-enumerable closed set is the sum of a perfect set and one that is finite or enumerable.*

Proof. Let C be a non-enumerable closed set, and let K be the set of all the points of condensation of C; since C is closed, $K \subset C$ (cor. to def. 25), and, by th. 40.1, $C-K$ is finite or enumerable. It remains only to prove that K is perfect, and since K is obviously closed, we have only to show that

$$K \neq 0 \quad \& \quad K \subset K'.$$

Now $K \neq 0$ by th. 40.1, and, if P is any point of K, then every sphere about P contains a non-enumerable subset of S, which subset clearly remains non-enumerable when P is removed from it; hence (th. 40.1), every sphere about P includes a point of K other than P, i.e. $P \in K'$, and this completes the proof.

§ 5. The Selection Axiom

The proofs of several theorems in the preceding sections have depended on the 'existence' of certain aggregates for which no 'constructive' rule was offered. The introduction of these aggregates is legitimized if we admit the following axiom:

Selection Axiom. Let α be an aggregate whose members are aggregates, none of which is empty, and no two of which have an element in common; let β be the sum of the members of α. Then β contains a sub-aggregate γ which has exactly one element in common with every member of α.

It will be noted that the axiom only asserts the *existence* of γ and is not concerned with the problem of how γ may be 'constructed'. The role which this axiom plays in the theory of aggregates is discussed in detail by A. Fraenkel in the work referred to on p. 3, and by W. Sierpiński in *Leçons sur les nombres transfinis*; here we shall content ourselves with a single detailed example of its application, namely to the proof that every infinite set contains a sequence of distinct points, a result that was assumed in th. 34.

Let S be an infinite set. If A is any non-empty subset of S, let $\pi(A)$ denote the aggregate of all pairs

$$(A, a), \text{ where } a \text{ is any member of } A.$$

Let α denote the aggregate of all possible aggregates $\pi(A)$ corresponding to all the subsets A of S. Since the members of α are mutually exclusive, there is, by the Selection Axiom, an aggregate γ, of pairs (A, a), which has just one member in common with each of the aggregates $\pi(A)$ composing α. This means that there exists a function $f(A)$ which assigns to every subset A of S a point belonging to A and denoted by $f(A)$. We now define a sequence of distinct points of S as follows: let $P_1 = f(S)$, and let S_1 be the set of the points of S different from P_1; S_1 is not empty since S is not finite, and so we may define P_2 as $f(S_1)$. More generally, when $P_1, P_2,..., P_n$ are defined, let S_n be the set of the points of S not included among $P_1, P_2,..., P_n$; again, $S_n \neq 0$, and so we may define P_{n+1} as $f(S_n)$. Since $P_{n+1} \in S_n$, it follows from the principle of induction that this defines a sequence of distinct points, $\{P_n\}$, contained in S.

Another detailed example of the use of the Selection Axiom will be found in the proof of th. 130. The axiom is also used implicitly in other existence theorems, e.g. ths. 107, 108, 111, 114, 124, and 174, whose proofs depend on the existence of certain sequences for which no precise rule is given; on the other hand, the exact specification of a sequence is sometimes a detail left to the reader, and its omission in such cases, to avoid burdening the proof, will of course not mean that the Selection Axiom is essential to the argument.

§6. General Principle of Convergence in R_n

Suppose $\{P_j\}$ is a sequence of points in R_n and that for every positive number ϵ there is an integer N such that $\operatorname{dist}(P_N, P_{N+p}) < \epsilon$ for all positive p; then $\{P_j\}$ is convergent.

Proof. Let N_r be the least N such that $\operatorname{dist}(P_N, P_{N+p}) < 2^{-r}$ for all positive p; then $N_1 \leqslant N_2 \leqslant ...$ and $\operatorname{dist}(P_{N_r}, P_{N_{r+1}}) < 2^{-r}$. If $P_j = (x_1^{(j)},..., x_n^{(j)})$, it follows that for each q from 1 to n $x_q^{(N_s)}$ tends to a finite limit, say ξ_q, as $s \to \infty$, and

$$|\xi_q - x_q^{(N_r)}| = |\sum_{s=r}^{\infty} \{x_q^{(N_{s+1})} - x_q^{(N_s)}\}| < \sum_{s=r}^{\infty} 2^{-s} = 2^{1-r}.$$

Let $L = (\xi_1,..., \xi_q)$. For all j exceeding N_r

$$\operatorname{dist}(P_j, P_{N_r}) + \operatorname{dist}(P_{N_r}, L) < 2^{-r} + \sum_{q=1}^{n} |\xi_q - x_q^{(N_r)}| < 2^{-r}(1 + 2n).$$

This implies that $\operatorname{dist}(P_j, L) \to 0$ as $j \to \infty$, i.e. $\{P_j\}$ converges to L.

II

§ 1. Functions defined in a Set of Points

Definition 26. If to every point P of a set S there is a real number $f(P)$, then f is called a *function of P defined in S*. If $P = (x_1, x_2, ..., x_n)$ and F is the function of the n variables $x_1, x_2, ..., x_n$ given by

$$F(x_1, x_2, ..., x_n) = f(P),$$

then we say that the function $F(x_1, x_2, ..., x_n)$ is defined in S and that $f(P)$ is its *corresponding point function*. In Chapter VI the notion of a function of P defined in S is extended so that $f(P)$ is a complex number, but, unless otherwise stated, $f(P)$ will denote a real function.

Definition 27. Let $f(P)$ be defined in S; then $M(f; S)$ and $m(f; S)$ denote respectively the upper and the lower bounds of the aggregate of the values of $f(P)$ when P runs through all points of S. The *oscillation* of $f(P)$ in S is denoted by $\omega(f; S)$, where

$$\omega(f; S) = M(f; S) - m(f; S),$$

whenever the right-hand side is defined.

For example, if

$$f(x) = \begin{cases} 1 \text{ when } x \text{ is rational} \\ 0 \text{ otherwise,} \end{cases}$$

then $\omega(f; I) = 1$ for every linear interval I.

Definition 28. Let $f(P)$ be defined in S and let Q be any point interior to S; let U_ϵ denote a sphere about Q of radius ϵ and contained in S. Now as ϵ decreases, so

$$M(f; U_\epsilon) \text{ decreases (or remains constant); while}$$

$$m(f; U_\epsilon) \text{ increases (or remains constant);}$$

hence we may define $M(f; Q)$, the *maximum of $f(P)$ at Q*, and $m(f; Q)$, the *minimum of $f(P)$ at Q*, by the equations

$$M(f; Q) = \lim_{\epsilon \to 0} M(f; U_\epsilon) \quad \& \quad m(f; Q) = \lim_{\epsilon \to 0} m(f; U_\epsilon).$$

If $f(x)$ is defined in J, a closed interval $[a, b]$, but not outside J, then $M(f; a) = \lim_{\epsilon \to 0} M(f; J U_\epsilon)$; similar definitions give the minimum of $f(x)$ at a and at b.

The *oscillation of* $f(P)$ *at* Q, denoted by $\omega(f; Q)$, is defined by

$$\omega(f; Q) = M(f; Q) - m(f; Q)$$

whenever the right-hand side exists.

Example. Let

$$f(x) = \begin{cases} 0 & \text{if } \quad x = 0 \\ \sin\dfrac{1}{x} & \text{if } \quad x \neq 0; \end{cases}$$

then $M(f; 0) = 1$, $m(f; 0) = -1$, and $\omega(f; 0) = 2$.

Theorem 41. *Let* $f(P)$ *be defined in a sphere* U *about a point* Q; *then* $\qquad \omega(f; Q) \geqslant \epsilon \quad$ *implies* $\quad \omega(f; U) \geqslant \epsilon.$

Proof. By defs. 27 and 28.

Theorem 42. *Let* $f(x)$ *be defined and bounded in a closed interval* J, *and let* ϵ *be freely chosen; put* $D(\epsilon) = J\mathscr{P}(x; \omega(f; x) \geqslant \epsilon)$; *then* $D(\epsilon)$ *is closed.*

Proof. Suppose $\qquad \xi \in J - D(\epsilon)$;

we shall show that ξ is not a limiting point of $D(\epsilon)$. Suppose

$$\omega(f; \xi) = \eta.$$

Since $\eta < \epsilon$, there is an interval I, centre ξ, such that, if x_1 and x_2 belong to IJ, then $|f(x_1) - f(x_2)| < \frac{1}{2}(\eta + \epsilon) < \epsilon$. Hence $ID(\epsilon) = 0$, which means that ξ is not a limiting point of $D(\epsilon)$. Since every limiting point of $D(\epsilon)$ must clearly belong to J, this proves the theorem.

Definition 29. The function $f(P)$ is said to be *continuous* at Q, if to every ϵ there is a δ such that

$$\text{dist}(P, Q) < \delta \quad \text{implies} \quad |f(P) - f(Q)| < \epsilon;$$

this implies that $f(P)$ is defined in some sphere about Q, and that $f(Q)$ is finite. The function $F(x_1, x_2, ..., x_n)$ is said to be continuous at $(\xi_1, \xi_2, ..., \xi_n)$ if its corresponding point function is continuous at $(\xi_1, \xi_2, ..., \xi_n)$. If $f(x)$ is defined in a closed interval $[a, b]$, then $f(x)$ is said to be *continuous throughout* $[a, b]$ if

(i) $f(x)$ is continuous at every point of (a, b),

(ii) $f(a)$ and $f(b)$ are finite, and

$$\lim_{x \to a+0} f(x) = f(a) \quad \& \quad \lim_{x \to b-0} f(x) = f(b).$$

Examples.

(i) If $f(x,y) = \begin{cases} \dfrac{xy}{x^2+y^2} & \text{when} \quad x^2+y^2 > 0 \\ 0 & \text{when} \quad x = y = 0, \end{cases}$

then $f(x,y)$ is not continuous at the origin since

$$f(0,0) = 0, \quad \text{while} \quad f(x,x) = \tfrac{1}{2} \quad \text{if} \quad x \neq 0.$$

(ii) If $f(x,y) = \begin{cases} \dfrac{xy^2}{x^2+y^2} & \text{when} \quad x^2+y^2 > 0 \\ 0 & \text{when} \quad x = y = 0, \end{cases}$

then $f(x,y)$ is continuous at the origin since

$$|f(x,y)| \leqslant |x|.$$

Theorem 43. *Let $f(P)$ be defined in a sphere about Q; then $f(P)$ is continuous at Q if and only if $\omega(f; Q) = 0$.*

Proof. The necessity of the given condition follows at once from defs. 28 and 29. On the other hand, if $\omega(f; Q) = 0$, then, by def. 28, to every ϵ there is a sphere U (depending on ϵ) about Q such that $M(f; U) - m(f; U) < \epsilon$, and this, by def. 29, implies the continuity of $f(P)$ at Q.

§ 2. The Riemann Integral

Definition 30. Let J denote a closed linear interval $[a,b]$; let N be any finite set of numbers, say $x_0, x_1, ..., x_n$, such that

$$a = x_0 < x_1 < x_2 < ... < x_n = b.$$

Then N is said to be a *net* over J, and the closed intervals $[x_{r-1}, x_r]$ $(r = 1, 2, ..., n)$ are called its *cells*. The *gauge* of N, denoted by $g(N)$, is given by

$$g(N) = \max(x_r - x_{r-1}) \quad (r = 1, 2, ..., n).$$

Definition 31. If the interval I is given by

$$a_r < x_r < b_r \quad (r = 1, 2, ..., n),$$

its *content*, cI, is defined as $\prod\limits_{r=1}^{n} (b_r - a_r)$; cI may also be denoted by $|I|$. If J is a closed linear interval $[a, b]$, then $|J|$ shall denote $b - a$.

The reader will recognize that cI agrees with the usual definitions of length, area, or volume, according as I is an interval of R_1, R_2, or R_3.

Definition 32. Let $f(x)$ be defined and bounded in J, a closed interval $[a, b]$. Let N be any net over J, and let $\delta_1, \delta_2,..., \delta_n$ be its cells; let

$$U(f; N) = \sum_{r=1}^{n} |\delta_r| M(f; \delta_r) \quad \text{and} \quad L(f; N) = \sum_{r=1}^{n} |\delta_r| m(f; \delta_r);$$

then $U(f; N)$ is called an *upper sum*, and $L(f; N)$ a *lower sum* of $f(x)$ over $[a, b]$.

The following theorem follows at once from defs. 32 and 27.

Theorem 44. *Let $f(x)$ be defined and bounded in a closed interval J; let N be any net over J, and $\delta_1, \delta_2,..., \delta_n$ its cells; then*

(i) $U(-f; N) = -L(f; N)$;

(ii) $|J| m(f; J) \leqslant L(f; N) \leqslant U(f; N) \leqslant |J| M(f; J)$;

(iii) $U(f; N) - L(f; N) = \sum_{r=1}^{n} \omega(f; \delta_r) |\delta_r|$.

Definition 33. Let $f(x)$ be defined and bounded in the closed interval $[a, b]$; then the lower bound of the aggregate of all possible upper sums of $f(x)$ over $[a, b]$ is called the *upper Riemann integral* of $f(x)$ over $[a, b]$, denoted by $\int_a^{\overline{b}} f(x)\, dx$; the upper bound of the aggregate of all possible lower sums of $f(x)$ over $[a, b]$ is called the *lower Riemann integral* of $f(x)$ over $[a, b]$, denoted by $\int_{\underline{a}}^{b} f(x)\, dx$; if and only if

$$\int_{\underline{a}}^{b} f(x)\, dx = \int_a^{\overline{b}} f(x)\, dx,$$

their common value is called the *Riemann integral* of $f(x)$ over $[a, b]$, and is denoted by $\int_a^b f(x)\, dx$ (in subsequent chapters, to avoid ambiguity, this integral may be denoted by $(R) \int_a^b f(x)\, dx$); $f(x)$ is then said to be *integrable in the Riemann sense* (*integrable-R*) over $[a, b]$. If $a < b$, then

$$\int_b^a f(x)\, dx = - \int_a^b f(x)\, dx$$

if the right-hand side exists. $\int_a^a f(x)\, dx$ is defined to be zero; $\int_a^b dx$ denotes $\int_a^b 1\, dx$, and $\int_a^b \dfrac{dx}{f(x)}$ denotes $\int_a^b \dfrac{1}{f(x)}\, dx$.

Theorem 45. *Let $f(x)$ be defined and bounded in J, a closed interval $[a, b]$, and let N_1 and N_2 be any nets over J; then*

$$|J|\, m(f; J) \leqslant L(f; N_1) \leqslant \int_{\underline{a}}^{b} f(x)\, dx \leqslant \int_{a}^{\overline{b}} f(x)\, dx$$

$$\leqslant U(f; N_2) \leqslant |J|\, M(f; J).$$

Lemma. If N_1 and N_2 are any two nets over J, then

(1) $L(f; N_1) \leqslant L(f; N_1 \dotplus N_2) \leqslant U(f; N_1 \dotplus N_2) \leqslant U(f; N_2).$

Proof of Lemma. Let $\delta_1, \delta_2, \dots, \delta_n$ be the cells of N_2; then $(N_1 \dotplus N_2)\delta_r$ is a net over δ_r: let $\Delta_r^{(1)}, \Delta_r^{(2)}, \dots, \Delta_r^{(q_r)}$ be its cells $(r = 1, 2, \dots, n)$. Then

(2) $$M(f; \Delta_r^{(s)}) \leqslant M(f; \delta_r) \quad \& \quad \sum_{\sigma=1}^{q_r} |\Delta_r^{(\sigma)}| = |\delta_r|$$

$$(1 \leqslant r \leqslant n; \ 1 \leqslant s \leqslant q_r),$$

and

$$U(f; N_2) = \sum_{r=1}^{n} |\delta_r|\, M(f; \delta_r) \quad \& \quad U(f; N_1 \dotplus N_2) = \sum_{r=1}^{n} \sum_{s=1}^{q_r} |\Delta_r^{(s)}|\, M(f; \Delta_r^{(s)}).$$

So, if

$$\theta_r = |\delta_r|\, M(f; \delta_r) - \sum_{s=1}^{q_r} |\Delta_r^{(s)}|\, M(f; \Delta_r^{(s)}) \quad (r = 1, 2, \dots, n),$$

then $$U(f; N_2) - U(f; N_1 \dotplus N_2) = \sum_{r=1}^{n} \theta_r,$$

and this, by (2), gives

$$U(f; N_2) \geqslant U(f; N_1 \dotplus N_2).$$

The proof of (1) is now easily completed, in virtue of th. 44 (i), by applying a similar argument to the function $-f(x)$ and interchanging the nets N_1 and N_2.

Proof of th. 45. By def. 33 and th. 44 (ii) it suffices to prove

(3) $$\int_{\underline{a}}^{b} f(x)\, dx \leqslant \int_{a}^{\overline{b}} f(x)\, dx.$$

Let N be any net over J; by (1) $L(f; N)$ does not exceed *any* of the upper sums of $f(x)$ over J, and so, by def. 33,

$$L(f; N) \leqslant \int_{a}^{\overline{b}} f(x)\, dx;$$

N being arbitrary this last formula implies (3), by def. 33.

Example. Let $f(x) = \begin{cases} 1 \text{ if } x \text{ is rational} \\ 0 \text{ otherwise}; \end{cases}$

then $m(f; \delta) = 0 \quad \& \quad M(f; \delta) = 1$ for every closed interval δ, so that

$$U(f;N) = 1 \quad \& \quad L(f;N) = 0 \text{ for every net } N \text{ over } [0,1];$$

hence

$$\overline{\int_0^1} f(x)\, dx = 1 \quad \& \quad \underline{\int_0^1} f(x)\, dx = 0.$$

The following three theorems follow at once from the definitions.

Theorem 46. *If $f(x)$ is defined and bounded in the closed interval $[a,b]$, then*

$$\overline{\int_a^b} -f(x)\, dx = -\underline{\int_a^b} f(x)\, dx.$$

Theorem 47.
$$\int_a^b -f(x)\, dx = -\int_a^b f(x)\, dx$$

if either side exists.

Theorem 48. *If $[a,b]$ is a closed interval, and k is a finite real number, then*

$$\int_a^b k\, dx = k(b-a).$$

Theorem 49. *Let $f(x)$ be defined and bounded in J, a closed interval $[a,b]$; then a necessary and sufficient condition for $f(x)$ to be integrable-R over J is that, to every ϵ there is a net N over J such that*

$$U(f;N) - L(f;N) < \epsilon.$$

Proof. Sufficiency follows at once from the formula (th. 45)

$$L(f;N) \leqslant \underline{\int_a^b} f(x)\, dx \leqslant \overline{\int_a^b} f(x)\, dx \leqslant U(f;N).$$

On the other hand, suppose $f(x)$ is integrable-R over J, and let ϵ be freely chosen. By def. 33 there exist nets N_1 and N_2 over J such that

$$0 \leqslant \int_a^b f(x)\, dx - L(f;N_1) < \tfrac{1}{2}\epsilon \quad \& \quad 0 \leqslant U(f;N_2) - \int_a^b f(x)\, dx < \tfrac{1}{2}\epsilon,$$

whence, by the lemma of th. 45,

$$U(f;N_1\dotplus N_2) - L(f;N_1\dotplus N_2) < \epsilon,$$

and this proves the necessity of the given condition.

Theorem 50. *Let $f(x)$ be defined, finite, and non-decreasing in J, a closed interval $[a, b]$; then $f(x)$ is integrable-R over J.*

Proof. Choose any positive integer n, and let N be the net whose points are given by

$$x_r = a + \frac{r}{n}(b-a) \quad (r = 0, 1, 2, ..., n).$$

Since $f(x)$ is non-decreasing in J,

$$m(f; [x_{r-1}, x_r]) = f(x_{r-1}) \quad \& \quad M(f; [x_{r-1}, x_r]) = f(x_r) \quad (r = 1, 2, ..., n);$$

hence

$$U(f; N) - L(f; N) = \frac{|J|}{n} \sum_{r=1}^{n} \{f(x_r) - f(x_{r-1})\} = \frac{|J|}{n} \{f(b) - f(a)\},$$

and since n is arbitrary, this implies that $f(x)$ is integrable-R over J (th. 49).

§ 3. Conditions for a Function to be Integrable-R

The reader will be familiar with the theorem (Hardy, § 156) that a function which is continuous throughout a closed interval J is integrable-R over J; in the theorems which follow we obtain conditions which are necessary and sufficient for a bounded function $f(x)$ to be integrable-R over J.

Theorem 51. *Suppose $f(x)$ is integrable-R over a closed interval J, and let ϵ and η be freely chosen positive numbers; then there is a net over J such that the sum of the lengths of those of its cells which include in their interiors points x, with $\omega(f; x) \geqslant \eta$, is less than ϵ.*

Proof. By ths. 49 and 44 (iii) N may be chosen over J so that

$$(1) \qquad \sum_{r=1}^{n} \omega(f; \delta_r) |\delta_r| < \eta\epsilon,$$

where δ_1, δ_2,..., δ_n are the cells of N.

Now, by th. 41, the oscillation of $f(x)$ in a cell which includes in its interior a point x, with $\omega(f; x) \geqslant \eta$, is not less than η. and this, by (1), gives the required result.

Definition 34. A set S in R_n is said to be *null* if to every ϵ there is a sequence of intervals, $\{I_r\}$, such that

$$S \subset \sum_{r=1}^{\infty}{}^* I_r \quad \& \quad \sum_{r=1}^{\infty} |I_r| < \epsilon.$$

If a condition is satisfied at all points of a given set A, except at the points of a null subset of A, then we say the condition is satisfied *almost everywhere* in A, or at *almost all* the points of A.

The expression 'almost everywhere' is often denoted by

$$p.p. \text{ } (presque \text{ } partout),$$

in accordance with the usage of the French and other writers.

The following theorem will suggest examples of null sets.

Theorem 52. *Let S be a finite or an enumerable set; then S is null.*

Proof. Let $\{P_r\}$ be a sequence of points including every member of S. Choose ϵ freely, and then to every positive integer r an interval I_r such that

$$P_r \in I_r \quad \& \quad |I_r| < \epsilon 2^{-r}.$$

Then

$$S \subset \sum_{r=1}^{\infty}{}^* I_r \quad \& \quad \sum_{r=1}^{\infty} |I_r| < \epsilon;$$

and this, by def. 34, means that S is null.

It is, however, not necessary for a null set to be enumerable; the existence of null sets which are perfect follows easily from th. 123.

Theorem 53. *Let $f(x)$ be integrable-R over J, a closed interval $[a, b]$; then $f(x)$ is continuous almost everywhere in J.*

Proof. With the notation of th. 42, put $D = \sum_{r=1}^{\infty}{}^* D(1/r)$; then D is the set of the points x of J at which $f(x)$ is discontinuous (th. 43), and so we have only to prove that D is null. Choose ϵ freely, and then choose any positive integer r. By th. 51 there is a finite number of intervals which cover the set $D(1/r)$, with the exception of those of its points which belong to a certain net, and the sum of the lengths of these intervals is less than $\epsilon 2^{-r}$. Since the net in question may itself be covered by a finite aggregate of intervals, the sum of whose lengths is less than $\epsilon 2^{-r}$, it follows that there is a finite number of intervals, say $I_r^{(1)}, I_r^{(2)}, \dots, I_r^{(n_r)}$, such that

$$(1) \qquad D\left(\frac{1}{r}\right) \subset \sum_{t=1}^{n_r}{}^* I_r^{(t)} \quad \& \quad \sum_{t=1}^{n_r} |I_r^{(t)}| < \epsilon 2^{1-r} \quad \& \quad n_r \geqslant 1.$$

By th. 6 the intervals $I_r^{(t)}$, where r runs through all positive integers and $1 \leqslant t \leqslant n_r$, can be arranged in a sequence, say $\{J_r\}$.

It follows from (1) that

$$D = \sum_{r=1}^{\infty}{}^* D\left(\frac{1}{r}\right) \subset \sum_{r=1}^{\infty}{}^* J_r \quad \& \quad \sum_{r=1}^{\infty} |J_r| = \sum_{r=1}^{\infty} \sum_{t=1}^{n_r} |I_r^{(t)}| < 2\epsilon;$$

and since ϵ is arbitrary, this means that D is null.

The aim of the next two theorems is to state a converse to th. 53, and so obtain sufficient conditions for a function to be integrable-R.

Theorem 54. *Let $f(x)$ be defined and bounded in J, a closed interval $[a, b]$, and let η be a finite number such that*

(1) $$x \in J \quad implies \quad \omega(f; x) < \eta;$$

then there is a net N over J such that

(2) $$U(f; N) - L(f; N) \leqslant \eta(b - a).$$

Proof. By th. 44 (iii), (2) will be proved if we can show (3) there is a net N over J such that

$$\omega(f; \delta) \leqslant \eta \text{ for every cell } \delta \text{ of } N.$$

Let $f(x)$ be defined outside J as follows:

$$f(x) = \begin{cases} f(a) & \text{if} \quad x < a \\ f(b) & \text{if} \quad x > b. \end{cases}$$

Then, by (1), every point x of J is the centre of an interval $I(x)$, say (α, β), such that

(4) $$\alpha \leqslant \xi_1 \leqslant \xi_2 \leqslant \beta \quad implies \quad |f(\xi_1) - f(\xi_2)| < \eta.$$

Since the intervals $I(x)$ are open (th. 14), it follows by th. 40 that there is a finite number of them, say $I(x_1)$, $I(x_2)$,..., $I(x_k)$, such that

(5) $$J \subset \sum_{r=1}^{k}{}^* I(x_r).$$

By (5) and (4), (3) will be proved if the following lemma is true.

Lemma. Let I_1, I_2,..., I_k be any finite number of linear intervals, and let J be a closed linear interval; then there is a net over J such that, if δ is any one of its cells and r is any integer from 1 to k, then

either $\quad \delta I_r = 0$, or else $\quad I_r \supset \delta^\circ$ (cf. def. 17).

Proof. Suppose

$$I_s = (a_s, b_s) \quad (s = 1, 2,..., k);$$

choose N so that it includes all those points a_s, b_s which belong to J. Then

(6) no point a_s or b_s is interior to any cell of N.

Let $[\lambda, \mu]$ be any cell of N, and suppose $[\lambda, \mu](a_r, b_r) \neq 0$; then

(7) $$a_r \leqslant \lambda < \mu \leqslant b_r,$$

for if (7) is false, it follows, since $[\lambda, \mu](a_r, b_r) \neq 0$, that

$$\lambda < a_r < \mu \quad \text{or} \quad \lambda < b_r < \mu,$$

which contradicts (6). Hence (7) is true, and the lemma is proved.

Theorem 55. *Let $f(x)$ be defined and bounded in J, a closed interval $[a, b]$, and let $f(x)$ be continuous almost everywhere in J; then $f(x)$ is integrable-R over J.*

Proof. With the notation of th. 53, we are given that $\sum\limits_{r=1}^{\infty}{}^{*} D(1/r)$ is null, and have to deduce that $f(x)$ is integrable-R over J. Choose ϵ freely, and choose any positive integer s; since $\sum\limits_{r=1}^{\infty}{}^{*} D(1/r)$ may be covered by a sequence of intervals the sum of whose lengths is less than ϵ, the same is true of $D(1/s)$, and since $D(1/s)$ is bounded and closed (th. 42), it follows by th. 38 that there is a finite number of intervals, say $I_1, I_2, \ldots, I_k$, such that

$$(1) \qquad D\left(\frac{1}{s}\right) \subset \sum_{r=1}^{k}{}^{*} I_r \quad \& \quad \sum_{r=1}^{k} |I_r| < \epsilon.$$

By the lemma to th. 54 there is a net N_0 over J such that, if δ is any one of its cells, then either $\delta \sum\limits_{r=1}^{k}{}^{*} I_r = 0$, or else δ° is contained in one of $I_1, I_2, \ldots, I_k$. Since the interiors of the cells of N_0 are mutually exclusive, it follows easily from (1) that the sum of the lengths of the cells of N_0 which include points of $D(1/s)$ is less than ϵ; or, if we put

$$\theta_r = \begin{cases} 1 & \text{if} \quad \delta_r . D(1/s) \neq 0 \\ 0 & \text{otherwise,} \end{cases}$$

where $\delta_1, \delta_2, \ldots, \delta_n$ are the cells of N_0, then

$$(2) \qquad \sum_{r=1}^{n} \theta_r |\delta_r| < \epsilon.$$

We now define a net N_r over each of the cells δ_r as follows:

if $\theta_r = 1$, let N_r consist of the end-points of δ_r;

if $\theta_r = 0$, then, since $x \in \delta_r$ implies $\omega(f; x) < 1/s$, N_r may be chosen (th. 54) so that

$$U(f; N_r) - L(f; N_r) \leqslant |\delta_r| \frac{1}{s}.$$

Then, on putting $N = \sum\limits_{r=1}^{n}{}^{*} N_r$, it follows at once that N is a net over J and that

$$(3) \qquad U(f; N) - L(f; N) = \sum_{r=1}^{n} \{ U(f; N_r) - L(f; N_r) \}.$$

Now clearly, by th. 44,

$$\theta_r \{ U(f; N_r) - L(f; N_r) \} \leqslant \omega(f; J) |\delta_r| \theta_r,$$

and $\qquad\qquad (1-\theta_r)\{U(f;N_r)-L(f;N_r)\} \leqslant |\delta_r|\dfrac{1}{s};$

hence, by (2),

$$\sum_{r=1}^{n}\{U(f;N_r)-L(f;N_r)\} \leqslant \omega(f;J)\sum_{r=1}^{n}|\delta_r|\,\theta_r+\frac{1}{s}\sum_{r=1}^{n}|\delta_r|$$

$$\leqslant \omega(f;J)\epsilon+|J|\frac{1}{s},$$

and so, since ϵ and s are arbitrary, it follows by (3) and th. 49 that $f(x)$ is integrable-R over J.

Example. Let $f(x)$ be defined in $[1,2]$ as follows:

$$f(x) = \begin{cases} 0 & \text{if } x \text{ is irrational} \\ \dfrac{(-1)^n}{n} & \text{if } x = m/n,\ m \text{ and } n \text{ being positive integers with} \\ & \text{no common factor.} \end{cases}$$

Then $f(x)$ is bounded in $[1,2]$ and is continuous except where x is rational; since the set of the rational points of $[1,2]$ is null (ths. 9 and 52), it now follows from th. 55 that $f(x)$ is integrable-R over $[1,2]$. The value of $\int_{1}^{2} f(x)\,dx$ will be found following th. 57.

Definition 35. Let J be a closed interval, and let $\phi(N)$ be a real number defined for every net N over J; then

$$\lim_{g(N)\to 0} \phi(N) = \lambda$$

means λ is a finite real number such that to every ϵ there is an η with the property:

$$\eta > 0, \quad \text{and} \quad g(N) < \eta \quad \text{implies} \quad |\phi(N)-\lambda| < \epsilon.$$

We come now to what may be regarded as a key theorem for the Riemann integral.

Theorem 56 (Darboux). *Let $f(x)$ be defined and bounded in J, a closed interval $[a,b]$, and let N be any net over J; then*

(1) $\qquad \lim_{g(N)\to 0} L(f;N) = \int_{a}^{b} f(x)\,dx \quad \& \quad \lim_{g(N)\to 0} U(f;N) = \overline{\int_{a}^{b}} f(x)\,dx.$

Proof. Choose ϵ freely and then N_1, a net over J, such that

(2) $\qquad\qquad 0 \leqslant \int_{a}^{b} f(x)\,dx - L(f;N_1) < \tfrac{1}{2}\epsilon.$

Let N be any net over J, and $\delta_1, \delta_2,..., \delta_n$ its cells. $(N_1\dotplus N)\delta_r$ is a net over δ_r: let $\Delta_1^{(r)}$, $\Delta_2^{(r)}$,..., $\Delta_{q_r}^{(r)}$ be its cells; clearly

$$(3) \quad L(f;N \dotplus N_1) - L(f;N) = \sum_{r=1}^{n} \left\{ \sum_{s=1}^{q_r} m(f;\Delta_s^{(r)}) \, |\Delta_s^{(r)}| - m(f;\delta_r) \, |\delta_r| \right\}.$$

Now, for every integer r from 1 to n,

$$\sum_{s=1}^{q_r} m(f;\Delta_s^{(r)}) \, |\Delta_s^{(r)}| - m(f;\delta_r) \, |\delta_r| \leqslant \omega(f;J) |\delta_r| \theta_r,$$

where
$$\theta_r = \begin{cases} 1 & \text{if } N_1 \delta_r^{\text{o}} \neq 0 \\ 0 & \text{otherwise.} \end{cases}$$

Hence, by (3) and the lemma to th. 45,

$$(4) \quad L(f;N_1) - L(f;N) \leqslant \omega(f;J) \sum_{r=1}^{n} |\delta_r| \, \theta_r \leqslant \omega(f;J) g(N) \sum_{r=1}^{n} \theta_r$$
$$\leqslant \omega(f;J) g(N) p,$$

where p is the number of points in N_1. Hence, if $g(N)$ is so small that

$$\omega(f;J) g(N) p < \tfrac{1}{2}\epsilon,$$

it follows by (4) and (2) that

$$0 \leqslant \int_{\underline{a}}^{b} f(x) \, dx - L(f;N) < \epsilon;$$

since ϵ is arbitrary, this implies the first part of (1). The second part of (1) may be deduced from the first part in virtue of ths. 46 and 44 (i), on replacing $f(x)$ by $-f(x)$.

Theorem 57. *Let $f(x)$ be defined and bounded in J, a closed interval $[a,b]$. Let N be any net over J and $\delta_1, \delta_2,..., \delta_n$ its cells; then*

(i) *if $f(x)$ is integrable-R over J, there is to every ϵ a positive number η such that*

$$g(N) < \eta \quad \text{implies} \quad \left| \sum_{r=1}^{n} f(\xi_r) \, |\delta_r| - \int_{a}^{b} f(x) \, dx \right| < \epsilon,$$

ξ_r being any point of δ_r ($r = 1, 2,..., n$);

(ii) *if there is a number l with the property that to every ϵ there is a positive number η such that*

$$g(N) < \eta \quad \text{implies} \quad \left| \sum_{r=1}^{n} f(\xi_r) \, |\delta_r| - l \right| < \epsilon$$

however the point ξ_r is chosen from δ_r ($r = 1, 2,..., n$), then $f(x)$ is integrable-R over J.

Proof. To prove (i) we observe that, from def. 32,

(1) $$L(f;N) \leqslant \sum_{r=1}^{n} f(\xi_r) \, |\delta_r| \leqslant U(f;N);$$

also, if $f(x)$ is integrable-R over J, we have, by th. 56,

$$\lim_{g(N)\to 0} L(f;N) = \lim_{g(N)\to 0} U(f;N) = \int_a^b f(x) \, dx,$$

and this, by (1), proves (i).

To prove (ii) suppose $f(x)$ is not integrable-R over J, and put

(2) $$\int_a^{\overline{b}} f(x) \, dx - \int_{\underline{a}}^b f(x) \, dx = 4\epsilon.$$

Choose any net N and take λ_r and μ_r in δ_r so that

(3) $$0 \leqslant M(f;\delta_r) - f(\mu_r) < \frac{\epsilon}{|J|} \quad \& \quad 0 \leqslant f(\lambda_r) - m(f;\delta_r) < \frac{\epsilon}{|J|};$$

by (3) and def. 32

(4) $$0 \leqslant U(f;N) - L(f;N) - \sum_{r=1}^{n} f(\mu_r) \, |\delta_r| + \sum_{r=1}^{n} f(\lambda_r) \, |\delta_r| < 2\epsilon,$$

and so, from (2), (4), and th. 45, we have

(5) $$\sum_{r=1}^{n} f(\mu_r) \, |\delta_r| - \sum_{r=1}^{n} f(\lambda_r) \, |\delta_r| > 2\epsilon.$$

Since (5) holds for $g(N)$ arbitrarily small, it is clear that the conditions laid down in (ii) are not satisfied by $f(x)$. Hence it follows that (ii) is true.

Example. To evaluate the integral discussed in the example following th. 55, we observe that every cell of every net over $[1,2]$ includes points ξ for which $f(\xi) = 0$; hence, since $f(x)$ is integrable-R over J, we have, by th. 57,

$$\int_1^2 f(x) \, dx = 0.$$

§ 4. Properties of the Riemann Integral

We now proceed to discuss some of the properties of the Riemann integral, and, more particularly, to discuss methods for its evaluation.

Theorem 58. *Let $f(x)$ be defined and bounded in J, a closed interval $[a,b]$, and suppose $a = x_0 < x_1 < \ldots < x_n = b$; then*

(1) $$\int_{\underline{a}}^b f(x) \, dx = \sum_{r=1}^{n} \int_{x_{r-1}}^{x_r} f(x) \, dx.$$

Proof. Let N_r be any net over $[x_{r-1}, x_r]$, and put $N = \sum_{r=1}^{n}{}^{*} N_r$; then N is a net over J, and

(2) $$L(f; N) = \sum_{r=1}^{n} L(f; N_r);$$

also, if each of the n numbers $g(N_r)$ $(r = 1, 2, ..., n)$ tends to zero, then so does $g(N)$, and so, by (2) and th. 56, we have (1).

Theorem 59. *Let $f(x)$ be defined and bounded in the closed interval $[a, b]$, and suppose $a < c < b$; then*

(1) $$\int_a^b f(x)\,dx = \int_a^c f(x)\,dx + \int_c^b f(x)\,dx$$

if either side exists.

Proof. By th. 58 and a similar result for upper integrals,

$$\int_a^{\overline{b}} f(x)\,dx - \int_{\underline{a}}^b f(x)\,dx$$

$$= \left\{ \int_a^{\overline{c}} f(x)\,dx - \int_{\underline{a}}^c f(x)\,dx \right\} + \left\{ \int_c^{\overline{b}} f(x)\,dx - \int_{\underline{c}}^b f(x)\,dx \right\};$$

now the sum of two non-negative numbers is zero if and only if each of them is zero; hence, by the last equation and th. 45, if one side of (1) exists, so does the other, and their equality follows from th. 58.

Theorem 60. *Let $f(x)$ be defined and bounded in the closed interval $[a, b]$; then*

$$\int_a^{\overline{b}} f(x)\,dx \leqslant (b-a)\,M(f;(a,b)) \quad \& \quad \int_{\underline{a}}^b f(x)\,dx \geqslant (b-a)\,m(f;(a,b)).$$

Proof. Choose ϵ so that $a+\epsilon < b-\epsilon$; by th. 58,

$$\int_{\underline{a}}^b f(x)\,dx = \int_{\underline{a}}^{a+\epsilon} f(x)\,dx + \int_{\underline{a+\epsilon}}^{b-\epsilon} f(x)\,dx + \int_{\underline{b-\epsilon}}^b f(x)\,dx,$$

and so, by th. 45,

(1) $$\int_{\underline{a}}^b f(x)\,dx \geqslant 2\,\epsilon m(f; J) + (b-a-2\epsilon)\,m(f; [a+\epsilon, b-\epsilon]);$$

since this is true for all sufficiently small ϵ, and since

$$m(f; [a+\epsilon, b-\epsilon]) \geqslant m(f;(a,b)),$$

it follows by (1) that

$$\int\limits_{\underline{a}}^{b} f(x)\,dx \geqslant (b-a)\,m(f;(a,b)).$$

A similar argument shows that

$$\int\limits_{a}^{\overline{b}} f(x)\,dx \leqslant (b-a)\,M(f;(a,b)).$$

Theorem 61. *If λ and μ are finite real numbers, then*

(1) $$\int\limits_{a}^{b} \{\lambda f(x)+\mu g(x)\}\,dx = \lambda \int\limits_{a}^{b} f(x)\,dx + \mu \int\limits_{a}^{b} g(x)\,dx$$

assuming the right-hand side of (1) *to be defined.*

Proof. The proof is divided into two parts.

(i) Suppose $a < b$, and $\lambda = \mu = 1$; put $h(x) = f(x)+g(x)$. Then $h(x)$, like $f(x)$ and $g(x)$, is bounded in $[a,b]$, and since for every subset S of $[a,b]$
$$M(h;S) \leqslant M(f;S)+M(g;S),$$
it follows that for every net N over $[a,b]$
$$U(h;N) \leqslant U(f;N)+U(g;N);$$
this, by th. 56, implies

(2) $$\int\limits_{a}^{\overline{b}} h(x)\,dx \leqslant \int\limits_{a}^{b} f(x)\,dx + \int\limits_{a}^{b} g(x)\,dx.$$

Similar reasoning shows that

(3) $$\int\limits_{\underline{a}}^{b} h(x)\,dx \geqslant \int\limits_{a}^{b} f(x)\,dx + \int\limits_{a}^{b} g(x)\,dx.$$

By (2), (3), and th. 45 we have

(4) $$\int\limits_{a}^{b} \{f(x)+g(x)\}\,dx = \int\limits_{a}^{b} f(x)\,dx + \int\limits_{a}^{b} g(x)\,dx.$$

(ii) Suppose $a < b$, $\lambda > 0$, and $\mu = 0$; put $j(x) = \lambda f(x)$. Clearly, for every net N over $[a,b]$, $U(j;N) = \lambda U(f;N)$, and so, by def. 33,

$$\int\limits_{a}^{\overline{b}} j(x)\,dx = \lambda \int\limits_{a}^{b} f(x)\,dx.$$

Similarly, $$\int\limits_{\underline{a}}^{b} j(x)\,dx = \lambda \int\limits_{a}^{b} f(x)\,dx,$$

and so

$$(5) \qquad \int_a^b \lambda f(x)\, dx = \lambda \int_a^b f(x)\, dx \quad \text{if} \quad \lambda > 0.$$

Now, by the aid of def. 33 and th. 47, every case of (1) can be resolved into cases examined under (i) and (ii). Hence, by (5) and (4), (1) is true in all cases.

Theorem 62. *Let $f(x)$ be integrable-R over J, a closed interval $[a,b]$, and let $F(x) = \int_a^x f(t)\, dt$; then*

(1) *$F(x)$ is continuous throughout J;*

(2) *if $a < \xi < b$, and $f(x)$ is continuous for $x = \xi$, then*
$$F'(\xi) = f(\xi).$$

Proof. By th. 59, $F(x)$ is defined and finite in J. Suppose $a < \xi < b$, and choose h to satisfy the condition

$$h \neq 0 \quad \& \quad a < \xi + h < b \quad \text{(i.e. } 0 < |h| < \min(\xi - a, b - \xi)\text{).}$$

By th. 59

$$(3) \qquad F(\xi + h) - F(\xi) = \int_\xi^{\xi + h} f(x)\, dx.$$

Hence, by th. 45,

$$|F(\xi + h) - F(\xi)| \leqslant |h\, M(|f|; J)|,$$

which, since $f(x)$ is bounded in J, implies the continuity of $F(x)$ for $x = \xi$. To prove

$$\lim_{x \to a + 0} F(x) = F(a) \quad \& \quad \lim_{x \to b - 0} F(x) = F(b)$$

the above argument is modified only by restricting the sign of h, and this completes the proof of (1). To prove (2) suppose $f(x)$ is continuous for $x = \xi$, and suppose $a \leqslant \xi + h \leqslant b$; by th. 48 and def. 33

$$(4) \qquad hf(\xi) = \int_\xi^{\xi + h} f(\xi)\, dx. \qquad (4)$$

By (3), (4), and th. 61, $h \neq 0$ implies

$$(5) \qquad \frac{F(\xi + h) - F(\xi)}{h} - f(\xi) = \frac{1}{h} \int_\xi^{\xi + h} \{f(x) - f(\xi)\}\, dx.$$

Choose ϵ freely, and then, since $f(x)$ is continuous for $x = \xi$, δ exists such that

$$(6) \qquad |\eta| < \delta \quad \text{implies} \quad |f(\xi) - f(\xi + \eta)| < \epsilon.$$

So, by (6) and th. 45,

$$|h| < \delta \quad \text{implies} \quad \left| \int\limits_{\xi}^{\xi+h} \{f(x) - f(\xi)\}\, dx \right| \leqslant |h|\,\epsilon,$$

which, with (5), gives

$$0 < |h| < \delta \quad \text{implies} \quad \left| \frac{F(\xi+h) - F(\xi)}{h} - f(\xi) \right| \leqslant \epsilon,$$

and this means $F'(\xi) = f(\xi)$.

Theorem 63. *Let $f(x)$ be integrable-R over the closed interval $[a, b]$, and let*

$$F(x) = \int\limits_{a}^{x} f(t)\, dt; \quad then \quad F'(x) = f(x) \ p.p. \ in \ [a, b].$$

Proof. By ths. 53 and 62.

§ 5. Riemann Integration of Derivatives

The reader will be familiar with the presentation of the elementary theory of integration as an aspect of the inverse problem to differentiation (Hardy, § 127).

Definition 36. Let $f(x)$ be defined in the interval (a, b); $F(x)$ is said to be a *primitive* of $f(x)$ in $[a, b]$ if

  (i) $F(a) = 0$,

  (ii) $F(x)$ is continuous throughout $[a, b]$, and

  (iii) $F'(x) = f(x)$ for every point x of (a, b).

When the function $f(x)$ is continuous throughout $[a, b]$ the problem of evaluating $\int\limits_{a}^{x} f(t)\, dt$ $(a \leqslant x \leqslant b)$ becomes identified with the problem of finding a primitive of $f(x)$ in $[a, b]$; and it is this principle which forms the basis of technique for the evaluation of integrals.

Theorem 64. *Let $f(x)$ be defined and finite in the interval (a, b); let $F(x)$ and $G(x)$ be primitives of $f(x)$ in $[a, b]$. Then*

$$F(x) = G(x) \quad in \quad [a, b].$$

Proof. Put $H(x) = F(x) - G(x).$

Then $H(x)$ is continuous throughout $[a, b]$, and $H(a) = 0$.

Hence, by the first mean-value theorem (Hardy, § 126), $H(x) = 0$ in $[a, b]$ if it is true that

(1) $a < x < b \quad \text{implies} \quad H'(x) = 0.$

Now, since $f(x)$ is finite throughout (a, b), it follows that $F'(x)$ and $G'(x)$ are equal and finite, and hence, that their difference is zero throughout (a, b). Hence

$$a < x < b \quad \text{implies} \quad H'(x) = F'(x) - G'(x) = 0,$$

which proves (1).

In brief, then, a *finite* function cannot have more than one primitive in $[a, b]$.

Theorem 65. *Let $f(x)$ be continuous throughout J, a closed interval $[a, b]$; then the Riemann integral*

$$\int_a^x f(t)\, dt \text{ is the unique primitive of } f(x) \text{ in } J.$$

Proof. Since $f(x)$ is continuous throughout J, $f(x)$ is bounded in J (Hardy, § 102); hence $f(x)$ is integrable-R over J (th. 55). It follows by th. 62 that

$$\int_a^x f(t)\, dt \text{ is a primitive of } f(x) \text{ in } J,$$

and, by th. 64, it is the unique primitive of $f(x)$ in J.

Bearing in mind the necessary and sufficient conditions for a function $f(x)$ to be integrable-R over the closed interval $[a, b]$, we must now consider the following questions:

(α) If $f(x)$ has a primitive in $[a, b]$, is it necessary that $f(x)$ be integrable-R over $[a, b]$?

(β) If $f(x)$ is integrable-R over $[a, b]$, is it necessary for $f(x)$ to have a primitive in $[a, b]$?

(γ) If $f(x)$ is integrable-R over $[a, b]$ and has a primitive in $[a, b]$, is it necessary that the primitive shall be identical with $\int_a^x f(t)\, dt$?

We shall first prove that the answer to (γ) is 'yes', and then show, by examples, that 'no' is the answer to (α) and (β).

Theorem 66. *Let $[a, b]$ be a closed interval, and let $F(x)$ be a function such that*

(1) $F'(x)$ *is defined and bounded in* $[a, b]$,

(2) $F'(x)$ *is continuous almost everywhere in* $[a, b]$;

then $\qquad\qquad \int_a^b F'(x)\, dx = F(b) - F(a).$

Proof. Let $x_0, x_1, ..., x_n$ be any finite set of points such that

$$a = x_0 < x_1 < ... < x_n = b.$$

Then

(3) $$F(b) - F(a) = \sum_{r=1}^{n} \{F(x_r) - F(x_{r-1})\}.$$

By the first mean-value theorem (Hardy, §125) there is to every integer r from 1 to n a point ξ_r such that

(4) $$x_{r-1} < \xi_r < x_r,$$

and

(5) $$F(x_r) - F(x_{r-1}) = (x_r - x_{r-1})F'(\xi_r).$$

By (5) and (3)

(6) $$\sum_{r=1}^{n} (x_r - x_{r-1})F'(\xi_r) = F(b) - F(a).$$

Now, by (1), (2), and th. 55, $F'(x)$ is integrable-R over $[a, b]$, and so, by th. 57, the left-hand side of (6) may be made arbitrarily close to $\int_a^b F'(x)\, dx$ by a suitable choice of the points $x_0, x_1, ..., x_n$. Hence, by (6),

$$\int_a^b F'(x)\, dx = F(b) - F(a).$$

Corollary. If $f(x)$ is integrable-R over $[a, b]$, and if $f(x)$ has a primitive in $[a, b]$, then this primitive must be $\int_a^x f(t)\, dt$.

Examples.

(i) Let $$F(x) = \begin{cases} x^2 \sin \pi/x & \text{if } x \neq 0 \\ 0 & \text{if } x = 0. \end{cases}$$

Then $$F'(0) = \lim_{h \to 0} h \sin \frac{\pi}{h} = 0,$$

and if $x \neq 0$, then $$F'(x) = 2x \sin \frac{\pi}{x} - \pi \cos \frac{\pi}{x}.$$

Hence $F'(x)$ is defined and bounded in $[-1, 1]$ and is continuous if $x \neq 0$ (it is easy to see that $F'(x)$ is discontinuous at $x = 0$). The conditions of th. 66 being therefore satisfied, we have

$$\int_{-1}^{1} F'(x)\, dx = F(1) - F(-1) = 0.$$

(ii) To prove that

$$\lim_{n\to\infty} \sum_{r=1}^{n} \frac{n}{n^2+r^2} = \tfrac{1}{4}\pi.$$

Proof. Let $F(x) = \arctan x$; then $F'(x) = (1+x^2)^{-1}$ in $[0,1]$, and so it follows from th. 66 that

(1) $$\int_0^1 (1+x^2)^{-1}\,dx = \int_0^1 F'(x)\,dx = F(1)-F(0) = \tfrac{1}{4}\pi.$$

Now, if n is any chosen positive integer, and N_n is the net whose cells are given by

$$\left[\frac{r-1}{n},\frac{r}{n}\right] \quad (r = 1, 2, ..., n),$$

it follows by th. 57 that

$$\lim_{n\to\infty}\left\{\sum_{r=1}^{n}\frac{1}{n}\left(1+\frac{r^2}{n^2}\right)^{-1} - \int_0^1 (1+x^2)^{-1}\,dx\right\} = 0,$$

and this, with (1), gives the required result.

Example. To show that the answer to (β) p. 47 is 'no'. Let

$$f(x) = \begin{cases} 0 & \text{if } -1 \leqslant x \leqslant 0 \\ 1 & \text{if } 0 < x \leqslant 1; \end{cases}$$

then $f(x)$ is bounded in $[-1,1]$ and continuous except for $x = 0$. Hence $f(x)$ is integrable-R over $[-1,1]$. Let

$$F(x) = \int_{-1}^{x} f(t)\,dt;$$

by the corollary to th. 66, *if* $f(x)$ has a primitive in $[-1,1]$, it must be $F(x)$; but

$$F(x) = \begin{cases} 0 & \text{if } -1 \leqslant x \leqslant 0 \\ x & \text{if } 0 < x \leqslant 1, \end{cases}$$

and so $F'(0)$ does not exist, which means that $f(x)$ has no primitive in $[-1,1]$.

Example. To show that the answer to (α) p. 47 is 'no'. We have to find a function $f(x)$ such that

$f(x)$ has a primitive in the closed interval $[a,b]$,

and $f(x)$ is not integrable-R over $[a,b]$.

For this to happen, either

(i) the set of the discontinuities of $f(x)$ in $[a,b]$ is null and $f(x)$ is unbounded in $[a,b]$, or else

(ii) the set of the discontinuities of $f(x)$ in $[a, b]$ is not null.

Following the lines of the example following th. 295, it is possible to construct an example of (ii) in which $f(x)$ is even *bounded* in $[a, b]$. The example given below illustrates (i). Let

$$F(x) = \begin{cases} x^2 \sin \dfrac{1}{x^2} & \text{if } 0 < x \leqslant 1 \\ 0 & \text{if } x = 0. \end{cases}$$

Then $F(x)$ is continuous throughout $[0, 1]$, and, since

$$\lim_{h \to 0} h \sin \frac{1}{h^2} = 0,$$

we have

$$F'(x) = \begin{cases} 0 & \text{if } x = 0 \\ 2x \sin \dfrac{1}{x^2} - \dfrac{2}{x} \cos \dfrac{1}{x^2} & \text{if } 0 < x \leqslant 1. \end{cases}$$

Thus $F'(x)$ is defined in $[0, 1]$, and is continuous except at $x = 0$. To show that $F'(x)$ is unbounded in $[0, 1]$, let n be any positive integer, and let $x_n = (2n\pi)^{-\frac{1}{2}}$. Then

$$\frac{2}{x_n} \cos x_n^{-2} = 2(2n\pi)^{\frac{1}{2}} \quad \& \quad 2x_n \sin x_n^{-2} = 0,$$

and hence

$$\lim_{n \to \infty} F'(x_n) = -\infty.$$

§ 6. Riemann Integration of Limit Functions

We now consider a common and important case of the problem of evaluating $(R) \int_a^b f(x)\, dx$, namely that which occurs when $f(x)$ is defined as the limit of a sequence of functions, each of which is integrable-R over $[a, b]$. More precisely, let $\{f_n(x)\}$ be a sequence of functions and $f(x)$ a function such that

(I) $(R) \int_a^b f_n(x)\, dx$ exists $(n = 1, 2, ...),$

and $\lim_{n \to \infty} f_n(x) = f(x)$ for every x in $[a, b]$;

in what circumstances is it true to write

(II) $(R) \int_a^b f(x)\, dx = \lim_{n \to \infty} (R) \int_a^b f_n(x)\, dx?$

To assert the truth of (II) is to assert three things:

(i) that $f(x)$ is integrable-R over $[a, b]$,

(ii) that $\lim_{n \to \infty} (R) \int_a^b f_n(x)\, dx$ exists,

(iii) that the two sides of (II) are equal.

The following examples illustrate the independence of (i), (ii), and (iii).

Examples.

(i) For every positive integer n let

$$f_n(x) = \begin{cases} n \sin \pi n x & \text{if } 0 \leqslant x < \dfrac{1}{n} \\[2mm] 0 & \text{if } \dfrac{1}{n} \leqslant x \leqslant 1. \end{cases}$$

Then
$$\lim_{n \to \infty} f_n(x) = 0 \quad \text{if } 0 \leqslant x \leqslant 1.$$

By ths. 59, 48, and 66, for every positive integer n,

$$\int_0^1 f_n(x)\, dx = \int_0^{1/n} n \sin \pi n x\, dx = -\frac{1}{\pi} \int_0^{1/n} \frac{d}{dx} \cos \pi n x\, dx = 2/\pi;$$

hence
$$\lim_{n \to \infty} \int_0^1 f_n(x)\, dx = \frac{2}{\pi} \neq \int_0^1 \lim_{n \to \infty} f_n(x)\, dx = 0.$$

(ii) Let $f_n(x)$ be defined as in (i), and put

$$g_n(x) = (-1)^n f_n(x);$$

then
$$\int_0^1 \lim_{n \to \infty} g_n(x)\, dx = 0 \quad \& \quad \int_0^1 g_n(x)\, dx = \frac{2}{\pi}(-1)^n,$$

and so
$$\lim_{n \to \infty} \int_0^1 g_n(x)\, dx \text{ does not exist.}$$

(iii) Let $\{x_n\}$ be a sequence consisting of all the rational points of $[0, 1]$, and for every positive integer n let

$$f_n(x) = \begin{cases} 1 & \text{if } x \text{ is among } x_1, x_2, ..., x_n \\ 0 & \text{otherwise,} \end{cases}$$

so that, in $[0, 1]$,

$$\lim_{n \to \infty} f_n(x) = \begin{cases} 1 & \text{if } x \text{ is rational} \\ 0 & \text{otherwise.} \end{cases}$$

It follows from the example to th. 45 that

$$\lim_{n \to \infty} f_n(x) \text{ is not integrable-}R \text{ over } [0,1].$$

However, since $f_n(x)$ is continuous except in a finite number of points, it follows that $f_n(x)$ is integrable-R over $[0,1]$, and, as in the example to th. 57,

$$\int_0^1 f_n(x)\, dx = 0 \quad (n = 1, 2, \ldots), \quad \text{whence} \quad \lim_{n \to \infty} \int_0^1 f_n(x)\, dx = 0.$$

It is, however, not difficult to find a condition which together with (I) implies (II).

Definition 37. Let $\{f_n(P)\}$ be a sequence of functions defined in a set S. Let $f(P)$ be defined and finite in S so that

(i) $P \in S$ implies $f(P) = \lim_{n \to \infty} f_n(P)$, and

(ii) to every ϵ there is an integer q such that, for *every* point P of S, $n \geqslant q$ implies $|f(P) - f_n(P)| < \epsilon$.

Then $f_n(P)$ is said to tend to $f(P)$ *uniformly* in S as n tends to infinity.

Examples.

(i) Suppose $0 < r_1 < r_2$ and $\sum_{n=1}^{\infty} a_n x^n$ converges for $x = r_2$; then, as n tends to infinity,

$$\sum_{\nu=1}^{n} a_\nu x^\nu \quad \text{tends to} \quad \sum_{\nu=1}^{\infty} a_\nu x^\nu \quad \text{uniformly in } [0, r_1].$$

Proof. Choose ϵ freely; since $\sum_{\nu=1}^{\infty} |a_\nu r_1^\nu| < \infty$ (Hardy, § 192), q may be chosen so that

$$\sum_{\nu=q}^{\infty} |a_\nu r_1^\nu| < \epsilon.$$

Hence, if $0 \leqslant x \leqslant r_1$ & $n \geqslant q$, we have

$$\left| \sum_{\nu=1}^{\infty} a_\nu x^\nu - \sum_{\nu=1}^{n} a_\nu x^\nu \right| < \epsilon,$$

which is the required result.

(ii) Let $f_n(x)$ be defined as in example (i) p. 51, and let $f(x) = 0$; then $f(x) = \lim_{n \to \infty} f_n(x)$ in $[0,1]$. However, $f_n(x)$ does not tend to $f(x)$ uniformly in $[0,1]$, for, if n is any positive integer,

$$\left| f\left(\frac{1}{2n}\right) - f_n\left(\frac{1}{2n}\right) \right| = n.$$

Theorem 67. *Let J be a closed interval $[a,b]$, and let $\{f_n(x)\}$ be a sequence of functions such that*

(1) $$(R) \int_a^b f_n(x)\, dx \text{ exists} \quad (n = 1, 2, ...),$$

and

(2) $f_n(x)$ *tends to $f(x)$ uniformly in J as n tends to infinity;*

then $$(R) \int_a^b f(x)\, dx = \lim_{n \to \infty} \int_a^b f_n(x)\, dx.$$

Proof. Choose ϵ freely, and then, in virtue of (2), choose q so that

(3) $$x \in J \quad \& \quad n \geqslant q \text{ implies } |f(x) - f_n(x)| < \epsilon.$$

Since $f_q(x)$ is bounded in J, so is $f(x)$, by (3). Let N be any net over J, and δ any one of its cells; by (3)

$$n \geqslant q \text{ implies } m(f_n; \delta) - \epsilon \leqslant m(f; \delta) \leqslant M(f; \delta) \leqslant M(f_n; \delta) + \epsilon,$$

and so, by def. 32, $n \geqslant q$ implies

$$L(f_n; N) - \epsilon|J| \leqslant L(f; N) \leqslant U(f; N) \leqslant U(f_n; N) + \epsilon|J|.$$

Hence, by (1), def. 33, and th. 56,

(4) $$n \geqslant q \text{ implies}$$

$$\int_a^b f_n(x)\, dx - \epsilon|J| \leqslant \underline{\int_a^b} f(x)\, dx \leqslant \overline{\int_a^b} f(x)\, dx \leqslant \int_a^b f_n(x)\, dx + \epsilon|J|;$$

ϵ being arbitrary, (4) implies

$$\underline{\int_a^b} f(x)\, dx = \overline{\int_a^b} f(x)\, dx,$$

and so (4) may be written

$$n \geqslant q \text{ implies } -\epsilon|J| \leqslant (R) \int_a^b f(x)\, dx - \int_a^b f_n(x)\, dx \leqslant \epsilon|J|,$$

which means $$(R) \int_a^b f(x)\, dx = \lim_{n \to \infty} \int_a^b f_n(x)\, dx.$$

Example. To evaluate $\displaystyle \int_0^{\frac{1}{2}} \frac{dx}{1 + x^5}.$

The series $1 - x^5 + x^{10} - ...$ converges to $(1 + x^5)^{-1}$ if $|x| < 1$, and so, by example (i) following def. 37, its partial sums converge uniformly in $[0, \frac{1}{2}]$. Hence, by th. 67,

$$\int_0^{\frac{1}{2}} \frac{dx}{1+x^5} = \lim_{n\to\infty} \int_0^{\frac{1}{2}} \sum_{r=0}^n (-1)^r x^{5r} \, dx$$

$$= \lim_{n\to\infty} \sum_{r=0}^n \int_0^{\frac{1}{2}} (-1)^r x^{5r} \, dx = \sum_{r=0}^\infty \left(\frac{1}{2}\right)^{5r+1} \frac{(-1)^r}{5r+1},$$

and so the answer required is given in the form of an infinite series.

§ 7. Cauchy-Riemann Integral

The definition of $(R) \int_a^b f(x) \, dx$ can sometimes be extended to include cases in which $f(x)$ is defined, though not necessarily bounded, in a set (a, b), where $(b-a)$ is not necessarily finite.

Definition 37.1. Suppose $a < b$ and $f(x)$ is defined in (a, b) so that

(i) if $a < \alpha < \beta < b$, then $f(x)$ is integrable-R over (α, β), and

(ii) there is a finite number k such that, if α and β tend *independently* to $a+0$ and $b-0$ respectively, then

$$(R) \int_\alpha^\beta f(x) \, dx \quad \text{tends to } k;$$

then $f(x)$ is said to be integrable in the *Cauchy-Riemann* sense (*integrable-CR*) over (a, b), and

$$(CR) \int_a^b f(x) \, dx \quad \text{denotes the number } k.$$

It follows easily from th. 62 (i) that

$$(CR) \int_a^b f(x) \, dx = (R) \int_a^b f(x) \, dx$$

if the right-hand side exists, and that, if either of the limits

$$\lim_{\alpha\to a+0} (R) \int_\alpha^b f(x) \, dx \quad \text{and} \quad \lim_{\beta\to b-0} (R) \int_a^\beta f(x) \, dx$$

exists and is finite, then its value is $(CR) \int_a^b f(x) \, dx$.

Examples.

(i) $(CR) \int_0^1 x^{-\frac{1}{2}} \, dx = 2$, since

$$0 < \alpha < 1 \quad \text{implies} \quad (R) \int_\alpha^1 x^{-\frac{1}{2}} \, dx = 2(1-\sqrt{\alpha}).$$

(ii) $(CR) \int\limits_{1}^{\infty} x^{-2}\, dx = 1$, since

$$1 < \beta < \infty \quad \text{implies} \quad (R) \int\limits_{1}^{\beta} x^{-2}\, dx = \left(1 - \frac{1}{\beta}\right).$$

(iii) If $f(x) = \begin{cases} 1 & \text{if } x \geqslant 0 \\ -1 & \text{if } x < 0, \end{cases}$ then $f(x)$ is not integrable-CR

over $(-\infty, \infty)$; for, although $(R) \int\limits_{-\alpha}^{\alpha} f(x)\, dx = 0$ for every posi-

tive finite number α, $\int\limits_{-\alpha}^{\alpha+1} f(x)\, dx = 1$, and so the limit postulated

in def. 37.1 does not exist.

§ 8. Geometric Interpretation of Riemann Integration

When $f(x)$ is bounded and non-negative in the closed interval $[a, b]$ we can interpret its upper and lower sums geometrically as follows.

Definition 38. Let $f(x)$ be defined and non-negative in the linear set S; then $\Omega_0(f; S)$ denotes the plane set

$$\mathscr{S}((x, y); x \in S \ \& \ 0 < y < f(x)).$$

Clearly, when S is a closed interval, $\Omega_0(f; S)$ is what we usually call the 'set of the points between the curve $y = f(x)$ and the x-axis'.

Let $f(x)$ be defined and bounded $(f(x) \geqslant 0)$ in J, a closed interval $[a, b]$. Let N be any net over J, and $\delta_1, \delta_2, ..., \delta_n$ its cells; for every integer r from 1 to n put

$$I_r = \mathscr{S}((x, y); x \in \delta_r^0 \ \& \ 0 < y < m(f; \delta_r)) \quad \text{(cf. def. 17)}$$

and $\qquad J_r = \mathscr{S}((x, y); x \in \delta_r \ \& \ 0 \leqslant y \leqslant M(f; \delta_r));$

then

(1) $$\sum_{r=1}^{n} I_r \subset \Omega_0(f; J) \subset \sum_{r=1}^{n}{}^{*} J_r.$$

Clearly, $\sum\limits_{r=1}^{n} I_r$ is a sum of intervals to which in elementary geometry we would assign the area

$$\sum_{r=1}^{n} |\delta_r|\, m(f; \delta_r) \quad \text{i.e.} \quad L(f; N);$$

also, $\sum\limits_{r=1}^{n}{}^{*} J_r$ is a union of closed intervals to which we would assign the area

$$\sum_{r=1}^{n} |\delta_r|\, M(f; \delta_r) \quad \text{i.e.} \quad U(f; N).$$

So, if we refer to the sets $\sum\limits_{r=1}^{n} I_r$ and $\sum\limits_{r=1}^{n}{}^{*} J_r$ as elementary figures, we see that the lower and upper sums of $f(x)$ over J are respectively the areas of elementary figures inscribed and circumscribed to the set $\Omega_0(f;J)$; moreover, when $f(x)$ is integrable-R over J, $\Omega_0(f;J)$ has the property that to every ϵ there is an elementary figure contained in $\Omega_0(f;J)$, and an elementary figure containing $\Omega_0(f;J)$, whose areas differ by less than ϵ (th. 49); in this case (Hardy, § 157) the 'area under the curve $y = f(x)$ between $x = a$ and $x = b$' is defined as

$$(R) \int_a^b f(x)\, dx.$$

This leads to the more general problem of defining a function which assigns to every plane set S a number $\alpha(S)$ which may be regarded as its area. Of such a function $\alpha(S)$ it would be natural to require that

   (i) if S is an elementary figure, then $\alpha(S)$ shall be the area assigned to S in elementary geometry, and

   (ii) if $S \subset T$, then $\alpha(S) \leqslant \alpha(T)$.

If $\alpha(S)$ satisfies (i) and (ii), it follows easily that

   (iii) if S is covered by the intervals $I_1, I_2,..., I_k$, then

$$\alpha(S) \leqslant \sum_{r=1}^{k} |I_r|,$$

and

   (iv) if S contains the mutually exclusive intervals $I_1, I_2,..., I_k$, then

$$\alpha(S) \geqslant \sum_{r=1}^{k} |I_r|.$$

These considerations suggest the following definitions:

Definition 39. Let S be any set in R_n; the *exterior Jordan content* of S ($\bar{c}S$) is defined as follows: if S is bounded, let $I_1, I_2,..., I_k$ be any *finite* number of intervals such that

$$S \subset \sum_{r=1}^{k}{}^{*} I_r, \quad \text{and let} \quad u = \sum_{r=1}^{k} |I_r|;$$

then $\bar{c}S$ is the lower bound of the aggregate of all possible such numbers u; if S is unbounded, $\bar{c}S = \infty$. The *interior Jordan content* of S ($\underline{c}S$) is defined as follows: let $I_1, I_2,..., I_k$ be any finite number of intervals such that

$$S \supset \sum_{r=1}^{k} I_r, \quad \text{and let} \quad v = \sum_{r=1}^{k} |I_r|;$$

then $\underline{c}S$ is the upper bound of α, the aggregate of all possible such numbers v ($\underline{c}S = 0$ if α is empty). If and only if $\underline{c}S = \bar{c}S < \infty$, then S is said to be *measurable in the Jordan sense* (*measurable-J*), and the common value of $\underline{c}S$ and $\bar{c}S$ is called the *content* of S (cS). The consistency of this with def. 31 is proved by th. 70.

Example. If S is a finite set of points, then $cS = 0$.

Theorem 68. *Let* $I_1, I_2,..., I_k$ *be a finite number of intervals in* R_n; *then there is a finite number of intervals, say* $C_1, C_2,..., C_q$, *with the following properties: If* s *is any integer from 1 to* k, *then*

(i) I_s *contains all those intervals* C_t *with which it has points in common, and*

(ii) *the content of* I_s *is the sum of the contents of the intervals* C_t *which are contained in* I_s.

Proof. To avoid obscuring an essentially simple idea, we prove the theorem for the special case $n = 2$. (Expressed geometrically, the idea of the proof is to produce all the sides of all the rectangles $I_1, I_2,..., I_k$ so as to produce a background of rectangles which have the required property.) Suppose

$$I_r = \mathscr{S}((x,y); a_1^{(r)} < x < b_1^{(r)} \quad \& \quad a_2^{(r)} < y < b_2^{(r)}) \quad (r = 1, 2,..., k),$$

and let $x_0, x_1,..., x_v$ be the set of all the numbers $a_1^{(r)}, b_1^{(r)}$ ($r = 1, 2,..., k$) arranged so that

(1) $$x_0 < x_1 < ... < x_v;$$

similarly, let $y_0, y_1,..., y_w$ be the set of the $a_2^{(r)}, b_2^{(r)}$ arranged so that

$$y_0 < y_1 < ... < y_w.$$

Allowing m to run from 1 to v and r from 1 to w, let

$$C(m,r) = \mathscr{S}((x,y); x_{m-1} < x < x_m \quad \& \quad y_{r-1} < y < y_r),$$

and let $C_1, C_2,..., C_q$ denote all the intervals so obtained (in fact, $q = vw$). Now consider any one of the intervals $I_1, I_2,..., I_k$, say I_s, and suppose

$$x_\lambda = a_1^{(s)} < b_1^{(s)} = x_\mu \quad \& \quad y_\rho = a_2^{(s)} < b_2^{(s)} = y_\sigma;$$

then I_s contains all those intervals $C(m,r)$ for which

$$\lambda + 1 \leqslant m \leqslant \mu \quad \& \quad \rho + 1 \leqslant r \leqslant \sigma,$$

the sum of whose contents is

$$\sum_{m=\lambda+1}^{\mu} \sum_{r=\rho+1}^{\sigma} (x_m - x_{m-1})(y_r - y_{r-1})$$

or
$$\sum_{m=\lambda+1}^{\mu} (x_m - x_{m-1}) \sum_{r=\rho+1}^{\sigma} (y_r - y_{r-1}),$$

which is equal to $(x_\mu - x_\lambda)(y_\sigma - y_\rho)$ or $|I_s|$. Hence it remains only to show that

(2) $I_s C(m, r) \neq 0$ implies $\lambda + 1 \leqslant m \leqslant \mu$ & $\rho + 1 \leqslant r \leqslant \sigma$.

Suppose then that $I_s C(m, r) \neq 0$, i.e.

$$(x_{m-1}, x_m)(a_1^{(s)}, b_1^{(s)}) \neq 0 \quad \& \quad (y_{r-1}, y_r)(a_2^{(s)}, b_2^{(s)}) \neq 0;$$

this implies $a_1^{(s)} < x_m$ & $b_1^{(s)} > x_{m-1}$,

i.e. $x_\lambda < x_m$ & $x_\mu > x_{m-1}$,

and so, by (1), $\lambda + 1 \leqslant m \leqslant \mu$.

A similar argument applied to the numbers y_r now completes the proof of (2).

Theorem 69. *If S is any set, then $\underline{c}S \leqslant \bar{c}S$.*

Proof. The theorem being trivial if S is unbounded, suppose S is bounded and that $I_1, I_2, ..., I_k$ are intervals such that

(1)
$$\sum_{r=1}^{\nu} I_r \subset S \subset \sum_{r=\nu+1}^{k}{}^{*} I_r,$$

where ν is some integer between 1 and k. Clearly the theorem will be proved if we can show that

(2)
$$\sum_{r=1}^{\nu} |I_r| \leqslant \sum_{r=\nu+1}^{k} |I_r|.$$

Let $C_1, C_2, ..., C_q$ be the aggregate of intervals defined in th. 68. As a result of that theorem, we may define a function $f(s, t)$ such that

$$f(s, t) = \begin{cases} 1 & \text{if } I_s C_t \neq 0, \quad \text{which implies} \quad C_t \subset I_s \\ 0 & \text{otherwise,} \end{cases}$$

and then $|I_s| = \sum_{t=1}^{q} f(s, t)|C_t|$ $(s = 1, 2, ..., k)$.

Hence (2) will be proved if we show that

$$\sum_{s=1}^{\nu} \sum_{t=1}^{q} f(s, t)|C_t| \leqslant \sum_{s=\nu+1}^{k} \sum_{t=1}^{q} f(s, t)|C_t|,$$

and for this it is clearly sufficient to prove that, if t is freely chosen from among $1, 2, ..., q$, then

(3)
$$\sum_{s=1}^{\nu} f(s, t) \leqslant \sum_{s=\nu+1}^{k} f(s, t).$$

Now since $I_1, I_2,..., I_\nu$ are mutually exclusive, no two of them can contain C_t, and so

$$\sum_{s=1}^{\nu} f(s,t) \leqslant 1;$$

on the other hand, if $\quad \sum_{s=1}^{\nu} f(s,t) = 1,$

then, by (1),

$$C_t I_\mu \neq 0 \quad \text{for some integer } \mu \text{ among } \nu+1, \nu+2,..., k,$$

and this implies $\qquad \sum_{s=\nu+1}^{k} f(s,t) \geqslant 1$

which proves (3).

We can now deduce that Jordan content is a generalization of the notion of geometric content.

Theorem 70. *Let I be an interval; then $\underline{c}I = \bar{c}I = |I|$.*

Proof. Since $I \subset I$, it follows from def. 39 that

$$\underline{c}I \geqslant |I| \quad \& \quad \bar{c}I \leqslant |I|,$$

which, together with th. 69, implies the required result.

Theorem 71. *If $A \subset B$, then $\bar{c}A \leqslant \bar{c}B$ & $\underline{c}A \leqslant \underline{c}B$.*

Proof. By def. 39.

Theorem 72. *Let J be a closed interval; then $\bar{c}J = |J^o|$.*

Proof. Suppose J is given by

$$a_r \leqslant x_r \leqslant b_r \quad (r = 1, 2,..., n),$$

and let I_ϵ be given by

$$a_r - \epsilon < x_r < b_r + \epsilon \quad (r = 1, 2,..., n);$$

then $\qquad J^o \subset J \subset I_\epsilon,$ and so (th. 71) $\quad \bar{c}J^o \leqslant \bar{c}J \leqslant \bar{c}I_\epsilon.$

Now by suitably choosing ϵ, it follows from th. 70 that $\bar{c}I_\epsilon$ may be made arbitrarily close to $|J^o|$, which is equal to $\bar{c}J^o$; hence it follows that $\bar{c}J = |J^o|$.

Theorem 73. *Let $S_1, S_2,..., S_k$ be any* finite *number of sets in R_n; then*

(1) $$\bar{c}(S_1 \dotplus S_2 \dotplus ... \dotplus S_k) \leqslant \bar{c}S_1 + \bar{c}S_2 + ... + \bar{c}S_k.$$

Proof. The theorem being trivial if one of the sets is unbounded, suppose they are all bounded, so that their union is likewise bounded. Choose ϵ freely, and then, to every integer r from 1 to k, a finite number of intervals, say $I_r^{(1)}, I_r^{(2)},..., I_r^{(n_r)}$, such that

$$S_r \subset \sum_{t=1}^{n_r}{}^* I_r^{(t)} \quad \& \quad \sum_{t=1}^{n_r} |I_r^{(t)}| \leqslant \bar{c}S_r + \frac{\epsilon}{k};$$

then the finite aggregate of intervals $I_r^{(t)}$, where r runs from 1 to k, and t from 1 to n_r, covers $\sum_{r=1}^{k}{}^{*}\, S_r$, and

$$\sum_{r=1}^{k}\sum_{t=1}^{n_r} |I_r^{(t)}| \leqslant \epsilon + \sum_{r=1}^{k} \bar{c}S_r.$$

Hence
$$\bar{c}\sum_{r=1}^{k}{}^{*}\, S_r \leqslant \epsilon + \sum_{r=1}^{k} \bar{c}S_r,$$

and since ϵ is arbitrary, this proves (1).

The sign $\leqslant$ in (1) of th. 73 cannot be replaced by $=$ even when the sets $S_1, S_2, \ldots, S_k$ are mutually exclusive; to see more clearly how this comes about, and also the reason why the restriction of th. 73 to a *finite* number of sets is essential, we require the following:

Theorem 74. *Let S be any set; then*

(1) $$\underline{c}S = \underline{c}S^{o};$$

(2) $$\bar{c}S = \bar{c}S^{c}.$$

Proof. To prove (1) it is sufficient, by th. 71, to show that $\underline{c}S^o \geqslant \underline{c}S$. To this end, suppose

$$I_1, I_2, \ldots, I_k \quad \text{are intervals such that} \quad \sum_{r=1}^{k} I_r \subset S;$$

since $\sum_{r=1}^{k} I_r$ is open (ths. 14 and 16), we have, by th. 24.1, that

$$\sum_{r=1}^{k} I_r \subset S^o, \quad \text{and this implies} \quad \underline{c}S \leqslant \underline{c}S^o.$$

To prove (2) we observe first that

if S is unbounded, then $\bar{c}S = \bar{c}S^c = \infty$, verifying (2).

Suppose S is bounded and that $I_1, I_2, \ldots, I_k$ are a finite number of intervals covering S; if J_r denotes the closed interval of which I_r is the interior, then $\sum_{r=1}^{k}{}^{*}\, J_r$ is closed (th. 28), and, since it contains S, it must also contain S^c (th. 24.1). Hence, by ths. 71, 73, and 72,

$$\bar{c}S^c \leqslant \bar{c}\sum_{r=1}^{k}{}^{*}\, J_r \leqslant \sum_{r=1}^{k} \bar{c}J_r = \sum_{r=1}^{k} |I_r|,$$

and this implies $\bar{c}S^c \leqslant \bar{c}S$; the proof of (2) is now completed by th. 71.

Example. Let A be the set of the rational points, and B the set of the irrational points of the interval $(0, 1)$. Clearly

$$A^o = B^o = 0, \quad \text{so that} \quad \underline{c}A = \underline{c}B = 0,$$

whereas $\quad A+B = (0,1),\quad$ so that $\quad \underline{c}(A+B) = 1\quad$ (th. 70).

Again
$$A^c = B^c = [0,1], \quad \text{so that}\quad \bar{c}A = \bar{c}B = 1 \quad \text{(th. 72)},$$
while
$$\bar{c}(A+B) = 1,$$
which is an example where
$$\bar{c}(A+B) < \bar{c}A + \bar{c}B.$$

The set A also shows that the restriction of th. 73 to finite aggregates of sets is essential; for, if we regard A as the sum of a sequence of sets S_r, each consisting of just one of the points of A, which we may do since A is enumerable (th. 9), then $\bar{c}A$, which is 1, *exceeds* $\sum_{r=1}^{\infty} \bar{c}S_r$, which is zero, since $\quad \bar{c}S_r = 0 \quad (r = 1, 2, ...)$.

Theorem 75. *Let $S_1, S_2, ..., S_k$ be any finite number of mutually exclusive sets of R_n, all of which are measurable-J; then*
$$\sum_{r=1}^{k} S_r \text{ is measurable-J} \quad \& \quad c\sum_{r=1}^{k} S_r = \sum_{r=1}^{k} cS_r.$$

Proof. Choose ϵ freely, and then to each integer r from 1 to k a finite number of intervals, $I_r^{(1)}, I_r^{(2)}, ..., I_r^{(n_r)}$ such that

(1) $$\sum_{t=1}^{n_r} I_r^{(t)} \subset S_r \quad \& \quad \sum_{t=1}^{n_r} |I_r^{(t)}| > \underline{c}S_r - \frac{\epsilon}{k}.$$

(A slight modification, left to the reader, is necessary if $cS_r = 0$.) By (1), the intervals
$$I_r^{(t)} \quad (r = 1, 2, ..., k; \ t = 1, 2, ..., n_r)$$
are mutually exclusive, their sum is contained in $\sum_{r=1}^{k} S_r$, and the sum of their contents exceeds
$$-\epsilon + \sum_{r=1}^{k} \underline{c}S_r;$$
ϵ being arbitrary, this implies

(2) $$\underline{c}\sum_{r=1}^{k} S_r \geqslant \sum_{r=1}^{k} \underline{c}S_r.$$

By (2) and ths. 73 and 69 it follows that
$$\sum_{r=1}^{k} \bar{c}S_r \geqslant \bar{c}\sum_{r=1}^{k} S_r \geqslant \underline{c}\sum_{r=1}^{k} S_r \geqslant \sum_{r=1}^{k} \underline{c}S_r,$$
and since each of the sets S_r is measurable-J, this implies
$$\bar{c}\sum_{r=1}^{k} S_r = \underline{c}\sum_{r=1}^{k} S_r = \sum_{r=1}^{k} cS_r < \infty.$$

The restriction of th. 75 to finite aggregates of sets is essential, just as it is to th. 73; the set A, in the example following th. 74, is not measurable-J although it is the sum of a sequence of sets each of which consists of a single point and therefore has content zero.

Although the theory of Jordan content is now only of historic interest, its intimate connexion with the Riemann integral, which the next theorem reveals, is worth examining, especially if we are to understand how it is that the Lebesgue integral, which is based on another theory of measure of sets, is free from many of the limitations of the Riemann integral; and it is instructive to note how exactly the deficiencies of the Riemann theory of integration are reflected in those of the theory of Jordan content. In the next theorem we obtain a geometrical interpretation of $\int_a^{\bar{b}} f(x)\,dx$ and $\int_{\underline{a}}^b f(x)\,dx$, when $f(x)$ is non-negative and bounded in $[a,b]$, in terms of the set of the points 'between the curve $y = f(x)$ and the x-axis'. Since $f(x)$ must be bounded in order that $\int_{\underline{a}}^b f(x)\,dx$ and $\int_a^{\bar{b}} f(x)\,dx$ shall be defined, the reader will easily see that the restriction of $f(x)$ to be non-negative is not a serious one.

Theorem 76. *Let $f(x)$ be defined, non-negative, and bounded in J, a closed interval $[a,b]$; then*

$$\underline{c}\Omega_0(f; J) = \int_{\underline{a}}^b f(x)\,dx \quad \& \quad \bar{c}\Omega_0(f; J) = \int_a^{\bar{b}} f(x)\,dx.$$

Proof. Let $a = x_0 < x_1 < \ldots < x_n = b$ define any net N over J, and let $\delta_r = [x_{r-1}, x_r]$; put

$$A_r = \mathscr{S}((x,y); x \in \delta_r^o \quad \& \quad 0 < y < m(f; \delta_r^o)) \quad (r = 1, 2, \ldots, n).$$

Then $A_r = 0$ or else A_r is an interval with content $|\delta_r| m(f; \delta_r^o)$; hence (def. 39), since $\sum_{r=1}^n A_r \subset \Omega_0(f; J)$,

$$\underline{c}\Omega_0(f; J) \geqslant \sum_{r=1}^n |\delta_r| m(f; \delta_r^o) \geqslant \sum_{r=1}^n |\delta_r| m(f; \delta_r) = L(f; N),$$

and so, by def. 33, $\underline{c}\Omega_0(f; J) \geqslant \int_{\underline{a}}^b f(x)\,dx$. To complete one-half of the theorem we have now to show that, if $\underline{c}\Omega_0(f; J) > 0$, then

$$(1) \qquad \underline{c}\Omega_0(f; J) \leqslant \int_{\underline{a}}^b f(x)\,dx;$$

to this end, let $I_1, I_2,..., I_k$ be any finite number of intervals satisfying

$$(2) \qquad \sum_{s=1}^{k} I_s \subset \Omega_0(f; J).$$

Choose N so that it includes all the extreme abscissae of $I_1, I_2,..., I_k$ (a_1 and b_1 being called the extreme abscissae of an interval given by $a_1 < x < b_1$ & $a_2 < y < b_2$). If we put

$$I_s^{(r)} = I_s \mathscr{S}((x,y); x \in \delta_r^o) \quad (s = 1, 2,..., k; \ r = 1, 2,..., n),$$

then clearly

$$(3) \qquad \sum_{r=1}^{n} I_s^{(r)} \subset I_s \quad \& \quad \sum_{r=1}^{n} |I_s^{(r)}| = |I_s| \quad (s = 1, 2,..., k),$$

where $|I|$ denotes zero if $I = 0$. Hence, by th. 58,

$$\int_{\underline{a}}^{b} f(x)\, dx - \sum_{s=1}^{k} |I_s| = \sum_{r=1}^{n} \int_{\underline{x_{r-1}}}^{x_r} f(x)\, dx - \sum_{s=1}^{k} \sum_{r=1}^{n} |I_s^{(r)}|$$

$$= \sum_{r=1}^{n} \left\{ \int_{\underline{x_{r-1}}}^{x_r} f(x)\, dx - \sum_{s=1}^{k} |I_s^{(r)}| \right\};$$

since the intervals $I_1, I_2,..., I_k$ have only to satisfy (2), it now follows by def. 39 that (1) will be proved if we show that

$$(4) \qquad \int_{\underline{x_{r-1}}}^{x_r} f(x)\, dx \geqslant \sum_{s=1}^{k} |I_s^{(r)}| \quad (r = 1, 2,..., n).$$

Now, if $(\xi, \eta) \in I_s^{(r)}$, then there is a number η' greater than η and such that $(x, \eta') \in I_s^{(r)}$ for every x in δ_r^o; since $I_s^{(r)} \subset \Omega_0(f; J)$, this means that $f(x) > \eta'$ for every x in δ_r^o, and hence $m(f; \delta_r^o) \geqslant \eta' > \eta$, which implies $(\xi, \eta) \in A_r$. It now follows that $\sum_{s=1}^{k} I_s^{(r)} \subset A_r$, and since the I_r are intervals or are empty, we have (th. 70)

$$\sum_{s=1}^{k} |I_s^{(r)}| \leqslant |A_r| = |\delta_r| \, m(f; \delta_r^o) \quad (r = 1, 2,..., n),$$

which, together with th. 60, proves (4). To prove

$$\bar{c}\Omega_0(f; J) = \int_{a}^{\overline{b}} f(x)\, dx,$$

we proceed along similar lines. If N is any net over J and $\delta_1, \delta_2,..., \delta_n$ are its cells, then $\Omega_0(f; J) \subset \sum_{r=1}^{n}{}^* \mathscr{S}((x,y); x \in \delta_r \ \& \ 0 \leqslant y \leqslant M(f; \delta_r))$, whence it follows that

$$\bar{c}\Omega_0(f; J) \leqslant \sum_{r=1}^{n} M(f; \delta_r)|\delta_r| = U(f; N),$$

and hence that $\qquad \bar{c}\Omega_0(f; J) \leqslant \int\limits_a^{\overline{b}} f(x)\, dx.$

To reverse this inequality, we proceed as follows. Let $I_1, I_2,..., I_k$ be a finite number of intervals covering $\Omega_0(f; J)$, and let N be chosen so as to include all the extreme abscissae of $I_1, I_2,..., I_k$ which belong to J. Let $I_s^{(r)}$ $(r = 1, 2,..., n;\ s = 1, 2,..., k)$ be defined as before, and let η be any number such that $0 < \eta < M(f; \delta_r)$, the integer r having been freely chosen. Then ξ exists in δ_r so that $(\xi, \eta) \in \Omega_0(f; \delta_r)$; hence there is a positive integer s such that $(\xi, \eta) \in I_s$, and since $\xi \in \delta_r$, we have

$$(\xi, \eta) \in J_s^{(r)}, \text{ where } J_s^{(r)} \text{ is the closed envelope of } I_s^{(r)};$$

consequently, $(x, \eta) \in J_s^{(r)}$ for *every* x in δ_r. It now follows that

$$\mathscr{S}((x, y);\ x \in \delta_r \ \& \ 0 < y < M(f; \delta_r)) \subset \sum_{s=1}^k {}^* J_s^{(r)},$$

and, applying ths. 71, 72, and 73, we have

$$|\delta_r|\, M(f; \delta_r) \leqslant \bar{c} \sum_{s=1}^k {}^* J_s^{(r)} \leqslant \sum_{s=1}^k \bar{c} J_s^{(r)} = \sum_{s=1}^k |I_s^{(r)}| \quad (r = 1, 2,..., n),$$

whence $\qquad U(f; N) \leqslant \sum_{r=1}^n \sum_{s=1}^k |I_s^{(r)}| = \sum_{s=1}^k \sum_{r=1}^n |I_s^{(r)}| = \sum_{s=1}^k |I_s|,$

so that $\qquad \int\limits_a^{\overline{b}} f(x)\, dx \leqslant \sum_{s=1}^k |I_s|;$

and since $I_1, I_2,..., I_k$ are any intervals covering $\Omega_0(f; J)$, it follows that

$$\int\limits_a^{\overline{b}} f(x)\, dx \leqslant \bar{c}\Omega_0(f; J),$$

which completes the proof.

Theorem 77. *Let $f(x)$ be defined, bounded, and non-negative in a closed interval J; then each of the following three statements implies the other two:*

(i) *$f(x)$ is integrable-R over J;*

(ii) *$f(x)$ is continuous almost everywhere in J;*

(iii) *the set $\Omega_0(f; J)$ is measurable-J.*

Proof. Since $f(x)$ is bounded in J, $\Omega_0(f; J)$ is bounded, and so the theorem follows at once from ths. 53, 55, and 76, and defs. 33 and 39.

Th. 77 enables us to assert that when a function $f(x)$ is defined, bounded, and non-negative in a closed interval J, the integrability-R of $f(x)$ over J may be regarded from two points of view:

(i) as prescribing the degree of 'irregularity' of $f(x)$, namely that the set of the discontinuities of $f(x)$ in J shall be null, or

(ii) as imposing a structural condition on $\Omega_0(f; J)$, namely that $\underline{c}\Omega_0(f; J) = \bar{c}\Omega_0(f; J)$, i.e. that $\Omega_0(f; J)$ be measurable-J.

We can now see how it is that a bounded function, defined as the limit of a sequence of integrable functions, may itself be non-integrable in the Riemann sense. Briefly, it is because the property of being continuous almost everywhere in a set is one which may be possessed by every member of a convergent sequence of functions without being possessed by their limit function; or, from the other point of view, because the union of a sequence of sets which are measurable-J need not itself be measurable-J.

Example. Let $\{x_r\}$ be a sequence consisting of all the rational points of J, the closed interval $[0, 1]$; for every positive integer n let

$$f_n(x) = \begin{cases} 1 & \text{if } x \text{ is among } x_1, x_2, \ldots, x_n \\ 0 & \text{otherwise,} \end{cases}$$

and let

$$f(x) = \begin{cases} 1 & \text{if } x \text{ is rational} \\ 0 & \text{otherwise,} \end{cases} \quad \text{i.e.} \quad f(x) = \lim_{n \to \infty} f_n(x).$$

$\left(\text{It is of interest to note that } f(x) \text{ is also given by the equation} \right.$

$$f(x) = \lim_{m \to \infty} \left\{ \lim_{n \to \infty} \cos^{2n}(m! \, x\pi) \right\}.\bigg)$$

We have already seen (example following th. 45) that $f(x)$ is not integrable-R over J, and we may now examine this case from the two points of view we have been discussing.

(i) For every positive integer n, the set of the discontinuities of $f_n(x)$ in J is finite and therefore null, but the set of the discontinuities of $f(x)$ in J is the whole of J. Now J is not null; for if it were, there would be a sequence of intervals, $\{I_r\}$, such that

$$J \subset \sum_{r=1}^{\infty}{}^* I_r \quad \& \quad \sum_{r=1}^{\infty} |I_r| < 1,$$

and so, by th. 38, an integer k such that

$$J \subset \sum_{r=1}^{k}{}^* I_r \quad \& \quad \sum_{r=1}^{k} |I_r| < 1,$$

which contradicts th. 72. Hence the set of the discontinuities of $f(x)$ in J is not null.

(ii) Let n be any positive integer, and choose ϵ freely; then $\Omega_0(f_n; J)$ is covered by the n intervals given by

$$|x - x_r| < \frac{\epsilon}{2n} \quad \& \quad 0 < y < 1 \quad (r = 1, 2, ..., n),$$

the sum of whose contents is ϵ; ϵ being arbitrary, this means $\bar{c}\Omega_0(f_n; J) = 0$, and so, by th. 69, $c\Omega_0(f_n; J) = 0$. But, if $S = \Omega_0(f; J)$, then clearly

$$S^o = 0 \quad \& \quad S^c = \mathscr{S}((x, y); 0 \leqslant x \leqslant 1 \ \& \ 0 \leqslant y \leqslant 1),$$

so that, by ths. 74 and 72,

$$0 = \underline{c}\Omega_0(f; J) < \bar{c}\Omega_0(f; J) = 1,$$

showing that $\Omega_0(f; J)$ is not measurable-J.

In the Lebesgue theory of measure, to which the next chapter is devoted, every set S has a number assigned to it, its 'exterior Lebesgue measure', and the essential difference between this number and $\bar{c}S$ is that the former is based on the use of *infinite* aggregates of covering intervals, whereas $\bar{c}S$ is defined (def. 39) in terms of finite aggregates of covering intervals. As a result of this modification, and of a new definition of measurability, we shall see that the union of a *sequence* of measurable sets is again measurable, and also that the measurability of $\Omega_0(f; J)$ in the new sense imposes on $f(x)$ a certain condition which is much weaker than that of continuity almost everywhere; moreover, if every member of a convergent sequence of functions satisfies this condition, the same is true of their limit function.

III

LEBESGUE MEASURE

In the last chapter we considered the problem of assigning a measure number to an arbitrary set in R_n; we discussed in detail one solution, namely the theory of Jordan content, which proceeds by approximating, in a certain sense, to the given set by finite sums of intervals. The sets which are measurable-J form a special and important class in this theory; the main feature of this class is that it always includes the sum of a *finite* number of its members, the content being additive (th. 75), but one of its chief deficiencies is that it does not always include the sum of a *sequence* of its members. We saw furthermore that the theory of the Riemann integral, which is essentially linked to this theory of measure, reflects exactly the same defect in the way it deals with a function which is defined as the limit of a sequence of integrable functions. The Lebesgue theory of measure solves the problem in a much more satisfactory way, and, as we shall see in Chapter V, forms the basis of a theory of integration which is free from the major defects of the Riemann theory.

§ 1. Exterior Lebesgue Measure

Definition 40. The *exterior Lebesgue measure* (m^*S) of any set S is the lower bound of a certain aggregate α of real numbers, defined as follows: $u \in \alpha$ if and only if there is a sequence of intervals, $\{I_r\}$, such that

$$S \subset \sum_{r=1}^{\infty}{}^* I_r \quad \& \quad \sum_{r=1}^{\infty} |I_r| = u.$$

It may of course happen that $m^*S = \infty$, for example, if $S = R_n$; but it does not follow that $m^*S = \infty$ whenever S is unbounded (cf. def. 39); for example, if S is the sum of the intervals $(n, n+2^{-n})$ $(n = 1, 2, ...)$, then clearly $m^*S \leqslant \sum_{n=1}^{\infty} 2^{-n}$. It should be noted that the intervals I_r, referred to in def. 40, must be contained in the same space as S; this is emphasized in the next theorem.

Theorem 78. *Let a be any finite real number, and let*

$$S = \mathscr{S}((P, y); y = a); \quad then \quad m^*S = 0.$$

Proof. Assuming $S \subset R_{n+1}$, let $\{I_r\}$ be a sequence of intervals such that $R_n = \sum_{r=1}^{\infty}{}^* I_r$. Choose ϵ freely, and then for every positive integer

r let J_r be the interval in R_{n+1} given by

$$J_r = \mathscr{S}\left((P,y); P \in I_r \quad \& \quad |a-y| < \frac{\epsilon . 2^{-r-1}}{|I_r|}\right);$$

then $\qquad |J_r| = \epsilon 2^{-r}, \quad$ and so $\quad \sum_{r=1}^{\infty} |J_r| = \epsilon;$

clearly $\qquad\qquad\qquad S \subset \sum_{r=1}^{\infty}{}^* J_r,$

and since ϵ is arbitrary, this means $m^*S = 0$.

It is usual to define the aggregate α, referred to in def. 40, so that it also includes all numbers u for which there is a *finite* number of intervals, $I_1, I_2,..., I_k$ say, such that

$$S \subset \sum_{r=1}^{k}{}^* I_r \quad \& \quad \sum_{r=1}^{k} |I_r| = u;$$

in other words, what is usually called m^*S is, in our notation, $\min(m^*S, \bar{c}S)$. The equivalence of the two definitions of m^*S follows from the next theorem.

Theorem 79. $\qquad\qquad m^*S \leqslant \bar{c}S.$

Proof. If S is unbounded, $\bar{c}S = \infty$, and the result is obvious. Suppose S is bounded; choose ϵ freely, and then a finite number of intervals, $I_1, I_2,..., I_k$ say, such that

(1) $\qquad\qquad S \subset \sum_{r=1}^{k}{}^* I_r \quad \& \quad \sum_{r=1}^{k} |I_r| < \bar{c}S + \epsilon.$

Let $I_{k+1}, I_{k+2},...$ be any intervals such that

$$|I_{k+s}| < \epsilon 2^{-s} \quad (s = 1, 2,...);$$

then, by (1),

$$S \subset \sum_{r=1}^{\infty}{}^* I_r \quad \& \quad \sum_{r=1}^{\infty} |I_r| < \bar{c}S + 2\epsilon.$$

Hence $m^*S < \bar{c}S + 2\epsilon$ for every ϵ, which means $m^*S \leqslant \bar{c}S$.

Theorem 80. *Let S be a closed bounded set; then $\bar{c}S = m^*S$.*

Proof. Let $\{I_r\}$ be a sequence of intervals covering S. By th. 38 there is an integer k such that

$$S \subset \sum_{r=1}^{k}{}^* I_r \quad \& \quad \sum_{r=1}^{k} |I_r| \leqslant \sum_{r=1}^{\infty} |I_r|;$$

hence, by defs. 40 and 39,

$$m^*S \geqslant \bar{c}S,$$

and this, together with th. 79, proves $m^*S = \bar{c}S$.

Theorem 81. *If $A \subset B$, then $m^*A \leqslant m^*B$.*

Proof. By def. 40.

Theorem 82. *If I is an interval, then*
$$I \subset S \subset I^c \quad \text{implies} \quad m^*S = cI.$$

Proof. Suppose I is given by
$$a_r < x_r < b_r \quad (r = 1, 2, ..., n),$$
and let J_ϵ be a closed interval given by
$$a_r + \epsilon \leqslant x_r \leqslant b_r - \epsilon \quad (r = 1, 2, ..., n).$$
Clearly $I^c \supset S \supset I \supset J_\epsilon,$
and so, by ths. 80, 72, and 81,
$$cI = m^*I^c \geqslant m^*S \geqslant m^*J_\epsilon = \prod_{r=1}^{n} (b_r - a_r - 2\epsilon);$$
and since ϵ may be made arbitrarily small, this implies $m^*S = cI$.

Th. 82 shows that we may, consistently with the usage of def. 31, adopt a more convenient notation for m^*S.

Definition 41. If S is any set, let $|S|$ denote m^*S. Thus, comparing defs. 41 and 36, it appears that $|S| = 0$ is equivalent to the statement 'S is null'; so we may restate th. 52 as

Theorem 83. *If S is finite or enumerable, then $|S| = 0$.*

When dealing with the theory of Jordan content, it was observed that the inequality (th. 73) $\bar{c}\left(\sum_{r=1}^{k}{}^* S_r\right) \leqslant \sum_{r=1}^{k} \bar{c}S_r$ cannot in general be extended to a *sequence* of sets $\{S_r\}$. The next theorem shows that this defect disappears when $\bar{c}$ is replaced by m^*.

Theorem 84. *Let $\{A_r\}$ be a sequence of sets in R_n; then*
$$\left|\sum_{r=1}^{\infty}{}^* A_r\right| \leqslant \sum_{r=1}^{\infty} |A_r|.$$

Proof. Choose ϵ freely, and then, to every positive integer r, a sequence of intervals, $I_{r,1}, I_{r,2},...$ say, such that
$$(1) \qquad A_r \subset \sum_{s=1}^{\infty}{}^* I_{r,s} \quad \& \quad \sum_{s=1}^{\infty} |I_{r,s}| \leqslant |A_r| + \epsilon 2^{-r}.$$
By th. 6 the intervals $I_{r,s}$, where r and s run through all positive integers, can be arranged in a sequence $\{J_t\}$, say; and
$$\sum_{t=1}^{\infty} |J_t| = \sum_{r=1}^{\infty} \sum_{s=1}^{\infty} |I_{r,s}|.$$

Hence, by (1),

$$\sum_{r=1}^{\infty}{}^* A_r \subset \sum_{t=1}^{\infty}{}^* J_t \quad \& \quad \sum_{t=1}^{\infty} |J_t| \leqslant \sum_{r=1}^{\infty} |A_r| + \epsilon,$$

and so it follows that

$$\left| \sum_{r=1}^{\infty}{}^* A_r \right| \leqslant \sum_{r=1}^{\infty} |A_r| + \epsilon \quad \text{for every } \epsilon,$$

and this gives the required result.

Theorem 85. *If A_1, A_2,..., A_k are a finite number of sets in R_n, then*

$$\left| \sum_{r=1}^{k}{}^* A_r \right| \leqslant \sum_{r=1}^{k} |A_r|.$$

Proof. By putting $A_r = 0$ for $r = k+1$, $k+2$,..., we obtain a sequence of sets A_r to which th. 84 may be applied to give the required result. This artificial method may of course be replaced by an argument on the lines of th. 73.

Theorem 86. *The union of a sequence, or of a finite number, of null sets is also null.*

Proof. By th. 84.

§ 2. Measurable Sets

Just as with th. 73, the inequality sign in ths. 84 and 85 cannot be replaced by the sign of equality even when the sets in question are mutually exclusive. It is more difficult to prove this by an example than was the case with th. 73; however, the set N discussed in th. 130 has the property that it is contained in an interval I such that

$$m^*I < m^*N + m^*(I-N).$$

Let us first consider the problem of finding conditions in which

(1) $AB = 0$ implies $|A+B| = |A|+|B|$.

It is in fact true (th. 103) that, if A is contained in an interval which has no points in common with B, then (1) is verified; in particular, (1) is always true if A is an interval. However, intervals are not the only sets which have this property. Let $\mathscr{L}$ be an aggregate of sets defined as follows:

$S \in \mathscr{L}$ if and only if for every pair of sets A and B such that

$$A \subset S \quad \& \quad B \subset \bar{S} \quad \text{it is true that} \quad |A+B| = |A|+|B|.$$

This aggregate $\mathscr{L}$ will be found to possess a number of simple properties of far-reaching importance; for example,

if S belongs to $\mathscr{L}$, so does $\bar{S}$;

if S and T belong to $\mathscr{L}$, so do $S \dotplus T$ and ST; if $\{S_r\}$ is a sequence of members of $\mathscr{L}$, then

$$\sum_{r=1}^{\infty} {}^* S_r \quad \text{and} \quad \prod_{r=1}^{\infty} S_r \quad \text{belong to } \mathscr{L}.$$

Definition 42. A set S is said to be *measurable* $(S \in \mathscr{L})$ if and only if for *every* pair of sets A and B such that

$$A \subset S \quad \& \quad B \subset \bar{S} \quad \text{it is true that} \quad |A+B| = |A|+|B|.$$

If and only if S is measurable, we may denote m^*S or $|S|$ by mS, which is said to be the *measure* of S. In practice we shall only use the symbol mS if we wish to draw attention to the measurability of S; thus the equation

$$mA = |B| \text{ is taken to imply that } A \text{ is measurable.}$$

It is often convenient to have the condition for measurability stated as in the following theorem:

Theorem 87. *If $S \subset R_n$, then $S \in \mathscr{L}$ if and only if*

(1)   *for every set W in R_n,* $\quad |W| = |WS|+|W\bar{S}|$.

Proof. Suppose S satisfies (1); then $A \subset S \ \& \ B \subset \bar{S}$ implies

$$|A+B| = |(A+B)S|+|(A+B)\bar{S}| = |A|+|B|,$$

which, by def. 42, means $S \in \mathscr{L}$.

On the other hand,

if $S \in \mathscr{L}$ & $W \subset R_n$, then $WS \subset S$ & $W\bar{S} \subset \bar{S}$,

and so, by def. 42,

$$|WS+W\bar{S}| = |WS|+|W\bar{S}|, \text{ which means that (1) is true.}$$

Theorem 88. *Suppose $S \subset R_n$ and*

(1) $W \subset R_n$ & $|W| < \infty$ *implies* $|W| \geqslant |WS|+|W\bar{S}|$;

then $S \in \mathscr{L}$.

Proof. Since $W = WS+W\bar{S}$, it follows by th. 85 that

(2) $W \subset R_n$ implies $|W| \leqslant |WS|+|W\bar{S}|$.

By (2) and (1)

(3) $W \subset R_n$ & $|W| < \infty$ implies $|W| = |WS|+|W\bar{S}|$;

and from (2)

(4) $\quad W \subset R_n \quad \& \quad |W| = \infty \quad$ implies $\quad \infty = |W| = |WS| + |W\bar{S}|.$

By (3), (4), and th. 87 $\qquad\qquad S \in \mathscr{L}.$

Theorem 89. *Every null set is measurable.*

Proof. Suppose $|S| = 0$, and that W is any set in the same space as S. By th. 81

$$|W\bar{S}| \leqslant |W| \quad \& \quad |WS| = 0; \quad \text{hence} \quad |W| \geqslant |WS| + |W\bar{S}|,$$

which, by th. 88, means $S \in \mathscr{L}.$

Theorem 90. *If S is measurable, so is $\bar{S}$.*

Proof. Since the complement of $\bar{S}$ is S, the result follows from def. 42.

Theorem 91. *Let A and B be measurable sets in R_n; then*

$$(A \dotplus B) \in \mathscr{L}.$$

Proof. Let W be any set in R_n; since

$$A \dotplus B = A + B\bar{A}, \quad \text{and since} \quad A \in \mathscr{L},$$
$$|W(A \dotplus B)| = |WA + WB\bar{A}| = |WA| + |WB\bar{A}|;$$

hence

(1) $\qquad |W(A \dotplus B)| + |W\bar{A}\bar{B}| = |WA| + |W\bar{A}B| + |W\bar{A}\bar{B}|.$

Since both A and B are measurable,

$$|WA| + |W\bar{A}B| + |W\bar{A}\bar{B}| = |WA| + |W\bar{A}| = |W|;$$

hence, by (1) and ths. 1 and 87, $(A \dotplus B) \in \mathscr{L}.$

Theorem 92. *If $A_1, A_2,..., A_k$ are measurable sets in R_n, then*

$$\sum_{r=1}^{k}{}^* A_r \in \mathscr{L}.$$

Proof. By induction from th. 91.

Theorem 93. *Let $A_1, A_2,..., A_k$ be measurable mutually exclusive sets in R_n; then*

(i) $\qquad W \subset R_n \quad \text{implies} \quad \left| W \sum_{r=1}^{k} A_r \right| = \sum_{r=1}^{k} |WA_r|;$

(ii) $\qquad\qquad m\Big(\sum_{r=1}^{k} A_r \Big) = \sum_{r=1}^{k} mA_r.$

Proof. Put $S_p = \sum\limits_{r=1}^{p} A_r \; (p = 1, 2,..., k)$; then

$$WS_{p+1} = WS_p + WA_{p+1} \quad \& \quad A_{p+1} \in \mathscr{L} \quad (p = 1, 2,..., k-1),$$

and so, by def. 42,
$$|WS_{p+1}| = |WS_p| + |WA_{p+1}|,$$
whence (i) follows by induction. On putting $W = R_n$ in (i), (ii) follows in virtue of th. 92.

Theorem 94. *Let $\{A_r\}$ be a sequence of measurable mutually exclusive sets in R_n, and let W be any set in R_n; then*

(i)
$$\left| W \sum_{r=1}^{\infty} A_r \right| = \sum_{r=1}^{\infty} |WA_r|;$$

(ii)
$$\sum_{r=1}^{\infty} A_r \quad \text{is measurable;}$$

(iii)
$$m\left(\sum_{r=1}^{\infty} A_r \right) = \sum_{r=1}^{\infty} mA_r.$$

Proof. Put $S_p = \sum_{r=1}^{p} A_r$ $(p = 1, 2, ...)$; by th. 93 (i)

(1)
$$|WS_p| = \sum_{r=1}^{p} |WA_r| \quad (p = 1, 2, ...);$$
by (1) and th. 81
$$\left| W \sum_{r=1}^{\infty} A_r \right| \geqslant \sum_{r=1}^{p} |WA_r| \quad (p = 1, 2, ...),$$
and so

(2)
$$\left| W \sum_{r=1}^{\infty} A_r \right| \geqslant \sum_{r=1}^{\infty} |WA_r|.$$
On the other hand, by th. 84,
$$\left| W \sum_{r=1}^{\infty} A_r \right| \leqslant \sum_{r=1}^{\infty} |WA_r|;$$
hence, by (2), we have (i).

By th. 92, $S_p \in \mathscr{L}$, so that

(3)
$$|W| = |WS_p| + |W\bar{S}_p| \quad (p = 1, 2, ...).$$

Put $A = \sum_{r=1}^{\infty} A_r$; by (1) and (i), $|WA| = \lim_{p \to \infty} |WS_p|$; also $W\bar{S}_p \supset W\bar{A}$, which implies $|W\bar{S}_p| \geqslant |W\bar{A}|$ $(p = 1, 2, ...)$; hence, by (3),
$$|W| \geqslant |WA| + |W\bar{A}|,$$
which, by th. 88, means $A \in \mathscr{L}$. Finally, (iii) follows from (i) and (ii) on putting $W = R_n$.

Theorem 95. *Let A and B be measurable sets in R_n; then*
$$AB \in \mathscr{L}.$$
Proof. By ths. 90 and 91, $(\bar{A} \dotplus \bar{B}) \in \mathscr{L}$; hence (th. 90) $AB \in \mathscr{L}$.

Theorem 96. *If $S_1, S_2,..., S_k$ are measurable sets in R_n, then*

$$\prod_{r=1}^{k} S_r \quad \text{is measurable.}$$

Proof. By induction from th. 95.

Theorem 97. *Suppose A and B are measurable sets, and $A \supset B$; then*

(i) $\qquad\qquad\qquad (A-B) \in \mathscr{L},$

(ii) $\qquad$ *if $mB < \infty$, then $m(A-B) = mA - mB$.*

Proof. By th. 90, $\bar{B} \in \mathscr{L}$; hence (th. 95) $A\bar{B} \in \mathscr{L}$, which means (i). Since $\qquad A = B + (A-B) \quad \& \quad B \in \mathscr{L},$

we have, by (i), $\qquad mA = mB + m(A-B),$

and this implies (ii).

Theorem 98. *Let $\{A_r\}$ be a sequence of measurable sets such that*

(1) $\qquad\qquad 0 = A_0 \subset A_1 \subset A_2 \subset ... \cdot \& \quad A = \sum_{r=1}^{\infty}{}^* A_r;$

then $\qquad\qquad\qquad mA = \lim_{n\to\infty} mA_n.$

Proof. By (1) $\qquad A = \sum_{r=1}^{\infty} (A_r - A_{r-1});$

hence, by ths. 97 (i) and 94 (iii),

$$mA = \lim_{n\to\infty} \sum_{r=1}^{n} m(A_r - A_{r-1}),$$

which, by th. 93 (ii), implies $mA = \lim_{n\to\infty} mA_n.$

Theorem 99. *Let $\{S_r\}$ be a sequence of measurable sets in R_n; then*

$$\sum_{r=1}^{\infty}{}^* S_r \in \mathscr{L}.$$

Proof. Put $\qquad A_r = \sum_{v=1}^{r}{}^* S_v \quad (r = 1, 2,...);$

then (th. 92) $\{A_r\}$ is a sequence of measurable sets; also

$$A_1 \subset A_2 \subset ... \quad \& \quad \sum_{r=1}^{\infty}{}^* S_r = \sum_{r=1}^{\infty}{}^* A_r;$$

hence, by th. 98, $\qquad \sum_{r=1}^{\infty}{}^* S_r \in \mathscr{L}.$

Theorem 100. *Let $\{A_r\}$ be a sequence of measurable sets in R_n; then*

$$\prod_{r=1}^{\infty} A_r \in \mathscr{L}.$$

Proof. By ths. 90 and 99

$$\sum_{r=1}^{\infty}{}^* \overline{A}_r \in \mathscr{L};$$

hence, by ths. 1 and 90, $\quad \prod_{r=1}^{\infty} A_r \in \mathscr{L}.$

Theorem 101. *Let $\{A_r\}$ be a sequence of measurable sets such that*

(1) $\qquad\qquad A_1 \supset A_2 \supset \ldots \quad \& \quad A = \prod_{r=1}^{\infty} A_r,$

(2) $\qquad\qquad\qquad mA_1 < \infty;$

then $\qquad\qquad\qquad mA = \lim_{r\to\infty} mA_r.$

Proof. Put $\quad B_r = A_1 - A_r \quad (r = 1, 2, \ldots);$
by (1), (2), and ths. 81 and 97 (ii)

(3) $\qquad\quad B_1 \subset B_2 \subset \ldots \quad \& \quad A_1 - A = \sum_{r=1}^{\infty}{}^* B_r,$
and

(4) $\qquad\quad mB_r = mA_1 - mA_r \quad (r = 1, 2, \ldots).$

By (3), (4), and th. 98

$$m(A_1 - A) = \lim_{r\to\infty} mB_r = mA_1 - \lim_{r\to\infty} mA_r;$$

hence, from (2) and ths. 100 and 97 (ii), we have

$$mA = \lim_{r\to\infty} mA_r.$$

The reader should note that th. 101 is not generally true if the condition (2) is relaxed; for example, if $A_r = (r, \infty)$, it will appear from ths. 104, 81, and 82 that

$$mA_r = \infty \quad (r = 1, 2, \ldots), \quad \text{so that} \quad \lim_{r\to\infty} mA_r = \infty;$$

nevertheless $A_1 \supset A_2 \supset \ldots \& \prod_{r=1}^{\infty} A_r$ is empty and therefore null.

We now proceed to the fundamental result that every interval in R_n is measurable; to prove this, it is convenient to represent an interval as an intersection of sets of a simpler character.

Definition 43. Let c be any finite real number, and r any one of the integers $1, 2, \ldots, n$; then

$$\mathscr{S}((x_1, x_2, \ldots, x_n); x_r > c) \quad \text{and} \quad \mathscr{S}((x_1, x_2, \ldots, x_n); x_r < c)$$

are called *special half-spaces* of R_n.

For example, the set of the points of a line which lie to one side of any chosen point of the line represents a special linear half-space; similarly, if R_2 is represented by a plane, a line parallel to one of the axes of coordinates divides R_2 into two special half-spaces.

Theorem 102. *Any special half-space H of R_n is measurable.*

Proof. Let W be any set in R_n; by th. 88 it is sufficient to show that

$$(1) \qquad\qquad |WH| + |W\bar{H}| \leqslant |W|.$$

Let $\{I_r\}$ be a sequence of intervals such that

$$W \subset \sum_{r=1}^{\infty}{}^{*} I_r; \quad \text{then} \quad WH \subset \sum_{r=1}^{\infty}{}^{*} HI_r \quad \& \quad W\bar{H} \subset \sum_{r=1}^{\infty}{}^{*} \bar{H}I_r;$$

hence (ths. 81 and 84)

$$(2) \quad |WH| + |W\bar{H}| \leqslant \sum_{r=1}^{\infty} |HI_r| + \sum_{r=1}^{\infty} |\bar{H}I_r| = \sum_{r=1}^{\infty} \{|HI_r| + |\bar{H}I_r|\}.$$

So, if (1) is true whenever W is an interval, (2) will imply

$$|WH| + |W\bar{H}| \leqslant \sum_{r=1}^{\infty} |I_r|,$$

and consequently (def. 40) that (1) is true for every set W. Hence the theorem will be proved if we show that, for every interval I in R_n,

$$(3) \qquad\qquad |I| = |IH| + |I\bar{H}|.$$

Suppose I is given by

$$a_r < x_r < b_r \quad (r = 1, 2, ..., n);$$

we may, without loss of generality, suppose H is given by $x_1 < c$. Since (3) is obviously true if $c \leqslant a_1$ or $c \geqslant b_1$, suppose

$$a_1 < c < b_1;$$

IH is then the interval given by

$$a_1 < x_1 < c \quad \& \quad a_r < x_r < b_r \quad (r = 2, 3, ..., n),$$

and $I\bar{H}$ is the set given by $c \leqslant x_1 < b_1 \,\& \, a_r < x_r < b_r \ (r = 2, 3, ..., n)$. Hence, by th. 82,

$$|IH| = (c - a_1) \prod_{r=2}^{n} (b_r - a_r) \quad \& \quad |I\bar{H}| = (b_1 - c) \prod_{r=2}^{n} (b_r - a_r),$$

so that $\qquad |IH| + |I\bar{H}| = (b_1 - a_1) \prod_{r=2}^{n} (b_r - a_r) = |I|,$

thus verifying (3).

Theorem 103. *Any interval I in R_n is measurable.*

Proof. Let I be given by
$$a_r < x_r < b_r \quad (r = 1, 2, ..., n),$$
and let H_r and K_r be the special half-spaces given by
$$x_r > a_r \quad \text{and} \quad x_r < b_r$$
respectively. Then $I = H_1 K_1 H_2 K_2 ... H_n K_n$,
and so, by ths. 102 and 96, $I \in \mathscr{L}$.

Theorem 104. *Any open set U is measurable.*

Proof. If $U = 0$, then $U \in \mathscr{L}$ (th. 89); if $U \neq 0$, there is, by th. 18, a sequence of intervals $\{I_r\}$ such that $U = \sum_{r=1}^{\infty}{}^* I_r$, and so, by ths. 103 and 99, $U \in \mathscr{L}$.

It follows from ths. 19, 103, 82, and 94 that the measure of any bounded open linear set is the sum of the lengths of the intervals which compose it.

Theorem 105. *Any closed set is measurable.*

Proof. By ths. 104 and 90.

Theorem 106. *Let S be any set, and let ϵ be freely chosen; then there is an open set U such that*
$$S \subset U \quad \& \quad mU \leqslant m^*S + \epsilon.$$

Proof. By def. 40, there is a sequence of intervals, $\{I_r\}$, such that
$$S \subset \sum_{r=1}^{\infty}{}^* I_r \quad \& \quad \sum_{r=1}^{\infty} |I_r| \leqslant m^*S + \epsilon.$$
Put $U = \sum_{r=1}^{\infty}{}^* I_r$; then U is open (ths. 14 and 16) and, since
$$U \subset \sum_{r=1}^{\infty}{}^* I_r,$$
it follows by th. 104 and def. 40 that $mU \leqslant \sum_{r=1}^{\infty} |I_r| \leqslant m^*S + \epsilon$. The reader should note that the sign $\leqslant$ may be replaced by $<$ in th. 106 if and only if $m^*S < \infty$.

Theorem 107. *To every set S there is a set S^* such that*
$$S \subset S^* \quad \& \quad mS^* = m^*S.$$

Proof. By th. 106 there is a sequence of open sets, $\{U_r\}$, such that

(1) $\qquad S \subset U_r \quad \& \quad mU_r \leqslant |S| + \dfrac{1}{r} \quad (r = 1, 2, ...).$

Put $S^* = \prod_{r=1}^{\infty} U_r$; by (1) and th. 100

(2) $\qquad\qquad S \subset S^* \quad \& \quad S^* \in \mathscr{L};$

also, for every positive integer n,

$S^* \subset U_n$, so that, by (1), (2), and th. 81, $|S| \leqslant mS^* \leqslant |S| + \dfrac{1}{n}$,

which implies $mS^* = |S|$.

The next theorem is an important generalization of th. 98.

Theorem 108. *Let $\{S_r\}$ be a sequence of sets such that*

(1) $\qquad\qquad S_1 \subset S_2 \subset \ldots \quad \& \quad S = \sum_{r=1}^{\infty *} S_r;$

then $\qquad\qquad |S| = \lim_{r \to \infty} |S_r|.$

Proof. By th. 81

$$|S_n| \leqslant |S_{n+1}| \leqslant |S| \quad (n = 1, 2, \ldots);$$

hence the theorem is proved if we show

(2) $\qquad\qquad \lim_{n \to \infty} |S_n| \geqslant |S|.$

To prove (2) we construct a sequence of sets, $\{T_r\}$, such that

(3) $\qquad\qquad T_1 \subset T_2 \subset \ldots.$

(4) $\qquad S_r \subset T_r \quad \& \quad mT_r = |S_r| \quad (r = 1, 2, \ldots);$

it then follows by (4) and th. 81 that

$$|S| \leqslant \left| \sum_{r=1}^{\infty *} T_r \right|,$$

and by (3), (4), and th. 98 that

$$\left| \sum_{r=1}^{\infty *} T_r \right| = \lim_{n \to \infty} mT_n = \lim_{n \to \infty} |S_n|,$$

which together imply (2). The sequence $\{T_r\}$ is constructed as follows: by th. 107 there is a sequence $\{S_r^*\}$ such that

(5) $\qquad S_r \subset S_r^* \quad \& \quad mS_r^* = |S_r| \quad (r = 1, 2, \ldots);$

put $\qquad\qquad T_r = \prod_{n=r}^{\infty} S_n^* \quad (r = 1, 2, \ldots).$

Obviously (3) is true; by (1) and (5), for every positive integer r,

$$S_r \subset T_r \subset S_r^*, \quad \text{and so (th. 81)} \quad |S_r| \leqslant |T_r| \leqslant |S_r^*| = |S_r|,$$

which means $|T_r| = |S_r|$; but T_r, as the intersection of a sequence of measurable sets, is measurable (th. 100), and so (4) is verified.

Theorem 109. *Let S be a measurable set in R_n; then there is a sequence of bounded measurable sets whose sum is S.*

Proof. Let U_r denote the sphere about the origin of radius r if r is a positive integer, and let $U_0 = 0$; then

$$(1) \qquad S = \sum_{r=1}^{\infty} S(U_r - U_{r-1}).$$

By ths. 14, 104, and 97 (i) $(U_r - U_{r-1}) \in \mathscr{L}$, and so, by th. 95, $S(U_r - U_{r-1}) \in \mathscr{L}$ for every positive integer r; hence (1) represents S as a sum of bounded measurable sets.

Theorem 110. *Let S be any measurable set, and ϵ any positive number; then there are sets H and K such that*

$(1) \qquad\qquad S+H$ *is open & $mH < \epsilon$,*

$(2) \qquad\qquad S-K$ *is closed & $mK < \epsilon$.*

Proof. Suppose $mS < \infty$; by th. 106 there is an open set U satisfying
$$S \subset U \quad \& \quad mU < mS + \epsilon.$$
Put $H = U - S$; then
$S+H$ is open, and, by th. 97 (ii), $mH = mU - mS < \epsilon$, verifying (1).
If $mS = \infty$, there is (th. 109) a sequence of bounded measurable sets, $\{S_r\}$, such that $S = \sum_{r=1}^{\infty} S_r$. By what we have just proved, there is, to every positive integer r, a set H_r such that
$$S_r + H_r \text{ is open} \quad \& \quad mH_r < \epsilon 2^{-r}.$$
Hence, if we put $\qquad H = \sum_{r=1}^{\infty}{}^* (S_r + H_r) - S,$

it follows that $S+H$ is a union of open sets, and $H \subset \sum_{r=1}^{\infty}{}^* H_r$. So, by th. 16, $S+H$ is open, and by ths. 81 and 84
$$|H| \leqslant \sum_{r=1}^{\infty} |H_r| < \epsilon.$$

Since H is the difference of two measurable sets, it is measurable (th. 97 (i)), and so (1) is verified.

To prove (2), we apply the result of (1) to the set $\bar{S}$ which, by th. 90, is measurable, and hence there is a set K such that
$$K + \bar{S} \text{ is open} \quad \& \quad mK < \epsilon.$$
Since $S-K$ is the complement of $K + \bar{S}$, it is closed (th. 26), and so (2) is satisfied.

The next theorem shows that every measurable set may be expressed in terms of a sequence of open sets and a null set.

Theorem 111. *Let S be any* measurable *set; then there is*

  (i) *a sequence of open sets, $\{U_r\}$, such that* $\left| \prod_{r=1}^{\infty} U_r - S \right| = 0,$

  (ii) *a sequence of closed sets, $\{C_r\}$, such that* $\left| S - \sum_{r=1}^{\infty *} C_r \right| = 0.$

Proof. By th. 110 there is a sequence of open sets, $\{U_r\}$, and a sequence of closed sets, $\{C_r\}$, satisfying

$$|U_r - S| < \frac{1}{r} \quad \& \quad |S - C_r| < \frac{1}{r} \quad (r = 1, 2, ...);$$

since for every positive integer n

$$\left(\prod_{r=1}^{\infty} U_r - S \right) \subset (U_n - S) \quad \& \quad \left(S - \sum_{r=1}^{\infty *} C_r \right) \subset (S - C_n),$$

(i) and (ii) are verified in virtue of th. 81.

§ 3. Interior Lebesgue Measure

The reader should note the distinction between ths. 110 and 106; th. 106 asserts that if S is *any* set, then to every ϵ there is a set H such that
$$(S + H) \text{ is open} \quad \& \quad m(S + H) \leqslant |S| + \epsilon,$$
but it affirms nothing of $|H|$. In fact, if S is not measurable, the lower bound of the aggregate of values of $|H|$, for which $(S + H)$ is measurable, is *positive*; this follows from the next theorem.

Theorem 112. *Let S be a set such that to every ϵ there is a set A satisfying the conditions*
$$A \in \mathscr{L} \quad \& \quad |A - S| < \epsilon;$$
then $S \in \mathscr{L}$.

Proof. By hypothesis there is a sequence of measurable sets, $\{A_r\}$, such that
$$|A_r - S| < \frac{1}{r} \quad (r = 1, 2, ...).$$

Put
$$A = \prod_{r=1}^{\infty} A_r;$$

then $A \in \mathscr{L}$ (th. 100), and $|A - S| = 0$ since (th. 81)
$$|A - S| \leqslant |A_n - S| < \frac{1}{n} \quad (n = 1, 2, ...).$$

Hence S is the difference of A, which is measurable, and a null set, and this, by ths. 89 and 97 (i), means $S \in \mathscr{L}$.

The result of the last theorem naturally raises the question of what can be said of $|A-S|$ when A alone is known to be measurable. This question can be answered precisely in terms of the following definition:

Definition 44. The *interior Lebesgue measure* $(m_* S)$ of any set S is the upper bound of the measures of measurable subsets of S.

Theorem 113. $A \subset B$ *implies* $m_* A \leqslant m_* B$.

Proof. By def. 44.

Theorem 114. *To every set S there is a set S_* such that*
$$S_* \subset S \quad \& \quad mS_* = m_* S.$$

Proof. By def. 44 there is a sequence of sets, $\{S_r\}$, such that

(1) $S_r \subset S \quad (r = 1, 2, ...) \quad \& \quad \lim_{r \to \infty} mS_r = m_* S.$

Put $$S_* = \sum_{r=1}^{\infty *} S_r;$$

then, by (1) and th. 99, S_* is a measurable subset of S, and so
$$mS_* \leqslant m_* S;$$
on the other hand, by th. 81,

$mS_* \geqslant mS_r \quad (r = 1, 2, ...),$ which, by (1), implies $mS_* \geqslant m_* S,$
and this completes the proof.

Theorem 115. *Suppose $A = B+C$ & $A \in \mathscr{L}$; then*

(1) $$mA = m^*B + m_* C.$$

Proof. By ths. 107 and 114 there are sets B^* and C_* such that

(2) $B \subset B^* \quad \& \quad mB^* = |B|,$

(3) $C \supset C_* \quad \& \quad mC_* = m_* C.$

Since $BC_* = 0$ & $C_* \in \mathscr{L}$, we have (def. 42)
$$|B| + mC_* = |B+C_*|;$$
hence, by (3) and th. 81, since $B+C_* \subset A$,

(4) $$|B| + m_* C \leqslant mA.$$

On the other hand, since $B^* \in \mathscr{L}$, we have (th. 87)

(5) $$mA = |AB^*| + |A-AB^*|;$$

now $A - AB^*$ is a measurable subset of C (ths. 95 and 97),
and so $$|A-AB^*| \leqslant m_* C;$$

also, by (2) and th. 81, $|AB^*| \leqslant |B^*| = m^*B$; hence, by (5),
$$mA \leqslant m^*B + m_* C,$$
which, with (4), gives (1).

Theorem 116. $m_* S \leqslant m^*S.$

Proof. By th. 81 and def. 44.

Theorem 117.

(i) $S \in \mathscr{L}$ implies $m_* S = m^*S;$

(ii) $m_* S = m^*S < \infty$ implies $S \in \mathscr{L}.$

Proof. Suppose $S \in \mathscr{L}$; since $S \subset S$, $m_* S \geqslant mS$ (def. 44), and so, by th. 116, we have (i).

Now let S be any set; by th. 114, S_* exists such that

(1) $S_* \subset S$ & $mS_* = m_* S;$

since

(2) $S = (S - S_*) + S_*,$

we have, by (1), (2), and def. 42,
$$|S| = |S - S_*| + |S_*| = |S - S_*| + m_* S;$$
hence $m_* S = m^*S < \infty$ implies $|S - S_*| = 0,$
and this, by (2) and ths. 89 and 91, implies $S \in \mathscr{L}$, which proves (ii).

Theorem 118. *Let S be any set in R_n; then*

(i) $\underline{c}S \leqslant m_* S \leqslant m^*S \leqslant \bar{c}S,$

(ii)   *if S is measurable-J, then $mS = cS < \infty.$*

Proof. Let $I_1, I_2,..., I_k$ be any finite number of intervals such that $\sum\limits_{r=1}^{k} I_r \subset S$; by ths. 93, 82, and 103,
$$m\Big(\sum_{r=1}^{k} I_r\Big) = \sum_{r=1}^{k} mI_r = \sum_{r=1}^{k} |I_r|,$$
and so, by def. 44, $m_* S \geqslant \sum\limits_{r=1}^{k} |I_r|$; hence (def. 39) $m_* S \geqslant \underline{c}S$, and this, together with ths. 116 and 79, gives (i).

If S is measurable-J, then, by def. 39 and (i),
$$m_* S = m^*S = cS < \infty,$$
and this, by th. 117 (ii), proves (ii).

Theorem 119. *Suppose $A = B + N$ & $|N| = 0$; then*

(i) $m_* A = m_* B$ & $|A| = |B|;$

(ii) $A \in \mathscr{L}$ *if and only if $B \in \mathscr{L}.$*

Proof. Suppose $S \subset A$ & $S \in \mathcal{L}$; then, by ths. 89 and 97 (ii),
$$S - SN \subset B \quad \& \quad m(S - SN) = mS.$$
Hence, by def. 44,
$$m_* B \geqslant m_* A, \quad \text{which together with th. 113 gives} \quad m_* A = m_* B.$$
Furthermore, by th. 85,
$$|A| \leqslant |B| + |N| = |B|,$$
and this, together with th. 81, completes the proof of (i). Since $N \in \mathcal{L}$ (th. 89), (ii) follows at once from ths. 91 and 97 (i).

Theorem 120.

(i) $\quad If \quad A = \sum\limits_{r=1}^{\infty} A_r, \quad then \quad m_* A \geqslant \sum\limits_{r=1}^{\infty} m_* A_r,$

(ii) $\quad If \quad A = \sum\limits_{r=1}^{k} A_r, \quad then \quad m_* A \geqslant \sum\limits_{r=1}^{k} m_* A_r.$

Proof. Suppose $A = \sum\limits_{r=1}^{\infty} A_r$; by th. 114 there is a sequence of sets, $\{B_r\}$, such that

(1) $\quad B_r \subset A_r \quad \& \quad mB_r = m_* A_r \quad (r = 1, 2, ...).$

Since the sets A_r are mutually exclusive, we have, by (1) and th. 94 (iii),
$$\sum_{r=1}^{\infty} B_r \subset A \quad \& \quad m\left(\sum_{r=1}^{\infty} B_r\right) = \sum_{r=1}^{\infty} mB_r = \sum_{r=1}^{\infty} m_* A_r,$$
which, by def. 44, implies the truth of (i). The proof of (ii) is established on similar lines.

Theorem 121. *Let $\{A_r\}$ be a sequence of mutually exclusive measurable sets in R_n; let*
$$A = \sum_{r=1}^{\infty} A_r, \quad \text{and let } W \text{ be any set in } R_n;$$
then $\quad m_*(WA) = \sum\limits_{r=1}^{\infty} m_*(WA_r).$

Proof. By th. 114 there is a set B such that
$$B \subset WA \quad \& \quad mB = m_*(WA).$$
Clearly $B = \sum\limits_{r=1}^{\infty} BA_r \quad \& \quad BA_r \subset WA_r \quad (r = 1, 2, ...);$
hence, by ths. 95 and 94 (iii),
$$m_*(WA) = mB = m\left(\sum_{r=1}^{\infty} BA_r\right) = \sum_{r=1}^{\infty} mBA_r \leqslant \sum_{r=1}^{\infty} m_*(WA_r);$$

but since $WA = \sum\limits_{r=1}^{\infty} WA_r$, th. 120 implies $m_*(WA) \geqslant \sum\limits_{r=1}^{\infty} m_*(WA_r)$; hence it follows that

$$m_*(WA) = \sum_{r=1}^{\infty} m_*(WA_r).$$

Theorem 122. *Let S be a measurable set in R_n, and let W be any set in R_n; then* $$m_* W = m_*(WS) + m_*(W\bar{S}).$$

Proof. By th. 90 S and $\bar{S}$ are mutually exclusive measurable sets; put

$$A_1 = S, \quad A_2 = \bar{S}, \quad \text{and} \cdot A_r = 0 \quad (r = 3, 4, ...),$$

and the required result follows from th. 121.

Theorem 123 (CANTOR). *Let J denote the closed interval $[0, 1]$, and let θ be any number satisfying $0 \leqslant \theta < 1$; then there is a set K contained in J such that*

(1)　　　　　　　　K is perfect　&　$mK = \theta$,

(2) *every sub-interval of J contains an interval free from points of K.*

Proof. The idea of the construction is to remove from J a sequence of mutually exclusive intervals, $\{I_r\}$, and then to show that the set of the remaining points satisfies the conditions for K. Put $\lambda = 1 - \theta$; remove from J a concentric interval of length $\frac{1}{3}\lambda$: the remaining set consists of two mutually exclusive closed intervals, each of length $\frac{1}{2}(1 - \frac{1}{3}\lambda)$. From each of these closed intervals remove a concentric interval of length $\frac{1}{9}\lambda$; the set of the points of J which remain consists of four mutually exclusive closed intervals, each of length $\frac{1}{4}(1 - \lambda\{\frac{1}{3} + \frac{2}{9}\})$; from each of these remove a concentric interval of length $\frac{1}{27}\lambda$, and so on. Let $\{I_r\}$ be the sequence of intervals removed by this infinite process. Since these are mutually exclusive, their sum, U, is an open set (th. 16) and, by th. 94 (iii),

$$mU = \sum_{r=1}^{\infty} mI_r = \lambda \sum_{\nu=0}^{\infty} \frac{2^\nu}{3^{\nu+1}} = \lambda.$$

Put $K = J\bar{U}$; then K is closed (ths. 26 and 27), and, by th. 97 (ii),

$$mK = mJ - mU = 1 - \lambda = \theta.$$

To show that K is perfect, we observe first that the end-points of J clearly belong to K'. Suppose then that $\xi \in K(0, 1)$; if $\xi \bar{\in} K'$, then ξ belongs to an interval I such that

$$I \subset J \quad \& \quad IK \text{ consists of } \xi \text{ alone.}$$

Since
$$J - K = \sum_{r=1}^{\infty} I_r,$$
this means that ξ is an end-point of two different intervals I_r, which is inconsistent with the method of constructing the sequence $\{I_r\}$. Finally, to prove (2), we observe that

$$J - \sum_{r=1}^{2^n} I_r$$

consists of closed intervals none of which exceeds 2^{-n} in length; hence K, i.e. $J - \sum_{r=1}^{\infty} I_r$, cannot contain an interval, which means that every sub-interval of J includes a point, and therefore contains a sub-interval, of the open set $\overline{K}$.

Theorem 124. (VITALI). *Suppose E is a set of points in R_n, and that α is an aggregate of closed cubes in R_n (or of closed intervals if $n = 1$) such that*

(1) *the union of the members of α has finite exterior measure,*

(2) *if $P \in E$, then every sphere about P contains a member of α which includes P;*

then there is a finite or an enumerable aggregate of mutually exclusive members of α whose sum includes almost all *the points of E.*

Proof. Suppose

(3)   the theorem is false.

Let K_1 be any member of α, and let $\{K_r\}$ be a sequence of members of α constructed as follows: suppose $K_1, K_2, ..., K_q$ have been chosen and that their sum is S_q; then $\overline{S}_q$ is open (ths. 28 and 25), and, by (3), $E\overline{S}_q \neq 0$; so, by (2), there are members of α contained in $\overline{S}_q$; choose K_{q+1} from among these so that

(4) the side of every member of α contained in $\overline{S}_q$ is less than twice that of K_{q+1}.

Now put $A = \sum_{r=1}^{\infty} K_r$; by (1) and th. 94 (iii),

(5) $\infty > |A| = \sum_{r=1}^{\infty} |K_r|.$

Choose ϵ freely, and then, in virtue of (5), choose N so that

(6) $\sum_{r=N}^{\infty} |K_r| < \epsilon.$

Suppose $P \in E\overline{A}$; since P belongs to $\overline{S}_N$, which is open, it follows, by (2), that there is a member of α, say K, which includes P and is contained in $\overline{S}_N$. Now, by (5), $\lim_{r \to \infty} |K_r| = 0$, and so, by (4), K cannot be contained in $\overline{S}_q$ for all values of q; hence there is an integer ν such that

(7) $$KS_{\nu-1} = 0 \quad \& \quad KK_\nu \neq 0 \quad \& \quad \nu > N.$$

By (7) and (4) it follows that K is contained in K_ν^*, the cube concentric with K_ν and such that $|K_\nu^*| = 5^n|K_\nu|$, and hence P, which belongs to K, belongs to $\sum_{r=N}^{\infty} {}^* K_r^*$. Hence, by def. 40 and (6),

$$|E\overline{A}| \leqslant \sum_{r=N}^{\infty} |K_r^*| = 5^n \sum_{r=N}^{\infty} |K_r| < \epsilon 5^n,$$

and since ϵ is arbitrary, this means $|E\overline{A}| = 0$, which is inconsistent with (3). Hence (3) is false, and the theorem is proved true.

The proof of th. 124 given above is due to S. Banach.

(If the members of α can be arranged in a sequence, the reader will easily see that a precise rule can be given for the selection of $\{K_r\}$; cf. th. 11.)

Theorem 125. *Suppose E is a set of points in R_n of finite exterior measure, and that α is an aggregate of closed cubes in R_n (or of closed intervals if $n = 1$) such that, if $P \in E$, then every sphere about P contains a member of α which includes P. Let ϵ be freely chosen; then there is a finite number of mutually exclusive members of α, say K_1, K_2,..., K_N, such that*

(1) $$\sum_{r=1}^{N} |K_r| - \epsilon \leqslant |E| \leqslant \left| \sum_{r=1}^{N} EK_r \right| + \epsilon.$$

Proof. By th. 106 there is an open set U such that

(2) $$E \subset U \quad \& \quad mU < |E| + \epsilon.$$

Let α^* be the aggregate of all the members of α which are contained in U; since every point of E is the centre of a sphere contained in U, it follows from the hypothesis on α that α^* satisfies all the conditions for α which are laid down in th. 124. Hence, by that theorem, there is a finite aggregate, or else a sequence $\{K_r\}$, of mutually exclusive members of α^* whose sum includes almost all the points of E. Assuming that the latter is true, it follows by th. 119 that

(3) $$|E| = \left| \sum_{r=1}^{\infty} EK_r \right|.$$

Since $\sum\limits_{r=1}^{\infty} K_r \subset U$, we have, by ths. 94 (iii) and 81, and (2),

(4) $$\sum_{r=1}^{\infty} |K_r| = \left| \sum_{r=1}^{\infty} K_r \right| \leqslant |U| < |E| + \epsilon < \infty;$$

hence N exists such that $\sum\limits_{r=N+1}^{\infty} |K_r| < \epsilon$, and so, by (3) and ths. 85, 81, and 84,

$$|E| \leqslant \left| \sum_{r=1}^{N} EK_r \right| + \left| \sum_{r=N+1}^{\infty} EK_r \right|$$

$$\leqslant \left| \sum_{r=1}^{N} EK_r \right| + \sum_{r=N+1}^{\infty} |K_r| < \left| \sum_{r=1}^{N} EK_r \right| + \epsilon,$$

which, together with (4), implies (1).

In the case where a finite aggregate of members of α^* includes almost all the points of E it is easy to see that this aggregate satisfies (1).

§ 4. Linear Transformations

Definition 45. If to every point P of S, a set in R_n, there is assigned a point of R_n, and this point is denoted by $F(P)$, we say that F *transforms* P into $F(P)$; the set of all points $F(P)$ obtained when P runs through S is denoted by $F(S)$, and F is said to transform S into $F(S)$. We shall also use the symbol $f(S)$, when $f(P)$ is a function defined in a set S, to denote the set of the values assumed by $f(P)$ as P runs through S. If

$$F((x_1, x_2, ..., x_n)) = (y_1, y_2, ..., y_n),$$

and the x_r and y_r are connected by a fixed system of linear equations

$$y_r = u_r + v_{r,1} x_1 + v_{r,2} x_2 + ... + v_{r,n} x_n \quad (r = 1, 2, ..., n),$$

then F is said to be a *linear transformation*.

Definition 46. If the equations defining a linear transformation F are of the form

$$y_r = u_r + v_r x_r \quad \& \quad v_r \neq 0 \quad (r = 1, 2, ..., n),$$

so that

$$F((x_1, x_2, ..., x_n)) = (u_1 + v_1 x_1, u_2 + v_2 x_2, ..., u_n + v_n x_n),$$

we shall denote the positive number $|v_1 v_2 ... v_n|$ by v, and in this case F will be called a *restricted linear transformation*. (We shall only be concerned with such restricted transformations.)

Definition 47. If F is a restricted linear transformation, and Q is any point of R_n, then the unique point P such that

$$F(P) = Q \quad \text{will be denoted by} \quad F^{-1}(Q),$$

and F^{-1} will be called the *inverse transformation* to F. In the notation of def. 46, if $Q = (y_1, y_2,..., y_n)$, then

$$F^{-1}(Q) = \left(\frac{y_1 - u_1}{v_1}, \frac{y_2 - u_2}{v_2},..., \frac{y_n - u_n}{v_n}\right).$$

The reader will recognize that in R_2 the geometrical transformations of figures by translation, reflection (about a point or about one of the axes of coordinates), or by uniform stretch (in which the point (x, y) is transformed into (x, ky)) may all be expressed by restricted linear transformations. The following simple theorem enables us to compare the metrical properties of a set with those of its transform.

Theorem 126. *If I is an interval, and F is a restricted linear transformation, then $F(I)$ is an interval and $|F(I)| = v|I|$.*

Proof. If I is given by

$$a_r < x_r < b_r \quad (r = 1, 2,..., n),$$

it is easily seen that $F(I)$ is the set of the points $(y_1, y_2,..., y_n)$ such that (in the notation of def. 46)

$$u_r + \min(v_r a_r, v_r b_r) < y_r < u_r + \max(v_r a_r, v_r b_r) \quad (r = 1, 2,..., n).$$

Hence $F(I)$ is an interval, and

$$|F(I)| = \prod_{r=1}^{n} \{\max(v_r a_r, v_r b_r) - \min(v_r a_r, v_r b_r)\}$$

$$= \prod_{r=1}^{n} |v_r| (b_r - a_r) = v|I|.$$

Theorem 127. *If F is a restricted linear transformation, then*

$$|F(S)| = v|S|.$$

Proof. Choose ϵ freely, and then a sequence of intervals, $\{I_r\}$, such that

(1) $$S \subset \sum_{r=1}^{\infty}{}^* I_r \quad \& \quad \sum_{r=1}^{\infty} |I_r| \leqslant |S| + \epsilon.$$

Since

$$F(S) \subset \sum_{r=1}^{\infty}{}^* F(I_r),$$

it follows by def. 40, th. 126, and (1) that

$$|F(S)| \leqslant \sum_{r=1}^{\infty} |F(I_r)| = \sum_{r=1}^{\infty} v|I_r| \leqslant v(|S| + \epsilon)$$

for every ϵ. This means

(2) $$|F(S)| \leqslant v|S|.$$

Now $F^{-1}(F(S)) = S$, and $1/v$ bears the same relation to F^{-1} as v

does to F. Hence we obtain, as an analogue of (2),

$$|S| = |F^{-1}(F(S))| \leqslant \frac{1}{v}|F(S)|,$$

which, with (2), gives $|F(S)| = v\,|S|$.

Theorem 128. *Let F be a restricted linear transformation and S any set in R_n; then $F(S) \in \mathscr{L}$ if and only if $S \in \mathscr{L}$.*

Proof. Suppose $W \subset R_n$; since $F(P)$ and $F(Q)$ are different if the points P and Q are different, it follows that

$$F(WS) \quad \text{and} \quad F(W\bar{S}) \quad \text{are mutually exclusive;}$$

hence, by def. 42, if $F(S) \in \mathscr{L}$, then

$$|F(W)| = |F(WS + W\bar{S})| = |F(WS)| + |F(W\bar{S})|,$$

which, by th. 127, means

$$|W| = |WS| + |W\bar{S}|;$$

so, by th. 87, $\qquad F(S) \in \mathscr{L}$ implies $S \in \mathscr{L}$.

On applying the transformation F^{-1} to the set $F(S)$, it now follows that $S \in \mathscr{L}$ implies $F(S) \in \mathscr{L}$.

Theorem 129. *If F is a restricted linear transformation, then*
$$m_* F(S) = v\,m_* S.$$

Proof. By th. 114, S_* exists such that

(1) $\qquad\qquad S_* \subset S \quad \& \quad mS_* = m_* S.$

By (1)

(2) $\qquad\qquad F(S_*) \subset F(S),$

and, from ths. 127 and 128, it follows that

$$mF(S_*) = v\,mS_*;$$

hence, by def. 44, (2), and (1),

(3) $\qquad\qquad m_* F(S) \geqslant v\,m_* S.$

Similarly, as in th. 127, it follows that $m_* S \geqslant (1/v)\,m_* F(S)$, which, with (3), gives the required result.

§ 5. Non-Measurable Sets

When we introduced the definition of a measurable set our purpose was to set up a class of sets of points whose exterior Lebesgue measures satisfy a certain condition of additivity. It is natural to ask: Do there exist sets which are not measurable?—a question which has been of some historical importance. The study of this problem has coincided with a period in which the foundations of the theory of aggregates have been critically scrutinized; and this criticism has revealed that the words and concepts, which we usually accept in building a theory of aggregates, conceal subtle difficulties of a logical character which have serious bearing on the problem of the non-measurable set.

To prove that there are non-measurable sets, there appear to be two obvious paths: either to 'produce' such a set, or else to show that the assumption of their non-existence contradicts some axiom of mathematics. The first alternative compels us to examine the conditions in which a set may be said to have been produced or constructed; if we decide that a set is only produced when a 'rule' is given by which it can be determined whether or not any assigned point belongs to the set, we are further compelled to specify the conditions in which a collection of propositions becomes a 'rule'. It may at once be said that no example of a non-measurable set has yet been given along these lines. It is by proceeding with the second alternative that results have been obtained; and the mathematical axiom which plays the important role in these results is the Selection Axiom, which we discussed briefly in § 5 of Chapter I.

Theorem 130. *There exists a non-measurable set.*

Proof. Let I denote the interval $(0, 1)$; if $\xi \in I$, let $R(\xi)$ denote the set of the numbers x such that

$$0 < x < 1 \quad \& \quad x - \xi \text{ is rational.}$$

Clearly, $\qquad\qquad y \in R(x) \quad \text{implies} \quad R(y) = R(x),$

and so the members of the aggregate of the sets $R(x)$, obtained when x runs through I, are mutually exclusive. Hence, by the Selection Axiom, there is a set S such that

(1) $S \subset I$, and if $x \in I$, then $SR(x)$ consists of a single point.

It is easy to prove that S is a linear non-measurable set. By th. 9 there is a sequence, say $r_1, r_2, \ldots$, consisting of all the rational numbers in the interval $(-1, 1)$; to every positive integer n let F_n be the transformation defined by $\qquad F_n(x) = x + r_n.$

Now if m and n are distinct positive integers, then $F_m(S) F_n(S) = 0$: for otherwise there are points ξ and η in S such that

$$\xi + r_m = \eta + r_n, \quad \text{i.e.} \quad \xi - \eta = r_n - r_m,$$

TH. 130] LEBESGUE MEASURE

which, by (1), implies $\xi = \eta$ and consequently $n = m$. We can now show that S is not measurable. Suppose $S \in \mathscr{L}$; by ths. 127 and 128, $mF_n(S) = mS$ $(n = 1, 2, \ldots)$, and so, since

$$\sum_{n=1}^{\infty} F_n(S) \subset (-1, 2),$$

we have, by ths. 82, 81, and 94,

$$3 \geqslant m\Big(\sum_{n=1}^{\infty} F_n(S) \Big) = \sum_{n=1}^{\infty} mF_n(S) = \sum_{n=1}^{\infty} mS;$$

hence $mS = 0$, and consequently $\left| \sum_{n=1}^{\infty} F_n(S) \right| = 0$. On the other hand, if $\xi \in I$, it follows by (1) that

$$\xi \in F_n(S) \quad \text{for some positive integer } n;$$

hence $$I \subset \sum_{n=1}^{\infty} F_n(S),$$

which contradicts the conclusion $\left| \sum_{n=1}^{\infty} F_n(S) \right| = 0$. Hence the assumption $S \in \mathscr{L}$ leads to a contradiction.

IV

SETS OF ORDINATES AND MEASURABLE FUNCTIONS

§ 1. Sets of Ordinates

WITH the Lebesgue theory of measure at our disposal, we can now generalize the problem of 'measuring the area under a curve'.

Definition 48. Let B be any set in R_n, and let $f(P)$ be a non-negative function defined in B; let

$$\Omega_0(f; B) = \mathscr{S}((P, y); P \in B \,\&\, 0 < y < f(P)),$$
$$\Omega_1(f; B) = \mathscr{S}((P, y); P \in B \,\&\, 0 < y \leqslant f(P));$$

then $\Omega_0(f; B)$ is called the *least*, and $\Omega_1(f; B)$ is called the *greatest set of ordinates* of $f(P)$ over B. The symbol $\Omega(f; B)$ is used to denote any set S satisfying

$$\Omega_0(f; B) \subset S \subset \Omega_1(f; B),$$

and S is called a set of ordinates of $f(P)$ over B.

It should be noted that $\Omega(f; B) \subset R_{n+1}$, so that $\Omega(f; B)$ is plane if B is linear, and three-dimensional if B is plane. The problem which we shall consider in this chapter is that of finding necessary and sufficient conditions for $\Omega(f; B)$ to be measurable (in the Lebesgue sense).

The next two theorems are obvious corollaries to def. 48.

Theorem 131.

(i) *If* $B = \sum\limits_{r=1}^{k} B_r$, *then* $\Omega_0(f; B) = \sum\limits_{r=1}^{k} \Omega_0(f; B_r)$;

(ii) *if* $B = \sum\limits_{r=1}^{\infty} B_r$, *then* $\Omega_0(f; B) = \sum\limits_{r=1}^{\infty} \Omega_0(f; B_r)$,

assuming in each case that one side of the result equation is defined.

Theorem 132. *If* $0 \leqslant f(P) \leqslant g(P)$ *for every point P of B, then*
$$\Omega_0(f; B) \subset \Omega_0(g; B) \quad \&\quad \Omega_1(f; B) \subset \Omega_1(g; B).$$

Theorem 133. *If* $0 < a < \infty$, *and* $g(P) = af(P)$, *then*

(i) $|\Omega_0(g; B)| = a\,|\Omega_0(f; B)|$ & $m_* \Omega_0(g; B) = a\,m_* \Omega_0(f; B)$;

(ii) $m\Omega_0(g; B) = a\,m\Omega_0(f; B)$,

assuming in each case that one side of the equation exists.

Proof. Let F be defined by

$$F((P,y)) = (P, ay);$$

then $\qquad F\{\Omega_0(f; B)\} = \Omega_0(g; B),$

and so (i) follows by ths. 127 and 129, and (ii) from ths. 128 and 127.

Theorem 134. *Let $\{f_n(P)\}$ be a sequence of non-negative functions defined in B.*

(i) *If $P \in B$ implies $f_1(P) \leqslant f_2(P) \leqslant \ldots$ & $f(P) = \lim\limits_{n\to\infty} f_n(P)$, then*

$$\Omega_0(f; B) = \sum_{n=1}^{\infty}{}^* \Omega_0(f_n; B);$$

(ii) *if $P \in B$ implies $f_1(P) \geqslant f_2(P) \geqslant \ldots$ & $f(P) = \lim\limits_{n\to\infty} f_n(P)$, then*

$$\Omega_1(f; B) = \prod_{n=1}^{\infty} \Omega_1(f_n; B).$$

Proof. By def. 48.

Theorem 135. *Let $f(P)$ be defined and non-negative in B; then*

(i) $|\Omega_0(f; B)| = |\Omega_1(f; B)|$ & $m_*\Omega_0(f; B) = m_*\Omega_1(f; B);$

(ii) $m\Omega_0(f; B) = m\Omega_1(f; B)$ *if either side exists.*

Proof. Let $\qquad f_n(P) = \left(1 + \dfrac{1}{n}\right)f(P).$

If n is a positive integer, then

$$\Omega_1(f; B) \subset \Omega_0(f_n; B) \quad \text{(def. 48)},$$

and hence, by ths. 81 and 133,

$$|\Omega_0(f; B)| \leqslant |\Omega_1(f; B)| \leqslant |\Omega_0(f_n; B)| = \left(1 + \frac{1}{n}\right)|\Omega_0(f; B)|,$$

which, since n is arbitrary, means $|\Omega_0(f; B)| = |\Omega_1(f; B)|$. Similarly, appealing to th. 113 instead of th. 81, we have

$$m_*\Omega_0(f; B) = m_*\Omega_1(f; B),$$

which completes the proof of (i). Now

$$(1) \qquad \Omega_1(f; B) = \prod_{n=1}^{\infty} \Omega_0(f_n; B) \quad \& \quad \Omega_0(f; B) = \sum_{n=2}^{\infty}{}^* \Omega_1(f_{-n}; B);$$

if the left-hand side of (ii) exists, then, by th. 133,

$$\Omega_0(f_n; B) \in \mathscr{L} \quad (n = 1, 2, \ldots);$$

hence, by (1) and th. 100, $\Omega_1(f; B) \in \mathscr{L}$. This, together with (i), proves

$$m\Omega_0(f; B) = m\Omega_1(f; B).$$

If $\Omega_1(f; B) \in \mathscr{L}$, we replace th. 100 by th. 99 in the above argument, and so complete the proof of (ii).

We now consider the problem of finding conditions in which $\Omega_0(f; B) \in \mathscr{L}$. The simplest case occurs when $f(P)$ is finite and constant in B.

§ 2. Cylinder Sets

Definition 49. Let h be any finite positive number; then the *cylinder on B of height h*, $\mathscr{C}(h; B)$, is defined by
$$\mathscr{C}(h; B) = \mathscr{S}((P, y); \; P \in B \; \& \; 0 < y < h).$$
B is called the *base*, $\mathscr{S}((P, 0); P \in B)$ is called the *bottom*, and $\mathscr{S}((P, h); P \in B)$ is called the *top* of the cylinder $\mathscr{C}(h; B)$. The reader should note that
$$\text{if } B \subset R_n, \quad \text{then} \quad \mathscr{C}(h; B) \subset R_{n+1};$$
hence the base and the bottom are distinct sets.

The aim of the next six theorems is to show that
$$m\mathscr{C}(h; B) = h \, mB$$
if either side is defined.

Theorem 136. $|\mathscr{C}(1; B)| \leqslant |B|$.

Proof. Let I_1, I_2,... be intervals such that
$$(1) \qquad\qquad B \subset \sum_{r=1}^{\infty *} I_r.$$
Now $\mathscr{C}(1; I_r)$ is an interval & $|\mathscr{C}(1; I_r)| = |I_r|$ $(r = 1, 2,...)$; hence, by (1),
$$\mathscr{C}(1; B) \subset \sum_{r=1}^{\infty *} \mathscr{C}(1; I_r) \quad \& \quad \sum_{r=1}^{\infty} |\mathscr{C}(1; I_r)| = \sum_{r=1}^{\infty} |I_r|,$$
which, by def. 40, implies $|\mathscr{C}(1; B)| \leqslant |B|$.

Thus, if $B \subset R_2$, th. 136 asserts that the *volume* of a cylinder of unit height does not exceed the *area* of its base.

Theorem 137. *Let B be bounded; then* $m_* \mathscr{C}(1; B) \geqslant m_* B$.

Proof. Let I be an interval containing B; then
$$(1) \qquad\qquad \mathscr{C}(1; I) = \mathscr{C}(1; B) + \mathscr{C}(1; I - B).$$
Now $\mathscr{C}(1; I)$ is an interval & $m\mathscr{C}(1; I) = mI$; hence, by (1) and th. 115,
$$mI = m\mathscr{C}(1; I) = m_* \mathscr{C}(1; B) + |\mathscr{C}(1; I - B)|,$$
which, together with ths. 136 and 115, proves
$$m_* \mathscr{C}(1; B) \geqslant mI - |I - B| = m_* B.$$

Theorem 138. *Let B be a measurable set; then $m\mathscr{C}(1; B) = mB$.*

Proof. If B is bounded, the result is a corollary of ths. 136, 137, and 117, for

$$mB \leqslant m_* \mathscr{C}(1; B) \leqslant m^* \mathscr{C}(1; B) \leqslant mB < \infty.$$

Hence, if B is the sum of a sequence of bounded measurable sets, $\{B_r\}$, it follows from ths. 94 and 131 that

$$mB = \sum_{r=1}^{\infty} mB_r = \sum_{r=1}^{\infty} m\mathscr{C}(1; B_r) = m\left(\sum_{r=1}^{\infty} \mathscr{C}(1; B_r)\right) = m\mathscr{C}(1; B),$$

which, by th. 109, proves the result when B is unbounded.

Theorem 139. *Let B be any set; then $|\mathscr{C}(1; B)| = |B|$.*

Proof. Let $\underline{\mathscr{C}}(1; S)$ denote the sum of the cylinder $\mathscr{C}(1; S)$, its top, and its bottom. Let V be any set such that

(1) $$V \text{ is open } \& \quad \underline{\mathscr{C}}(1; B) \subset V.$$

Let U be the set of all points P such that $(P, y) \in V$ for all y satisfying $0 \leqslant y \leqslant 1$; by (1)

(2) $$B \subset U \quad \& \quad \underline{\mathscr{C}}(1; U) \subset V.$$

We first show that U is open. Let P be any point of U, and suppose $P \bar{\in} U^o$; then there is a sequence $\{P_r\}$ such that

(3) $$\lim_{r \to \infty} P_r = P \quad \& \quad P_r \in \bar{U} \quad (r = 1, 2, \ldots).$$

By (3) and the definition of U, there is a sequence $\{(P_r, y_r)\}$ such that

(4) $$0 \leqslant y_r \leqslant 1 \quad \& \quad (P_r, y_r) \in \bar{V} \quad (r = 1, 2, \ldots);$$

by (3) and (4) the sequence $\{(P_r, y_r)\}$ is bounded, and so (th. 32) contains a convergent sub-sequence, whose limit, by (3) and (4), must be of the form (P, θ), where $0 \leqslant \theta \leqslant 1$. Furthermore, $\bar{V}$ being closed (th. 26), it follows by (4) and th. 35 that $(P, \theta) \in \bar{V}$ which contradicts the hypothesis $P \in U$. Hence $P \in U$ implies $P \in U^o$, i.e. U is open. Since $U \in \mathscr{L}$ (th. 104), it now follows from (2) and ths. 81 and 138 that

$$mV \geqslant m\mathscr{C}(1; U) = mU \geqslant |B|$$

for every open set V which contains $\underline{\mathscr{C}}(1; B)$; hence, by th. 106, $|\underline{\mathscr{C}}(1; B)| \geqslant |B|$, which, together with th. 136, proves

(5) $$|\mathscr{C}(1; B)| \leqslant |B| \leqslant |\underline{\mathscr{C}}(1; B)|.$$

Now, by th. 78, both the top and the bottom of $\mathscr{C}(1; B)$ are null sets; hence, by ths. 86 and 119,

$$|\mathscr{C}(1; B)| = |\underline{\mathscr{C}}(1; B)|, \quad \text{so that (5) means} \quad |\mathscr{C}(1; B)| = |B|.$$

Theorem 140. *Suppose* $\mathscr{C}(1; B) \in \mathscr{L}$; *then* $B \in \mathscr{L}$.

Proof. Let W be any set in the same space as B; then

(1) $$\mathscr{C}(1; W) = \mathscr{C}(1; WB) + \mathscr{C}(1; W\bar{B}),$$

and

(2) $$\mathscr{C}(1; WB) \subset \mathscr{C}(1; B) \quad \& \quad \mathscr{C}(1; W\bar{B})\mathscr{C}(1; B) = 0.$$

Since $\mathscr{C}(1; B) \in \mathscr{L}$, it follows by (2), (1), and def. 42, that

$$|\mathscr{C}(1; W)| = |\mathscr{C}(1; WB)| + |\mathscr{C}(1; W\bar{B})|,$$

which, by th. 139, means

$$|W| = |WB| + |W\bar{B}|.$$

Hence, by th. 87, $B \in \mathscr{L}$.

Theorem 141. *If* $0 < h < \infty$, *and* B *is any set, then*

(i) $|\mathscr{C}(h; B)| = h\,|B|$,

(ii) $m\mathscr{C}(h; B) = h\,mB$ *if either side exists.*

Proof. Since $\mathscr{C}(1; B) = \Omega_0(f; B)$, where $f(P) = 1$ for every point P of B, the result follows from th. 133 on putting $a = h$.

Theorem 142. *Let* $f(P)$ *be defined and non-negative in a null set* B; *then*

$$|\Omega_0(f; B)| = 0.$$

Proof. Since $$\Omega_0(f; B) \subset \sum_{r=1}^{\infty}{}^{*}\,\mathscr{C}(r; B),$$

it follows by ths. 141 and 86 that $\Omega_0(f; B)$ is contained in a null set, and is therefore null.

§ 3. Measurable Functions

We are now in a position to discuss conditions for the measurability of $\Omega_0(f; B)$ in the more general case when $f(P)$ is not constant in B.

Theorem 143. *Let* $f(P)$ *be defined and non-negative in* B; *then* $\Omega_0(f; B)$ *is the union of a sequence of cylinders (except when* $f(P) = 0$ *for every point* P *of* B, *in which case* $\Omega_0(f; B) = 0$).

Proof. By th. 9 there is a sequence, $\{h_r\}$, consisting of all the positive rational numbers. Let

$$B_r = B \cdot \mathscr{S}(P; f(P) > h_r) \quad (r = 1, 2, \dots);$$

clearly

(1) $$\sum_{r=1}^{\infty}{}^{*}\,\mathscr{C}(h_r; B_r) \subset \Omega_0(f; B).$$

On the other hand, if $(P, y) \in \Omega_0(f; B)$, there is a positive rational number, say h_ν, such that $0 < y < h_\nu < f(P)$, which means that $(P, y) \in \mathscr{C}(h_\nu; B_\nu)$; hence

$$\Omega_0(f; B) \subset \sum_{r=1}^{\infty}{}^* \mathscr{C}(h_r; B_r),$$

and this, together with (1), gives the required result.

Since the measurability of a cylinder is equivalent to the measurability of its base (ths. 138 and 140), th. 143 at once suggests a condition sufficient for the measurability of $\Omega_0(f; B)$.

Definition 50. Let B be a measurable set, let $f(P)$ be defined in B, and let $B(a) = B \cdot \mathscr{S}(P; f(P) > a)$; the function $f(P)$ is said to be *measurable in* B if and only if $B(a) \in \mathscr{L}$ for *every* real number a. A function of the n real variables $x_1, x_2, \ldots, x_n$ is said to be measurable in B if its corresponding point function is measurable in B. It should be noted that def. 50 is not restricted to functions that are non-negative in B.

Theorem 144. *Let $f(P)$ be non-negative and measurable in B; then*

$$\Omega_0(f; B) \in \mathscr{L}.$$

Proof. With the notation of th. 143

(1) $$\Omega_0(f; B) = \sum_{r=1}^{\infty}{}^* \mathscr{C}(h_r; B_r).$$

By def. 50, $B_r \in \mathscr{L}$, and so (th. 138) $\mathscr{C}(h_r; B_r) \in \mathscr{L}$ for every positive integer r. Hence, by (1) and th. 99, $\Omega_0(f; B) \in \mathscr{L}$.

We shall now show that, when $B \in \mathscr{L}$ and $f(P)$ is non-negative in B, the measurability of $f(P)$ in B and the measurability of $\Omega_0(f; B)$ are exactly equivalent.

Theorem 145. *Let $f(P)$ be defined and positive in B, and suppose*

$$\Omega_0(f; B) \in \mathscr{L}; \quad then \quad B \in \mathscr{L}.$$

Proof. With the notation of th. 143, for every positive integer r put

(1) $$S_r = \Omega_0(f; B) \cdot \mathscr{S}((P, y); y < h_r),$$

(2) $$F_r((P, y)) = \left(P, \frac{y}{h_r}\right).$$

Since $S_r \supset \mathscr{C}(h_r; B_r)$, it follows that

$$F_r(S_r) \supset F_r(\mathscr{C}(h_r; B_r)) = \mathscr{C}(1; B_r) \quad (r = 1, 2, \ldots),$$

so that, since $f(P) > 0$ for every point P of B, i.e. $B = \sum_{r=1}^{\infty}* B_r$, we have

(3) $$\sum_{r=1}^{\infty}* F_r(S_r) \supset \sum_{r=1}^{\infty}* \mathscr{C}(1; B_r) = \mathscr{C}(1; B).$$

On the other hand, by (2) and (1),

$$F_r(S_r) \subset \mathscr{C}(1; B) \quad (r = 1, 2,...);$$

hence, by (3),

(4) $$\sum_{r=1}^{\infty}* F_r(S_r) = \mathscr{C}(1; B).$$

Now, by (1), S_r is the intersection of a special half-space and $\Omega_0(f; B)$, which is measurable by hypothesis; hence, by ths. 102 and 95, $S_r \in \mathscr{L}$, and consequently (th. 128)

$$F_r(S_r) \in \mathscr{L} \quad (r = 1, 2,...).$$

Hence, by (4) and th. 99,

$$\mathscr{C}(1; B) \in \mathscr{L}, \quad \text{and this means} \quad B \in \mathscr{L} \text{ (th. 140)}.$$

Th. 145 is not true if we replace the condition

'$f(P) > 0$'   by   '$f(P) \geqslant 0$'   for every point P of B;

for, if $B \bar{\in} \mathscr{L}$ and $f(P) = 0$ in B, then $\Omega_0(f; B)$ will be empty and therefore measurable without B being measurable.

Theorem 146. *Let $f(P)$ be defined and non-negative in a measurable set B, and suppose $\Omega_0(f; B) \in \mathscr{L}$; then $f(P)$ is measurable in B.*

Proof. Let $B(a) = B.\mathscr{S}(P; f(P) > a)$; suppose $0 < a < \infty$. (The idea of the proof may be pictured when B is a linear set in this way: that part of the set $\Omega_0(f; B)$ which lies above the line $y = a$ may, by translation, be transformed into the least set of ordinates of a *positive* function defined in $B(a)$; an application of th. 145 then gives the result.)

Suppose $B \subset R_n$, and let $H(a)$ be the special half-space in R_{n+1} given by $x_{n+1} > a$; let $S(a) = \Omega_0(f; B)H(a)$. Define F by

$$F((P, y)) = (P, y - a),$$

and let $g(P) = f(P) - a;$

then

(1) $$F(S(a)) = \Omega_0(g; B(a)).$$

Now $S(a)$ is the intersection of $\Omega_0(f; B)$, which is measurable by hypothesis, and a special half-space; hence (ths. 102 and 95)

$$S(a) \in \mathscr{L} \quad \text{and consequently (th. 128)} \quad F(S(a)) \in \mathscr{L}.$$

So, by (1), $\qquad\qquad \Omega_0(g; B(a)) \in \mathscr{L}.$

Since $P \in B(a)$ implies $g(P) > 0$, this means (th. 145) that $B(a) \in \mathscr{L}$. We have thus shown that,

$$\text{if } 0 < a < \infty, \quad \text{then} \quad B(a) \in \mathscr{L}.$$

Now $B(\infty) = 0$, and, if $a \leqslant 0$, $B(a)$ is the measurable set B; hence $B(a) \in \mathscr{L}$ for every real number a.

The remainder of this chapter is devoted to discussing the principal properties of measurable functions.

Theorem 147. *Let $f(P)$ be defined in a null set Z; then*
$$f(P) \text{ is measurable in } Z.$$

Proof. By def. 50 and ths. 89 and 81.

Theorem 148. *If $f(P)$ is measurable in B, then $f(P)$ is measurable in every measurable subset of B.*

Proof. By def. 50 and th. 95.

Theorem 149. *If α is a finite or an enumerable aggregate of sets in each of which $f(P)$ is measurable, then $f(P)$ is measurable in the union of the members of α.*

Proof. By def. 50 and th. 99.

Theorem 150. *Let $f(P)$ be measurable in B, and let a be any real number; let*

$$S_1(a) = B . \mathscr{S}(P; f(P) \geqslant a), \qquad S_2(a) = B . \mathscr{S}(P; f(P) < a),$$
$$S_3(a) = B . \mathscr{S}(P; f(P) \leqslant a), \qquad S_4(a) = B . \mathscr{S}(P; f(P) = a);$$

then $\qquad\qquad S_r(a) \in \mathscr{L} \quad (r = 1, 2, 3, 4).$

Proof. Clearly $S_1(-\infty)$ is B, which is measurable by hypothesis. If $a > -\infty$, there is a sequence $\{a_r\}$ such that

$$a_1 < a_2 < a_3 < \dots \quad \& \quad \lim_{r \to \infty} a_r = a;$$

it is easily seen from def. 50 that

$$S_1(a) = \prod_{r=1}^{\infty} B(a_r),$$

and hence, by hypothesis and th. 100, $S_1(a) \in \mathscr{L}$. Since

$$S_2(a) = B - S_1(a) \quad \& \quad S_3(a) = B - B(a),$$

it follows by th. 97 (i) that $S_2(a) \in \mathscr{L} \ \& \ S_3(a) \in \mathscr{L}$. Finally,

$$S_4(a) = S_1(a) S_3(a),$$

and so $S_4(a) \in \mathscr{L}$ (th. 95).

Theorem 151. *Let $f(P)$ be defined in B, and such that*

$$B.\mathscr{S}(P;f(P) \geqslant a) \in \mathscr{L}$$

for every real number a; then $f(P)$ is measurable in B.

Proof. Let

$$S_1(a) = B.\mathscr{S}(P;f(P) \geqslant a) \quad \& \quad B(a) = B.\mathscr{S}(P;f(P) > a);$$

then, knowing that $S_1(a) \in \mathscr{L}$ for every real number a, we must prove that

$$B \in \mathscr{L} \quad \& \quad B(a) \in \mathscr{L} \quad \text{for every real number } a.$$

Since $B = S_1(-\infty)$, we have $B \in \cdot \mathscr{L}$. Now $B(\infty)$ being empty is measurable, and, if $a < \infty$, there is a sequence $\{a_r\}$ such that $a_1 > a_2 > \dots$ & $\lim_{r \to \infty} a_r = a$, and it is easily seen that

$$B(a) = \sum_{r=1}^{\infty}{}^* S_1(a_r);$$

hence, by th. 99, $B(a) \in \mathscr{L}$.

Theorem 152. *Let $\{f_r(P)\}$ be a sequence of functions measurable in B; let $g(P)$ denote the upper bound, and $h(P)$ the lower bound of the aggregate of the numbers $f_1(P)$, $f_2(P),\dots$; then $g(P)$ and $h(P)$ are measurable in B.*

Proof. Let a be any real number, and put

$$G(a) = B.\mathscr{S}(P;g(P) > a),$$

and $\qquad G_r(a) = B.\mathscr{S}(P;f_r(P) > a) \quad (r = 1, 2,\dots);$

clearly $\qquad\qquad G(a) = \sum_{r=1}^{\infty}{}^* G_r(a),$

and so, by def. 50 and th. 99, $G(a) \in \mathscr{L}$; hence, since $B \in \mathscr{L}$, $g(P)$ is measurable in B. Now put

$$L(a) = B.\mathscr{S}(P;h(P) \geqslant a),$$

and $\qquad L_r(a) = B.\mathscr{S}(P;f_r(P) \geqslant a) \quad (r = 1, 2,\dots);$

then $\qquad\qquad L(a) = \prod_{r=1}^{\infty} L_r(a),$

and so, by ths. 150 and 100, $L(a) \in \mathscr{L}$; hence (th. 151) $h(P)$ is measurable in B.

Definition 51. Let $\{a_r\}$ be a sequence of real numbers; for every positive integer n let g_n be the upper bound and h_n the lower bound of the aggregate of the numbers a_n, $a_{n+1},\dots$; then the lower bound of the aggregate of the numbers g_1, $g_2,\dots$ is denoted by $\overline{\lim}_{r \to \infty} a_r$, and the upper bound of the aggregate of the numbers h_1, $h_2,\dots$ is denoted by

$\lim_{r \to \infty} a_r$. If $\overline{\lim}_{r \to \infty} a_r = \underline{\lim}_{r \to \infty} a_r = a$, we write $\lim_{r \to \infty} a_r = a$. If $\{f_r(P)\}$ is a sequence of functions defined in B, then the function $\overline{\lim}_{r \to \infty} f_r(P)$ is defined in B, and is called the *upper limit* function in B of the sequence $\{f_r(P)\}$; a similar definition explains the *lower limit* function, $\underline{\lim}_{r \to \infty} f_r(P)$.

Example. If θ is any finite real number, then $\overline{\lim}_{n \to \infty} \cos n\theta = 1$.

Proof. Suppose θ has been freely chosen, and let $g = \overline{\lim}_{n \to \infty} \cos n\theta$. With the notation of def. 51, if $a_n = \cos n\theta$, then

(1) $\qquad\qquad 1 \geqslant g_1 \geqslant g_2 \geqslant \dots \ \& \ \lim_{n \to \infty} g_n = g \leqslant 1.$

Now to every positive integer r there is a positive integer n_r such that
$$|g_r - \cos n_r \theta| < 2^{-r} \ \& \ n_r \geqslant r;$$
it follows from (1) that

(2) $\qquad\qquad\qquad \lim_{r \to \infty} \cos n_r \theta = g,$

and hence that

(3) $\qquad\qquad\qquad \lim_{r \to \infty} |\sin n_r \theta| = (1 - g^2)^{\frac{1}{2}}.$

Let m be any chosen positive integer; then
$$n > m \quad \text{implies} \quad g_{n-m} \geqslant \max\{\cos(n+m)\theta, \cos(n-m)\theta\}, \quad \text{i.e.}$$

(4) $\quad n > m$ implies $g_{n-m} \geqslant \cos n\theta \cos m\theta + |\sin n\theta \sin m\theta|.$

On allowing n to run through the values $n_1, n_2, \dots$, it follows from (1), (2), (3), and (4) that
$$1 \geqslant g \geqslant g \cos m\theta + (1 - g^2)^{\frac{1}{2}} |\sin m\theta|,$$
and if we consider this formula for $m = n_1, n_2, \dots$, it follows that
$$1 \geqslant g \geqslant g^2 + (1 - g^2) = 1,$$
which gives the required result.

(I am indebted to Dr. T. Estermann for this elegant proof.)

The consistency of def. 51 with the usual definition of the limit of a sequence of numbers, or of a sequence of functions, is proved in the following theorem, in which 'lim' is used as in def. 51.

Theorem 153.

(i) *If* $\lim_{r \to \infty} a_r = \lambda$ & $|\lambda| < \infty$, *then to every* ϵ *there is an integer* $m(\epsilon)$ *such that* $n > m(\epsilon)$ *implies* $|a_n - \lambda| < \epsilon$;

(ii) *if* $\lim\limits_{r\to\infty} a_r = \infty$, *then to every integer N there is an integer $m(N)$ such that $n > m(N)$ implies $a_n > N$.*

Proof.

(i) Suppose $\lim\limits_{r\to\infty} a_r = \lambda$ & $|\lambda| < \infty$. Choose ϵ freely; then, with the notation of def. 51, p exists such that

$$\lambda - \epsilon < h_p \leqslant g_p < \lambda + \epsilon,$$

and so $n > p$ implies $\lambda - \epsilon < a_n < \lambda + \epsilon.$

(ii) Suppose $\lim\limits_{r\to\infty} a_r = \infty$; then to every integer N there is an integer $m(N)$ such that $h_{m(N)} > N$; hence

$$n > m(N) \quad \text{implies} \quad a_n > N.$$

Theorem 154. *Let $\{a_n\}$ be a sequence of real numbers; then*

(i) $$\varliminf_{n\to\infty} a_n \leqslant \varlimsup_{n\to\infty} a_n,$$

(ii) $$\varliminf_{n\to\infty}(-a_n) = -\varlimsup_{n\to\infty} a_n.$$

Proof. Let n be any chosen positive integer; with the notation of def. 51

$$h_p \leqslant g_n \quad (p = 1, 2, \ldots),$$

which implies $$\varliminf_{p\to\infty} a_p \leqslant g_n \quad (n = 1, 2, \ldots);$$

hence (i) is true.

To prove (ii) we need only observe that, if g_n' and h_n' are respectively the upper and the lower bounds of the aggregate of the numbers $-a_n, -a_{n+1}, \ldots$, then, with the notation of def. 51,

$$h_n' = -g_n \quad \& \quad g_n' = -h_n \quad (n = 1, 2, \ldots),$$

and the result follows at once.

Theorem 155. *If $f_1(P), f_2(P), \ldots$ are measurable in B, so are*

$$\varliminf_{r\to\infty} f_r(P) \quad \text{and} \quad \varlimsup_{r\to\infty} f_r(P).$$

Proof. By def. 51 and repeated application of th. 152.

Corollary. If every member of a convergent sequence of functions is measurable in B, so is their limit function.

We noticed, p. 65, that a function may be discontinuous at every point of a set B although it is defined as the limit of a sequence of functions each of which is continuous almost everywhere in B; but, as we now see, a function which is defined as the limit of a sequence of functions measurable in B must itself be measurable in B; in brief, measurability is not lost in a passage to a limit, whereas continuity almost everywhere may be lost in such a process.

Theorem 156. *Suppose $f_1(P)$ and $f_2(P)$ are measurable in B, and $f_3(P) = f_1(P) + f_2(P)$ for every point P of B; then $f_3(P)$ is measurable in B.*

Proof. Put
$$B_r(a) = B \cdot \mathscr{S}(P; f_r(P) > a) \quad (r = 1, 2, 3).$$
By hypothesis,

(1) $B_1(a) \in \mathscr{L}$ & $B_2(a) \in \mathscr{L}$ for every real number a.

Since $f_3(P)$ is defined in B,
$$B_3(-\infty) = B_1(-\infty) B_2(-\infty),$$
and hence, by (1) and th. 95, $B_3(-\infty) \in \mathscr{L}$.

Suppose $|a| < \infty$; then $f_3(P) > a$, i.e. $f_1(P) > a - f_2(P)$, if and only if there is a rational number, say λ, such that
$$f_1(P) > \lambda \quad \& \quad \lambda > a - f_2(P), \quad \text{i.e.} \quad f_1(P) > \lambda \quad \& \quad f_2(P) > a - \lambda.$$
Hence, if $\{b_r\}$ is a sequence consisting of all rational numbers (th. 8), $P \in B_3(a)$ if and only if there is a positive integer n such that $P \in B_1(b_n) B_2(a - b_n)$, which means

(2) $$B_3(a) = \sum_{n=1}^{\infty}{}^* B_1(b_n) B_2(a - b_n).$$

By (2), (1), and ths. 95 and 99, $B_3(a) \in \mathscr{L}$. To complete the proof that $f_3(P)$ is measurable in B it remains only to remark that $B_3(\infty)$ is empty and therefore measurable, and that $B \in \mathscr{L}$.

Theorem 157. *Let $f(P)$ be measurable in B, and let λ be any finite real number different from zero; then*
$$\lambda f(P) \text{ is measurable in } B.$$

Proof. Let a be any real number; then
$$\lambda f(P) > a \quad \text{means} \quad \begin{cases} f(P) > \dfrac{a}{\lambda} & \text{if } \lambda > 0, \\ f(P) < \dfrac{a}{\lambda} & \text{if } \lambda < 0. \end{cases}$$
Hence, by th. 150, $B \cdot \mathscr{S}(P; \lambda f(P) > a) \in \mathscr{L}$ for every real number a, and so, since $B \in \mathscr{L}$, $\lambda f(P)$ is measurable in B.

Theorem 158. *Let $f(P)$ and $g(P)$ be measurable in B, and let λ and μ be any finite non-zero real numbers; then $\lambda f(P)+\mu g(P)$ is measurable in the subset of B in which it is defined.*

Proof. Put $\lambda f(P) = \phi(P)$ and $\mu g(P) = \psi(P)$;

$$B_1 = B.\mathscr{S}(P;\phi(P) = \infty), \qquad B_2 = B.\mathscr{S}(P;\phi(P) = -\infty),$$

$$B_3 = B.\mathscr{S}(P;\psi(P) = \infty), \qquad B_4 = B.\mathscr{S}(P;\psi(P) = -\infty),$$

and let $$A = B -\!(B_1 B_4 + B_2 B_3).$$

Then A is the subset of B in which $\{\phi(P)+\psi(P)\}$ is defined. Now B_1, B_2, B_3, B_4 are all measurable (th. 150), and so, by ths. 95, 91, and 97, $A \in \mathscr{L}$; hence, by ths. 157 and 148, $\phi(P)$ and $\psi(P)$ are measurable in A, and so their sum, i.e.

$$\lambda f(P)+\mu g(P), \quad \text{is measurable in } A \text{ (th. 156)}.$$

Theorem 159. *Let $f(P)$ be measurable in B; then so is $|f(P)|$.*

Proof. Let a be any real number; then

$$B.\mathscr{S}(P;|f(P)| > a) = B.\mathscr{S}(P;f(P) > a) \dotplus B.\mathscr{S}(P;f(P) < -a);$$

hence, by hypothesis and ths. 150 and 91, $B.\mathscr{S}(P;|f(P)| > a) \in \mathscr{L}$; since $B \in \mathscr{L}$, this means that $|f(P)|$ is measurable in B.

Theorem 160. *Let $f(P)$ be defined and constant in a measurable set B; then $f(P)$ is measurable in B.*

Proof. Suppose $f(P) = \mu$ in B, and let a be any real number; then

$$B.\mathscr{S}(P;f(P) > a) = \begin{cases} 0 & \text{if} \quad a \geqslant \mu \\ B & \text{if} \quad a < \mu, \end{cases}$$

which, since $B \in \mathscr{L}$, implies that $f(P)$ is measurable in B.

Theorem 161. *Let $f(P)$ be measurable in B, and let λ and μ be any real numbers; let*

$$\phi(P) = \begin{cases} f(P) & \text{if} \quad |f(P)| < \lambda \\ \mu & \text{otherwise;} \end{cases}$$

then $\phi(P)$ *is measurable in B.*

Proof. Let $$A = B.\mathscr{S}(P;|f(P)| < \lambda);$$

by ths. 159 and 150, $A \in \mathscr{L}$, and so (th. 148) $f(P)$ is measurable in A. Hence, by th. 149, it is sufficient to show that $\phi(P)$ is measurable in $B-A$. Now $\phi(P)$ is constant in $B-A$, and, by th. 97 (i), $(B-A) \in \mathscr{L}$; hence (th. 160) $\phi(P)$ is measurable in $B-A$.

Theorem 162. *Let $f(P)$ be continuous at every point of a set B, and let a be any real number; then there is an open set U such that $B(a) = BU$, where $B(a) = B.\mathscr{S}(P;f(P) > a)$.*

Proof. Suppose $f(P)$ is defined in A, and let U be the interior of $A(a)$. Since $f(P)$ is continuous at every point of B, it follows easily from def. 29 that
$$P \in B(a) \quad \text{implies} \quad P \in UB;$$
on the other hand,
$$P \in UB \quad \text{implies} \quad f(P) > a \quad \& \quad P \in B, \quad \text{i.e.} \quad P \in B(a).$$
Hence $B(a) = UB$; and, by th. 15, U is open.

Theorem 163. *If $f(P)$ is continuous at every point of a measurable set B, then $f(P)$ is measurable in B.*

Proof. Since every open set is measurable (th. 104), it follows by ths. 162 and 95 that the measurability of B implies that of $B(a)$ for every real number a.

Corollary (i). If $f(x)$ is continuous throughout a closed interval J, then $f(x)$ is bounded and measurable in J.

Proof. $f(x)$ is bounded in J (Hardy, § 102) and measurable in J^o (th. 163), and the result now follows from ths. 147 and 149.

Corollary (ii). If $f(P)$ is defined in a measurable set B and is continuous p.p. in B, then $f(P)$ is measurable in B (ths. 119 (ii), 147, and 163).

The following theorem states, roughly, that any continuous function of two *finite* measurable functions is itself measurable. Particular cases of this theorem have already been proved (ths. 156, 157, and 159) without restricting the functions to be finite.

Theorem 164. *Let $f_1(P)$ and $f_2(P)$ be finite functions measurable in B. Let A be the set of all points (x,y) for which there is a point P of B such that $x = f_1(P)$ & $y = f_2(P)$, and let $g(x,y)$ be a given function continuous at every point of A; then $g(f_1(P),f_2(P))$ is measurable in B.*

Proof. Let $h(P) = g(f_1(P),f_2(P))$, and let a be any real number; put
$$A(a) = A.\mathscr{S}((x,y);g(x,y) > a) \quad \text{and} \quad B(a) = B.\mathscr{S}(P;h(P) > a).$$
By th. 162 and def. 29 there is a plane open set U such that $A(a) = AU$, and it now follows easily that
$$(1) \qquad B(a) = B.\mathscr{S}(P;(f_1(P),f_2(P)) \in U).$$

If $U = 0$, then $B(a)$ is empty and therefore measurable; otherwise, there is a sequence of plane intervals, $\{I_r\}$, such that (th. 18) $U = \sum\limits_{r=1}^{\infty} {}^* I_r$, and so, by (1),

(2) $$B(a) = \sum_{r=1}^{\infty} {}^* B \cdot \mathscr{S}(P;(f_1(P),f_2(P)) \in I_r).$$

By (2) and th. 99, $B(a)$ is proved measurable if we show

(3) $$B \cdot \mathscr{S}(P;(f_1(P),f_2(P)) \in I_r) \in \mathscr{L} \quad (r = 1,2,...).$$

Suppose I is a plane interval given by

$$a_1 < x < b_1 \quad \& \quad a_2 < y < b_2;$$

let $\quad S = B \cdot \mathscr{S}(P; a_1 < f_1(P) < b_1) \cdot \mathscr{S}(P; a_2 < f_2(P) < b_2).$

Since $f_1(P)$ and $f_2(P)$ are measurable in B, it follows by th. 150 and a repeated application of th. 95 that $S \in \mathscr{L}$. This proves (3) and completes the proof of the theorem.

Theorem 165. *Let $f_1(P)$ and $f_2(P)$ be finite and measurable in B* *then* $$f_1(P)f_2(P) \quad \text{is measurable in } B.$$

Proof. By th. 164, on putting $g(x,y) = xy$.

Theorem 166. *Let $f(x)$ be defined in a measurable linear set B, and suppose*

(1) $\quad x_1 < x_2 \quad implies \quad f(x_1) \leqslant f(x_2) \quad if \; x_1 \; and \; x_2 \; belong \; to \; B;$

then $f(x)$ is measurable in B.

Proof. Let a be any real number; there are three possibilities for $B(a)$, the set $B \cdot \mathscr{S}(x; f(x) > a)$:

(i) $B(a) = 0,\quad$ or (ii) $B(a) = B,\quad$ or (iii) $B(a) \neq 0 \; \& \; B - B(a) \neq 0.$

In cases (i) and (ii) $B(a)$ is clearly measurable. In case (iii) let ξ be the lower bound of the aggregate $B(a)$; then $|\xi| < \infty$. It now follows by (1) that

$$B(a) = \begin{cases} B \cdot \mathscr{S}(x; x \geqslant \xi) & \text{if } f(\xi) > a \\ B \cdot \mathscr{S}(x; x > \xi) & \text{otherwise.} \end{cases}$$

In either case, by ths. 104, 105, and 95, $B(a) \in \mathscr{L}$.

Theorem 167. *Let $f(x)$ be measurable in B, and let $g(t)$ be a non-decreasing function of t defined for all real numbers t; then $g(f(x))$ is measurable in B.*

Proof. Let a be any real number, and let
$$B(a) = B \cdot \mathscr{S}(x; g(f(x)) > a).$$
If $B(a) = 0$, then $B(a) \in \mathscr{L}$; otherwise, let η be the lower bound of the aggregate of the real numbers t for which $g(t) > a$. Then
$$B(a) = \begin{cases} B \cdot \mathscr{S}(x; f(x) \geqslant \eta) & \text{if } g(\eta) > a \\ B \cdot \mathscr{S}(x; f(x) > \eta) & \text{otherwise.} \end{cases}$$
So, since $f(x)$ is measurable in B, it follows by th. 150 that $B(a) \in \mathscr{L}$; and since $B \in \mathscr{L}$, this means $g(f(x))$ is measurable in B.

Theorem 168. *Let $f(x)$ be measurable in $(-\infty, \infty)$, and let λ and μ be any finite real numbers, $\lambda \neq 0$; then*
$$f(\lambda x + \mu) \text{ is measurable in } (-\infty, \infty).$$

Proof. Let a be any real number, and put
$$B(a) = \mathscr{S}(x; f(x) > a) \quad \text{and} \quad C(a) = \mathscr{S}(x; f(\lambda x + \mu) > a).$$
Let F be the transformation defined by
$$F(x) = \frac{x - \mu}{\lambda}.$$
Since $x \in C(a)$ means $x \in F(B(a))$, it follows easily that
$$C(a) = F(B(a)),$$
and so (th. 128) $C(a)$ is, like $B(a)$, measurable.

Theorem 169. *Let $f(P)$ be non-negative and measurable in B; then*

(i) $$|\Omega_1(f; B) - \Omega_0(f; B)| = 0;$$

(ii) *every set of ordinates of $f(P)$ over B has the same measure.*

Proof. Let O denote the origin of coordinates, and let n be any chosen positive integer; put
$$B_n = B \cdot \mathscr{S}(P; f(P) < n) \cdot \mathscr{S}(P; \text{dist}(O, P) < n);$$
then B_n is the intersection of a sphere and a measurable set (th. 150), and hence B is measurable (ths. 95, 14, and 104). It follows (th. 148) that $f(P)$ is bounded and measurable in the bounded set B_n, and hence (ths. 144 and 135)
$$m\Omega_0(f; B_n) = m\Omega_1(f; B_n) < \infty.$$
This implies (th. 97 (ii)) that $\Omega_1(f; B_n) - \Omega_0(f; B_n)$ is null, and hence, by th. 86,
$$|\Omega_1(f; B) - \Omega_0(f; B)| = \left| \sum_{n=1}^{\infty} {}^* \{\Omega_1(f; B_n) - \Omega_0(f; B_n)\} \right| = 0,$$
which proves (i). It now follows, by (i) and th. 81, that any given set

of ordinates of $f(P)$ over B differs from $\Omega_0(f; B)$ by a null set, and so (ii) follows from ths. 144 and 119.

Theorem 170. *Let $f(P)$ be non-negative and measurable in B; then there is a sequence of functions, $\{f_r(P)\}$, such that, for every positive integer r, $f_r(P)$ is bounded and measurable in B, and assumes only a finite number of values as P runs through B, and*

$$(1) \qquad 0 \leqslant f_1(P) \leqslant f_2(P) \leqslant \ldots \quad \& \quad f(P) = \lim_{r \to \infty} f_r(P) \quad \text{in } B.$$

Proof. (The idea of the construction may be easily pictured when B is linear as follows: to obtain $f_r(x)$ we draw the line $y = r$, and divide the strip $0 \leqslant y < r$ into $r2^r$ strips of equal width: these, together with the strip $y \geqslant r$, make up the half-plane $y \geqslant 0$; the ordinate of the function $f_r(x)$ which stands on any point x of B is then obtained by retaining only that part of the corresponding ordinate of $f(x)$ which lies below the highest strip intersected by it.)

Let r be any positive integer; put

$$(2) \quad f_r(P) = \begin{cases} r & \text{if } f(P) \geqslant r \\ (s-1)2^{-r} & \text{if s is a positive integer not exceeding $r2^r$} \\ & \text{and } (s-1)2^{-r} \leqslant f(P) < s2^{-r}. \end{cases}$$

Then $f_r(P)$ assumes only a finite number of values as P runs through B, and since, by (2) and ths. 150 and 95, the set of the points of B at which it assumes any of these values is measurable, it follows by ths. 160 and 149 that $f_r(P)$ is measurable in B; moreover $f_r(P)$ is bounded in B, since the values assumed by $f_r(P)$ are all finite. To prove that (1) is satisfied, we observe first that,

$$\text{if} \quad f_r(P) = s2^{-r}, \quad \text{then} \quad f(P) \geqslant s2^{-r} \quad \& \quad 0 \leqslant s \leqslant r2^r;$$

hence $\qquad f(P) \geqslant 2s2^{-(r+1)} \quad \& \quad 0 \leqslant 2s < (r+1)2^{r+1},$

which, by (2), implies

$$f_{r+1}(P) \geqslant 2s2^{-r-1} = f_r(P).$$

Now if $f(P) < \infty$, it follows by (2) that

$$r > f(P) \quad \text{implies} \quad 0 \leqslant f(P) - f_r(P) < 2^{-r},$$

and so $\qquad\qquad\qquad \lim_{r \to \infty} f_r(P) = f(P).$

Finally, by (2),

$$\text{if} \quad f(P) = \infty, \quad \text{then} \quad f_r(P) = r \quad (r = 1, 2, \ldots),$$

and so (1) is satisfied.

§ 4. Lusin's Theorem

It was shown in th. 111 that to every measurable set S there is a sequence of open sets whose intersection differs from S by a null set; a similar underlying simplicity is to be found with measurable functions, and the aim of the next four theorems is to show that, to every finite function $f(x)$ measurable in $(-\infty,\infty)$, there is a sequence of functions which are continuous in $(-\infty,\infty)$ and which converge almost everywhere to $f(x)$.

The proof of th. 171, which contains the principal result, is due to L. W. Cohen.

Theorem 171. *Let $f(P)$ be measurable in B, and let ϵ be freely chosen; then there is a closed set K such that*

(1) $$K \subset B \quad \& \quad m(B-K) < \epsilon,$$

and

(2) *if $\{P_n\}$ is a sequence of points of K converging to some point P_0,*
    then $$f(P_0) = \lim_{n \to \infty} f(P_n).$$

Proof. Let $\{r_n\}$ be a sequence consisting of all the rational numbers (th. 8), and for every positive integer n put

$$G_n = B \cdot \mathscr{S}(P; f(P) \geqslant r_n).$$

Then, for every n, $G_n \in \mathscr{L}$ (th. 150), and hence (th. 110) there is a set S_n such that

(3) $$G_n - S_n \text{ is closed} \quad \& \quad mS_n < \tfrac{1}{3}\epsilon \, 2^{-n}.$$

Put $$A = B - \sum_{n=1}^{\infty}{}^{*} S_n;$$

by ths. 99, 84, and 97

$$A \in \mathscr{L} \quad \& \quad m(B-A) < \tfrac{1}{3}\epsilon.$$

Suppose $\{P_n\}$ is a sequence of points of A converging to a point P_0 of A; then

(4) $$f(P_0) \geqslant \varlimsup_{n \to \infty} f(P_n),$$

for otherwise there is a rational number, say r_ν, such that

(5) $\quad f(P_0) < r_\nu \leqslant f(P_n)$ for infinitely many values of n,

and so, since $AG_\nu \subset G_\nu - S_\nu$, and $(G_\nu - S_\nu)$ is closed by (3), it follows from (5) and th. 35 that

$$P_0 \in G_\nu - S_\nu, \quad \text{which implies} \quad f(P_0) \geqslant r_\nu,$$

contradicting (5). Hence (4) is true.

Now $-f(P)$ is measurable in A (ths. 148 and 157), and so, on reasoning as above, there is a measurable set A_1 such that $A_1 \subset A$ & $m(A-A_1) < \frac{1}{3}\epsilon$, and, if $\{P_n\}$ is a sequence of points of A_1 converging to a point P_0 of A_1, then $-f(P_0) \geqslant \varlimsup_{n\to\infty}(-f(P_n))$, which, by th. 154, means $f(P_0) \leqslant \varliminf_{n\to\infty} f(P_n)$; and hence, since $A_1 \subset A$, it follows by (4) and th. 154 that $f(P_0) = \lim_{n\to\infty} f(P_n)$. By th. 110 there is a closed set K such that
$$K \subset A_1 \quad \& \quad m(A_1-K) < \tfrac{1}{3}\epsilon,$$
and it follows by th. 35 and the properties proved of A_1, that K satisfies (2). Finally,
$$B-K = (B-A)+(A-A_1)+(A_1-K),$$
and so, by th. 85, K also satisfies (1).

Theorem 172. *Let $f(x)$ be finite and measurable in I, a linear interval (a,b), and let ϵ be freely chosen; then there is a function $g(x)$ such that*

(1) $\qquad g(a) = g(b) = 0 \quad \& \quad g(x)$ is continuous throughout $[a,b]$,

(2) $\qquad\qquad\qquad m\{I \cdot \mathscr{S}(x;f(x) \neq g(x))\} < \epsilon,$

(3) $\qquad\qquad\qquad M(|g|;I) \leqslant M(|f|;I).$

Proof. By th. 171 there is a closed set K such that

(4) $\qquad\qquad\qquad m(I-K) < \epsilon,$

and

(5) if $x_1, x_2,\ldots$ belong to K and $x_0 = \lim_{n\to\infty} x_n$, then $f(x_0) = \lim_{n\to\infty} f(x_n)$.
Define $g(x)$ in $[a,b]$ as follows:

(6) $g(x) = \begin{cases} 0 & \text{if } x = a \text{ or } x = b \\ f(x) & \text{if } x \in K \\ f(\lambda)+\dfrac{x-\lambda}{\mu-\lambda}\{f(\mu)-f(\lambda)\} & \text{if } \lambda < x < \mu \text{ and } (\lambda,\mu) \text{ is an} \\ & \text{interval of } I \text{ contiguous to } K. \end{cases}$

Clearly $g(x)$ satisfies (3), and, in virtue of (4), also satisfies (2). Suppose ξ is freely chosen so that $a \leqslant \xi < b$, and let h denote a variable positive number; we shall show that

(7) $\qquad\qquad\qquad \lim_{h\to 0} g(\xi+h) = g(\xi).$

If (λ,μ) is an interval of I contiguous to K, and $\lambda \leqslant \xi < \mu$, then $g(x)$ is linear in some closed interval $[\xi,\xi']$, and so (7) is true. Suppose then that ξ is a limiting point of $K[\xi, b]$. Choose δ freely; since $\xi \in K$, it follows easily from (5) and (6) that there is a positive number η such that

(8) $0 < x-\xi < \eta$ & $x \in K$ implies $|g(x)-g(\xi)| < \delta$.

Since $g(x)-g(\xi)$ is a monotone function of x in every interval of I contiguous to K, it follows that the restriction '$x \in K$' contained in (8) is unnecessary, which means that (7) is true. A similar argument shows that

$$a < \xi \leqslant b \quad \text{implies} \quad \lim_{h \to 0} g(\xi-h) = g(\xi),$$

and so (1) is satisfied.

Theorem 173 (LUSIN). *Let $f(x)$ be finite and measurable in $(-\infty, \infty)$, and let ϵ be freely chosen; then there is a function $g(x)$ such that*

(1) $g(x)$ *is continuous in* $(-\infty, \infty)$,

(2) $m\{\mathscr{S}(x; f(x) \neq g(x))\} < \epsilon$,

(3) $M(|g|; R_1) \leqslant M(|f|; R_1)$.

Proof. By th. 172 there is to every integer n a function $g_n(x)$ such that $g_n(x)$ is continuous throughout $[n-1, n]$, vanishes for $x = n-1$ and $x = n$, and satisfies the conditions

$$m\{[n-1, n].\mathscr{S}(x; g_n(x) \neq f(x))\} < \epsilon 2^{-|n|-2},$$

and $M(|g|; [n-1, n]) \leqslant M(|f|; [n-1, n])$.

It is now easily seen, by th. 84, that the function $g(x)$, defined as being equal to $g_n(x)$ in $[n-1, n]$ satisfies the conditions (1), (2), and (3).

Theorem 174. *Let $f(x)$ be finite and measurable in $(-\infty, \infty)$; then there is a sequence of functions, $\{g_n(x)\}$, which are continuous in $(-\infty, \infty)$ and such that*

(1) $\lim_{n \to \infty} g_n(x) = f(x)$ *p.p. in* $(-\infty, \infty)$,

(2) $M(|g_n|; R_1) \leqslant M(|f|; R_1)$ $(n = 1, 2, ...)$.

Proof. By th. 173 there is a sequence, $\{g_n(x)\}$, of functions continuous in $(-\infty, \infty)$, satisfying (2), and such that

(3)   if $H_n = \mathscr{S}(x; g_n(x) \neq f(x))$, then $mH_n < 2^{-n}$.

By (3) and ths. 99 and 84, for every positive integer r,

$$m\left\{\sum_{n=r}^{\infty}{}^* H_n\right\} \leqslant \sum_{n=r}^{\infty} mH_n < 2^{1-r},$$

and so, if
$$H = \prod_{r=1}^{\infty} \sum_{n=r}^{\infty}{}^* H_n,$$

it follows by th. 81 that H is null; hence $\{g_n(x)\}$ satisfies (1) if

(4) $x \in \bar{H}$ implies $\lim_{n \to \infty} g_n(x) = f(x).$

Now, if $x \in \bar{H}$, there is a positive integer ν such that

$$x \,\bar{\in}\, \sum_{n=\nu}^{\infty}{}^* H_n,$$

which, by the definition of H_n, means

$$g_n(x) = f(x)   \text{whenever}   n \geqslant \nu,$$

and this proves (4).

V

LEBESGUE INTEGRAL OF A NON-NEGATIVE FUNCTION

THE Lebesgue integral, which we are about to define, is a generalization of the Riemann integral. We have seen (ths. 76 and 77) that, if $f(x)$ is defined and non-negative in a closed interval J, then the equation

$$c\Omega_0(f; J) = (R) \int_a^b f(x)\,dx, \quad \text{where } J = [a, b],$$

is true if either side exists, and that this will happen if and only if $f(x)$ satisfies two conditions:

  (i) $f(x)$ must be bounded in J,

 (ii) the set of the points x of J at which $f(x)$ is discontinuous must be null.

The Lebesgue theory of measure, which is now at our disposal, permits a vast extension to the solution of the problem of areas partially solved by the Riemann integral (or, what comes to the same thing, by the theory of Jordan content). The main features of the generalization are:

(1) J, the range of integration, is replaced by any measurable set B in R_n,

(2) the condition of boundedness is relaxed entirely,

(3) the condition (ii) above, which may be said to prescribe the degree of '*irregularity*' of the function which is integrable, is replaced by the much weaker restriction that the function $f(P)$ must be measurable in B.

The reader will realize that the theory of the Lebesgue integral for non-negative functions is obtained largely by a restatement, in new terms, of the properties of measurable sets; and that the marked simplicity of the new integral is a reflection of the broad and simple properties which characterize the Lebesgue theory of measure. The greater fitness of the resulting theory for the ordinary purposes of analysis is best illustrated by the remarkable way in which it deals with functions defined as limits of integrable functions; for example, the equations

$$\int_a^b \lim_{n\to\infty} f_n(x)\,dx = \lim_{n\to\infty} \int_a^b f_n(x)\,dx$$

and
$$\int_a^b \sum_{n=1}^{\infty} f_n(x) \, dx = \sum_{n=1}^{\infty} \int_a^b f_n(x) \, dx,$$

which are true in rather restricted conditions for Riemann integrals, are true in greatly extended circumstances when the integrals are taken in the Lebesgue sense. It is to this added simplicity and power that the Lebesgue integral owes its importance.

In virtue of ths. 144 and 146 we may now enunciate

Definition 52. Let $f(P)$ be defined and non-negative in a measurable set B; then, if
$$f(P) \text{ is measurable in } B,$$

or, what is the same thing,
$$\Omega_0(f; B) \in \mathscr{L},$$

the *Lebesgue integral of* $f(P)$ *over* B, $\int_B f(P) \, dP$, is defined by
$$\int_B f(P) \, dP = m\Omega_0(f; B).$$

If $\int_B f(P) \, dP < \infty$, then $f(P)$ is said to be *summable over* B.

Definition 53.

(i) If $a < b$, then
$$\int_a^b f(x) \, dx \text{ denotes the Lebesgue integral of } f(x) \text{ over } (a, b).$$

(If $a > -\infty$, the same symbol is used to denote the integral of $f(x)$ over $\mathscr{S}(x; a \leqslant x < b)$; similar remarks apply to b if $b < \infty$; however, the four possible integrals which may be represented by the one symbol $\int_a^b f(x) \, dx$ are all equal when they exist (ths. 177 and 181)).

(ii) If $a > b$, then $\quad \int_a^b f(x) \, dx = - \int_b^a f(x) \, dx.$

(iii) If $a = b$, then $\quad \int_a^b f(x) \, dx = 0.$

That the Lebesgue integral is a generalization of the Riemann integral, for non-negative functions, is proved by the following:

Theorem 175. *Let $f(x)$ be non-negative and integrable-R over a closed interval J; then $f(x)$ is summable over J, and its Riemann and Lebesgue integrals over J are equal.*

Proof. By ths. 77 and 118

$$c\Omega_0(f; J) = m\Omega_0(f; J)$$

and so, by th. 76 and def. 52, J being measurable (th. 105), we have the result.

Theorem 176. *Let $f(P)$ be non-negative and measurable in A; then*

$$B \in \mathscr{L} \quad \& \quad B \subset A \quad implies \quad \int_B f(P)\, dP \leqslant \int_A f(P)\, dP.$$

Proof. $B \subset A$ implies $\Omega_0(f; B) \subset \Omega_0(f; A)$;

also, if $B \in \mathscr{L}$, then $f(P)$ is measurable in B (th. 148). Hence the result follows from th. 81 and def. 52.

Theorem 177.

(i) *Suppose $B = \sum\limits_{r=1}^{k} B_r$ and $f(P)$ is non-negative and measurable in each of the sets $B_1, B_2,..., B_k$; then*

$$\int_B f(P)\, dP = \sum_{r=1}^{k} \int_{B_r} f(P)\, dP.$$

(ii) *Suppose $B = \sum\limits_{r=1}^{\infty} B_r$ and $f(P)$ is non-negative and measurable in each of the sets $B_1, B_2,...$; then*

$$\int_B f(P)\, dP = \sum_{r=1}^{\infty} \int_{B_r} f(P)\, dP.$$

Proof of (ii). By th. 131, $\Omega_0(f; B) = \sum\limits_{r=1}^{\infty} \Omega_0(f; B_r)$, and hence (ths. 144 and 94)

$$m\Omega_0(f; B) = \sum_{r=1}^{\infty} m\Omega_0(f; B_r);$$

since $B \in \mathscr{L}$ (th. 99), this gives the required result in virtue of def. 52. The proof of (i) is on exactly the same lines.

Theorem 178. *Let $f(x)$ be a non-negative function measurable in (a, b); then*

(i) *if α and β tend independently to $a+0$ and $b-0$ respectively, then*

$$\int_\alpha^\beta f(x)\, dx \quad tends\ to \quad \int_a^b f(x)\, dx;$$

(ii) *if $f(x)$ is integrable-CR over (a, b), then*

$$\int_a^b f(x)\, dx = (CR) \int_a^b f(x)\, dx.$$

Proof. Let $\{a_n\}$ and $\{b_n\}$ be any chosen sequences such that $a_1 > a_2 > \ldots \,\&\, \lim\limits_{n\to\infty} a_n = a$, and $a_1 = b_1 < b_2 < \ldots \,\&\, \lim\limits_{n\to\infty} b_n = b$. Let

$$A_r = \mathscr{S}(x; a_{r+1} \leqslant x < a_r) \quad \text{and} \quad B_r = \mathscr{S}(x; b_r \leqslant x < b_{r+1});$$

then each of the sets $A_1,\, A_2,\ldots,\, B_1,\, B_2,\ldots$ consists of an interval together with one of its end-points and is easily seen to be measurable; hence $f(x)$ is measurable in each of these sets (th. 148) and, since $(a, b) = \sum\limits_{r=1}^{\infty} (A_r + B_r)$, it follows from th. 177 that

$$\int_a^b f(x)\, dx = \lim_{n\to\infty} \left\{ \sum_{r=1}^n \left(\int_{A_r} f(x)\, dx + \int_{B_r} f(x)\, dx \right) \right\} = \lim_{n\to\infty} \int_{a_{n+1}}^{b_{n+1}} f(x)\, dx,$$

which implies (i).

Suppose now that $f(x)$ is integrable-CR over (a, b); by def. 37.1 if $a < \alpha < \beta < b$, then $f(x)$ is integrable-R over (α, β), and as α and β tend independently to a and b respectively,

$$(1) \qquad\qquad (R) \int_\alpha^\beta f(x)\, dx \quad \text{tends to} \quad (CR) \int_a^b f(x)\, dx.$$

By th. 175 $\qquad\qquad (R) \int_\alpha^\beta f(x)\, dx = \int_\alpha^\beta f(x)\, dx,$

and so (ii) follows from (1) and (i).

Examples.

(i) If $\alpha > 0$, then $\qquad \int_0^\infty e^{-\alpha t}\, dt = 1/\alpha.$

(ii) $\qquad\qquad \int_1^\infty \dfrac{dx}{x^{1+\alpha}} = \begin{cases} 1/\alpha & \text{if } \alpha > 0 \\ \infty & \text{if } \alpha \leqslant 0. \end{cases}$

(iii) $\qquad\qquad \int_0^1 x^{\alpha-1}\, dx = \begin{cases} 1/\alpha & \text{if } \alpha > 0 \\ \infty & \text{if } \alpha \leqslant 0. \end{cases}$

Proofs. The cases where $\alpha > 0$ follow at once from th. 178 (ii) and th. 65. If $\alpha \leqslant 0$, then, by th. 175, for every positive integer n we have

$$\int_{1/n}^1 x^{\alpha-1}\, dx = (R) \int_{1/n}^1 x^{\alpha-1}\, dx = \begin{cases} \log n & \text{if } \alpha = 0 \\ (1/\alpha)(1 - n^{-\alpha}) & \text{if } \alpha < 0, \end{cases}$$

and since $x^{\alpha-1}$ is continuous and therefore measurable in $(0, 1)$, the proof of (iii) is completed by th. 178 (i). The proof of (ii) is similarly completed.

Theorem 179. *If $f(P)$ and $g(P)$ are measurable in B, and $P \in B$ implies $0 \leqslant f(P) \leqslant g(P)$, then $\int\limits_B f(P)\, dP \leqslant \int\limits_B g(P)\, dP$; if $g(P)$ is summable over B, so is $f(P)$.*

Proof. By ths. 132 and 81.

Theorem 180. *If $f(P)$ is non-negative and measurable in B, and $0 < a < \infty$, then*

$$\int\limits_B af(P)\, dP = a \int\limits_B f(P)\, dP.$$

Proof. By th. 133.

Example.

(i) $e^{-t}t^{x-1}$ is summable over $(0, \infty)$ if $x > 0$ but not if $x \leqslant 0$; when $x > 0$, we define

$$\Gamma(x) = \int\limits_0^\infty e^{-t}t^{x-1}\, dt.$$

(ii) $\Gamma(m+1) = \int\limits_0^\infty e^{-t}t^m\, dt = m!$ if m is a positive integer.

(iii) If $\lambda > 0$, then $\int\limits_0^\infty e^{-\lambda t}t^m\, dt = m!\,\lambda^{-m-1}$ (m as in (ii)).

Proof. For every x, $e^{-t}t^{x-1}$ is a non-negative continuous function of t in $(0, \infty)$, and therefore (th. 163 and def. 52) $\int\limits_0^\infty e^{-t}t^{x-1}\, dt$ exists. It follows easily from th. 179 that

$$\int\limits_0^1 e^{-1}t^{x-1}\, dt \leqslant \int\limits_0^1 e^{-t}t^{x-1}\, dt \leqslant \int\limits_0^1 t^{x-1}\, dt,$$

and so, by th. 180 and example (iii) following th. 178,

$$\int\limits_0^1 e^{-t}t^{x-1}\, dt \text{ is finite if } x > 0, \text{ and } \int\limits_0^1 e^{-t}t^{x-1}\, dt = \infty \text{ if } x \leqslant 0.$$

By th. 177 it remains, to prove (i), only to show that

(1) $e^{-t}t^{x-1}$ is summable over $(1, \infty)$ if $x > 0$.

Now, x being fixed, $t^x e^{-\frac{1}{2}t}$ is bounded in $(1, \infty)$ (Hardy, § 206), and so there is an integer k such that

$$e^{-t}t^{x-1} < ke^{-\frac{1}{2}t} \text{ in } (1, \infty);$$

hence, by ths. 179 and 180,

$$\int_1^\infty e^{-t}t^{x-1}\,dt \leqslant \int_1^\infty k\,e^{-\frac{1}{2}t}\,dt = k\int_1^\infty e^{-\frac{1}{2}t}\,dt \leqslant k\int_0^\infty e^{-\frac{1}{2}t}\,dt,$$

and the proof of (1) is completed by example (i) following th. 178.

It is possible to deduce (ii) and (iii) from the theorems on Lebesgue integration by parts (th. 242) and on change of variable (th. 241); alternatively, we may argue with Riemann integrals as follows: choose $\lambda > 0$ and m a positive integer; then

$$t > 0 \quad \text{implies} \quad \frac{d}{dt}(e^{-\lambda t}t^m) = me^{-\lambda t}t^{m-1}-\lambda e^{-\lambda t}t^m.$$

Hence, if n is any positive integer,

$$\frac{d}{dt}(e^{-\lambda t}t^m) \quad \text{is continuous throughout } [0,n],$$

and so, by ths. 65 and 61,

$$(2) \qquad (R)\int_0^n me^{-\lambda t}t^{m-1}\,dt -(R)\int_0^n \lambda e^{-\lambda t}t^m\,dt = e^{-\lambda n}n^m.$$

Now, by th. 175, the integrals in (2) may be taken in the Lebesgue sense, and so (th. 178)

$$m\int_0^\infty e^{-\lambda t}t^{m-1}\,dt = \lambda\int_0^\infty e^{-\lambda t}t^m\,dt + \lim_{n\to\infty} e^{-\lambda n}n^m = \lambda\int_0^\infty e^{-\lambda t}t^m\,dt.$$

It now follows by induction that

$$\int_0^\infty e^{-\lambda t}t^m\,dt = \lambda^{-m}m!\int_0^\infty e^{-\lambda t}\,dt,$$

and both (ii) and (iii) now follow from example (i) following th. 178.

Theorem 181. *If $f(P)$ is non-negative in a null set B, then*

$$\int_B f(P)\,dP = 0.$$

Proof. By ths. 142 and 89.

Example. If B is the set of all the rational points of R_n and $f(P)$ is any non-negative function defined in B, then $\int_B f(P)\,dP = 0$ (ths. 8, 83, and 181).

Theorem 182. *If $B \in \mathscr{L}$ & $a \geqslant 0$, then $\int_B a\,dP = a\,mB$, the right-hand side being replaced by zero if one if its factors is zero and the other ∞.*

Proof. The case $|B| = 0$ has been dealt with in th. 181; if $a = 0$, the result follows from def. 52, and the case $0 < a < \infty$ follows from th. 141. Finally, by ths. 160 and 179, and what we have already proved in this theorem,

$$0 < a < \infty \quad \text{implies} \quad \int_B \infty \, dP \geqslant \int_B a \, dP = a \, mB,$$

and this means $\quad \int_B \infty \, dP = \infty \quad \text{if} \quad mB > 0.$

Example. Let $f(x) = \begin{cases} 1 & \text{if} \quad x \text{ is rational} \\ 0 & \text{if} \quad x \text{ is irrational}; \end{cases}$

then $\qquad \int_{-\infty}^{\infty} f(x) \, dx = 0.$

Proof. Let A be the set of all irrational numbers, and B the set of all rational numbers; by the example to th. 181

$$\int_B f(x) \, dx = 0;$$

also, since A is measurable (ths. 89 and 90), we have (th. 182)

$$\int_A f(x) \, dx = 0,$$

and so, by th. 177,

$$\int_{-\infty}^{\infty} f(x) \, dx = \int_A f(x) \, dx + \int_B f(x) \, dx = 0.$$

Theorem 183. *Let $f(P)$ be non-negative, bounded, and measurable in B, and suppose $mB < \infty$; then $f(P)$ is summable over B.*

Proof. Let $a = M(f; B)$; then, by ths. 179 and 182,

$$\int_B f(P) \, dP \leqslant \int_B a \, dP = a \, mB < \infty.$$

Theorem 184. *Let $f(P)$ be non-negative in B and summable over B; then*

$$f(P) < \infty \quad p.p. \text{ in } B.$$

Proof. Let $\qquad B_0 = B . \mathscr{S}(P; f(P) = \infty);$

then $B_0 \in \mathscr{L}$ (th. 150), and so, by th. 176,

$$\int_{B_0} \infty \, dP = \int_{B_0} f(P) \, dP \leqslant \int_B f(P) \, dP < \infty,$$

which, by th. 182, is only possible if $|B_0| = 0$.

Theorem 185. *Let $f(P)$ be non-negative and measurable in B, and such that*

$$\int_B f(P)\,dP = 0; \quad then \quad f(P) = 0 \quad p.p. \ in \ B.$$

Proof. Let $\qquad B(a) = B.\mathscr{S}(P; f(P) > a);$

then, by ths. 182, 179, and 176,

$\qquad 0 < a < \infty$ implies

$$a\,mB(a) = \int_{B(a)} a\,dP \leqslant \int_{B(a)} f(P)\,dP \leqslant \int_B f(P)\,dP = 0,$$

which requires $\qquad\qquad |B(a)| = 0.$

Hence (th. 86) $\qquad \sum_{r=1}^{\infty}{}^{*} B\!\left(\frac{1}{r}\right),$ i.e. $B(0)$, is null.

Theorem 186. *Suppose $f_1(P), f_2(P),\ldots$ are measurable in B, and $P \in B$ implies $0 \leqslant f_1(P) \leqslant f_2(P) \leqslant \ldots$; then*

$$\int_B \lim_{n\to\infty} f_n(P)\,dP = \lim_{n\to\infty} \int_B f_n(P)\,dP.$$

Proof. By ths. 132 and 134 (i)

$$\Omega_0(f_1; B) \subset \Omega_0(f_2; B) \subset \ldots \quad \& \quad \Omega_0\!\left(\lim_{n\to\infty} f_n; B\right) = \sum_{n=1}^{\infty}{}^{*} \Omega_0(f_n; B),$$

and the result follows from th. 98.

The reader should note the remarkable simplicity of th. 186, and compare it with the limitations of the Riemann integral illustrated by the example following th. 77.

Theorem 187. *Let $f_1(P), f_2(P),\ldots$ be non-negative and measurable in B; suppose*

(1) $\qquad\qquad P \in B \quad implies \quad f_1(P) \geqslant f_2(P) \geqslant \ldots$

and $\qquad\qquad f_1(P)$ *is summable over B;*

then $\qquad \int_B \lim_{n\to\infty} f_n(P)\,dP = \lim_{n\to\infty} \int_B f_n(P)\,dP < \infty.$

Proof. By ths. 132 and 134 (ii)

$$\Omega_1(f_1; B) \supset \Omega_1(f_2; B) \supset \ldots \quad \& \quad \Omega_1\!\left(\lim_{n\to\infty} f_n; B\right) = \prod_{n=1}^{\infty} \Omega_1(f_n; B);$$

hence, since $m\Omega_0(f_1; B) < \infty$, the result follows from ths. 101 and 135 (ii).

Example. Let x be any real number, $x > 1$; then

$$\lim_{n\to\infty} n(x^{1/n}-1) = \log x.$$

Proof. If we put $\qquad f_n(t) = t^{1/n-1},$

then $\qquad 1 < t < x \quad$ implies $\quad f_1(t) \geqslant f_2(t) \geqslant \ldots,$

and, by ths. 175 and 65,

$$\int_1^x f_n(t)\, dt = n(x^{1/n}-1) \quad (n = 1, 2, \ldots).$$

Since $f_1(t) = 1$ in $(1, x)$, it now follows from th. 187 that

$$\lim_{n\to\infty} n(x^{1/n}-1) = \int_1^x \lim_{n\to\infty} f_n(t)\, dt = \int_1^x \frac{dt}{t} = (R)\int_1^x \frac{dt}{t} = \log x.$$

It should be observed that th. 187 is false if the assumption of summability of $f_1(P)$ over B is merely replaced by its measurability in B; for example, let

$$f_n(x) = \begin{cases} 1 & \text{if } x > n \\ 0 & \text{otherwise}; \end{cases} \quad \text{then} \quad \lim_{n\to\infty} f_n(x) = 0 \quad \text{in } (0,\infty).$$

However, it is easily seen from ths. 177 and 182 that

$$\int_0^\infty f_n(x)\, dx = \int_n^\infty dx = \infty \quad (n = 1, 2, \ldots),$$

whereas $\qquad \displaystyle\int_0^\infty \lim_{n\to\infty} f_n(x)\, dx = 0.$

Theorem 188. *Let $f(P)$ be non-negative and measurable in B, and suppose $a \geqslant 0$; then*

(1) $$\int_B \{a+f(P)\}\, dP = \int_B a\, dP + \int_B f(P)\, dP.$$

Proof. The case $a = \infty$ follows at once from ths. 181 and 182. If $0 \leqslant a < \infty$, let the transformation F be defined by

$$F((P,y)) = (P, a+y),$$

and let $\qquad g(P) = a + f(P).$

Then $g(P)$ is measurable in B (ths. 156 and 160), and so (th. 169 (ii))

$\int_B g(P)\,dP$ is the measure of any set of ordinates of $g(P)$ over B; hence

$$(2) \qquad \int_B g(P)\,dP = m[\Omega_1(a; B) + F\{\Omega_0(f; B)\}].$$

Now, by ths. 135 and 160, $m\Omega_1(a; B) = \int_B a\,dP$, and, by ths. 128 and 127,

$$m[F\{\Omega_0(f; B)\}] = m\Omega_0(f; B) = \int_B f(P)\,dP;$$

hence (1) follows from (2) and th. 93 (ii).

Theorem 189. *Let $f(P)$ and $g(P)$ be non-negative and measurable in B; then*

$$\int_B \{f(P)+g(P)\}\,dP = \int_B f(P)\,dP + \int_B g(P)\,dP.$$

Proof. Suppose first that $f(P)$ assumes only a finite number of values, $y_1, y_2,..., y_\lambda$, all finite. Let

$$B_s = B.\mathscr{S}(P; f(P) = y_s) \quad (s = 1, 2,...,\lambda).$$

Then (th. 150) $B_s \in \mathscr{L}$, and so, by ths. 148 and 188,

$$\int_{B_s} \{f(P)+g(P)\}\,dP = \int_{B_s} f(P)\,dP + \int_{B_s} g(P)\,dP \quad (s = 1, 2,...,\lambda).$$

Hence, by th. 177, since $\quad B = \sum_{s=1}^{\lambda} B_s,$

$$(1) \qquad \int_B \{f(P)+g(P)\}\,dP = \int_B f(P)\,dP + \int_B g(P)\,dP.$$

Now consider the most general case for $f(P)$; by th. 170 there is a sequence of functions, $\{f_n(P)\}$, such that

(2) $f_n(P)$ $(n = 1, 2,...)$ is bounded and measurable in B, and assumes only a finite number of values,

and

(3) $P \in B$ implies $0 \leqslant f_1(P) \leqslant f_2(P) \leqslant ...$ & $\lim\limits_{n\to\infty} f_n(P) = f(P)$.

By (2) and what we have already proved

$$\int_B \{f_n(P)+g(P)\}\,dP = \int_B f_n(P)\,dP + \int_B g(P)\,dP \quad (n = 1, 2,...),$$

and so, by (3) and th. 186,

$$(4) \qquad \lim_{n\to\infty} \int_B \{f_n(P)+g(P)\}\,dP = \lim_{n\to\infty} \int_B f_n(P)\,dP + \int_B g(P)\,dP$$

$$= \int_B f(P)\,dP + \int_B g(P)\,dP.$$

Moreover, by (3), $P \in B$ implies

$$0 \leqslant f_1(P)+g(P) \leqslant f_2(P)+g(P) \leqslant \ldots \quad \& $$
$$\lim_{n \to \infty} \{f_n(P)+g(P)\} = f(P)+g(P).$$

Hence, by (4) and th. 186, we have (1) in the general case.

Theorem 190. *Let $f_1(P)$, $f_2(P)$,..., $f_k(P)$ be non-negative and measurable in B; then*

$$\int_B \sum_{r=1}^{k} f_r(P)\, dP = \sum_{r=1}^{k} \int_B f_r(P)\, dP.$$

Proof. By induction from th. 189.

Theorem 191. *Let $\{f_r(P)\}$ be a sequence of functions, non-negative and measurable in B; then*

$$\int_B \sum_{r=1}^{\infty} f_r(P)\, dP = \sum_{r=1}^{\infty} \int_B f_r(P)\, dP.$$

Proof. Put $g_k(P) = \sum_{r=1}^{k} f_r(P)$; then $P \in B$ implies

$$0 \leqslant g_1(P) \leqslant g_2(P) \leqslant \ldots \quad \& \quad \lim_{k \to \infty} g_k(P) = \sum_{r=1}^{\infty} f_r(P).$$

Hence, by ths. 186 and 190,

$$\int_B \sum_{r=1}^{\infty} f_r(P)\, dP$$
$$= \lim_{k \to \infty} \int_B g_k(P)\, dP = \lim_{k \to \infty} \sum_{r=1}^{k} \int_B f_r(P)\, dP = \sum_{r=1}^{\infty} \int_B f_r(P)\, dP.$$

Example. Let p and q be finite positive numbers; then

$$\int_0^1 \frac{x^{p-1}}{1+x^q}\, dx = \frac{1}{p} - \frac{1}{p+q} + \frac{1}{p+2q} - \frac{1}{p+3q} + \ldots .$$

Proof. If $0 < x < 1$, then

$$x^{p-1}(1+x^q)^{-1} = x^{p-1}(1-x^q+x^{2q}-x^{3q}+\ldots) = \sum_{n=0}^{\infty} f_n(x),$$

where $\qquad f_n(x) = (1-x^q)x^{p-1+2nq} > 0;$

hence, by th. 191, since the functions $f_n(x)$ are continuous and therefore measurable in $(0,1)$,

$$(1) \qquad \int_0^1 x^{p-1}(1+x^q)^{-1}\, dx = \sum_{n=0}^{\infty} \int_0^1 f_n(x)\, dx.$$

Now, for every positive integer n,

$f_n(x)$ is of the form $x^\alpha - x^\beta$ where $\alpha > -1$ & $\beta > -1$;

hence, by ths. 175 and 66,

$$\int_0^1 f_n(x)\,dx = (CR)\int_0^1 (x^{p-1+2nq} - x^{p-1+2nq+q})\,dx$$

$$= \frac{1}{p+2nq} - \frac{1}{p+(2n+1)q},$$

and the result now follows by (1) since

$$\lim_{n\to\infty}(p+2nq)^{-1} = 0.$$

Corollaries.

(i) $\qquad 1 - \tfrac{1}{2} + \tfrac{1}{3} - \tfrac{1}{4} + \ldots = \log 2 \quad (p=1, q=1);$

(ii) $\qquad 1 - \tfrac{1}{3} + \tfrac{1}{5} - \tfrac{1}{7} + \ldots = \tfrac{1}{4}\pi \quad (p=1, q=2);$

in each case the integral in question is evaluated as a Riemann integral, relying on th. 65; in (i) the primitive is $\log(1+x)$, and in (ii) arc tan x.

The reader will be struck by the simplicity of treatment for the integral of a function which is defined as the limit of a *monotone* sequence of functions. To deal with the more general case of functions defined as limits, we consider such functions in relation to the *monotone* sequences by which they are defined as upper or lower limits.

Theorem 192 (FATOU). *Let $f_1(P)$, $f_2(P)$,… be non-negative and measurable in B; then*

(1) $$\int_B \varliminf_{n\to\infty} f_n(P)\,dP \leqslant \varliminf_{n\to\infty} \int_B f_n(P)\,dP.$$

Proof. Let r be any chosen positive integer. For every point P of B let $h_r(P)$ denote the lower bound of the aggregate of the numbers $f_r(P), f_{r+1}(P),\ldots$. Then (th. 152)

$h_r(P)$ is measurable in B & $h_r(P) \leqslant f_n(P) \quad (n = r, r+1,\ldots)$,

and hence, by th. 179,

(2) $$\int_B h_r(P)\,dP \leqslant \int_B f_n(P)\,dP \quad (n = r, r+1,\ldots).$$

By (2) and def. 51

(3) $$\int_B h_r(P)\,dP \leqslant \varliminf_{n\to\infty} \int_B f_n(P)\,dP \quad (r = 1, 2,\ldots).$$

But $P \in B$ implies

$$0 \leqslant h_1(P) \leqslant h_2(P) \leqslant \dots \quad \& \quad \lim_{r \to \infty} h_r(P) = \varliminf_{n \to \infty} f_n(P);$$

hence, by (3) and th. 186, we have (1).

Example. Let $f_n(x) = nx^{n-1}$ in $(0, 1)$; then

$$\int_0^1 f_n(x)\, dx = (R) \int_0^1 nx^{n-1}\, dx = 1 \quad (n = 1, 2, \dots),$$

while

$$\lim_{n \to \infty} f_n(x) = 0 \quad \text{in } (0, 1),$$

so that

$$0 = \int_0^1 \lim_{n \to \infty} f_n(x)\, dx < \lim_{n \to \infty} \int_0^1 f_n(x)\, dx = 1.$$

Theorem 193. *Let $f_1(P), f_2(P), \dots$ be non-negative and measurable in B, and let $F(P)$ be a function summable over B and such that, for every positive integer r,*

(1) $P \in B \quad implies \quad 0 \leqslant f_r(P) \leqslant F(P)$;

then

(2) $$\infty > \int_B \varlimsup_{n \to \infty} f_n(P)\, dP \geqslant \varlimsup_{n \to \infty} \int_B f_n(P)\, dP.$$

Proof. Let r be any chosen positive integer. For every point P of B let $g_r(P)$ denote the upper bound of the aggregate of the numbers $f_r(P), f_{r+1}(P), \dots$. Then (th. 152)

$$g_r(P) \text{ is measurable in } B \quad \& \quad F(P) \geqslant g_r(P) \geqslant f_n(P)$$
$$(n = r, r+1, \dots).$$

Hence, by th. 179 and def. 51,

(3) $\infty > \int_B g_r(P)\, dP \geqslant \varlimsup_{n \to \infty} \int_B f_n(P)\, dP \quad (r = 1, 2, \dots).$

But $P \subset B$ implies

$$g_1(P) \geqslant g_2(P) \geqslant \dots \quad \& \quad \lim_{r \to \infty} g_r(P) = \varlimsup_{n \to \infty} f_n(P).$$

Hence, by (3) and th. 187, we have (2).

The summability of $F(P)$ over B is essential to th. 193; this is illustrated by the example quoted after th. 187, in which

$$f_n(x) = \begin{cases} 1 & \text{if } x > n \\ 0 & \text{otherwise}; \end{cases}$$

for this sequence of functions we have

$$0 = \int_0^\infty \lim_{n \to \infty} f_n(x)\, dx < \lim_{n \to \infty} \int_0^\infty f_n(x)\, dx = \infty.$$

It is now easy to deduce a standard theorem for the integration of non-negative functions which are defined as limits of sequences of non-negative summable functions.

Theorem 194. *Let* $f_1(P), f_2(P),...$ *be measurable in* B, *and such that*

(1) $\qquad\qquad \lim\limits_{n\to\infty} f_n(P)$ *exists for every point* P *of* B,

and

(2) *there is a function* $F(P)$, *summable over* B, *and such that, for every positive integer* r *and every point* P *of* B,

$$0 \leqslant f_r(P) \leqslant F(P).$$

Then

(3) $\qquad \int\limits_B \lim\limits_{n\to\infty} f_n(P)\, dP = \lim\limits_{n\to\infty} \int\limits_B f_n(P)\, dP < \infty.$

Proof. By (1)

$$\lim\limits_{n\to\infty} f_n(P) = \varliminf\limits_{n\to\infty} f_n(P) = \varlimsup\limits_{n\to\infty} f_n(P)$$

for every point P of B; hence, by (2) and ths. 193 and 192,

$$\varlimsup\limits_{n\to\infty} \int\limits_B f_n(P)\, dP \leqslant \int\limits_B \lim\limits_{n\to\infty} f_n(P)\, dP \leqslant \varliminf\limits_{n\to\infty} \int\limits_B f_n(P)\, dP,$$

while $\qquad\qquad \varlimsup\limits_{n\to\infty} \int\limits_B f_n(P)\, dP < \infty;$

and this means (3).

Example. $\qquad \lim\limits_{n\to\infty} \int\limits_0^\infty \dfrac{dt}{(1+t/n)^n t^{1/n}} = 1.$

Proof. Let $\qquad f_n(t) = \left\{ \left(1+\dfrac{t}{n}\right)^n t^{1/n} \right\}^{-1};$

then (Hardy, p. 136 and § 208)

(1) $\qquad\qquad \lim\limits_{n\to\infty} f_n(t) = e^{-t}$ in $(0,\infty).$

Now in $(0,\infty)$ the non-negative functions $f_n(t)$ are continuous and therefore measurable; so, by (1) and th. 194, since

$$\int\limits_0^\infty e^{-t}\, dt = 1 \quad \text{(example (i) following th. 178),}$$

the result is proved if we define a function $F(t)$ summable over $(0,\infty)$ and such that

(2) $\qquad 0 < t < \infty$ implies $f_n(t) \leqslant F(t) \quad (n = 2, 3,...).$

Let n be any positive integer, $n \geqslant 2$; it follows easily that, if $1 < t < \infty$, then

$$f_n(t) \leqslant \left(1 + \frac{t}{n}\right)^{-n} = \left\{ \sum_{m=0}^{n} \binom{n}{m}\left(\frac{t}{n}\right)^m \right\}^{-1} \leqslant \left\{ \tfrac{1}{2}n(n-1)\frac{t^2}{n^2} \right\}^{-1} \leqslant 4t^{-2},$$

while, if $0 < t \leqslant 1$, then $f_n(t) < t^{-1/n} \leqslant t^{-\frac{1}{2}}$; so, if we put

$$F(t) = \begin{cases} t^{-\frac{1}{2}} & \text{if} \quad 0 < t \leqslant 1 \\ 4t^{-2} & \text{if} \quad 1 < t < \infty, \end{cases}$$

(2) is satisfied. The proof that $F(t)$ is summable over $(0, \infty)$ is left to the reader.

VI

INTEGRALS OF FUNCTIONS WHICH ARE SOMETIMES NEGATIVE

§ 1. Real Functions

THE definition of $\int\limits_B f(P) \, dP$ as $m\Omega_0(f; B)$, when $f(P)$ is non-negative and measurable in B, arose in connexion with the problem of measuring the 'area between a curve $y = f(x)$ and the x-axis'. Now, if $f(x)$ is sometimes negative and sometimes positive, the set of the points between the curve $y = f(x)$ and the x-axis is composed of two parts, namely that part which lies above the axis, and that part which lies below it. If each of these parts is measurable in the Lebesgue sense, and at least one of them has finite measure, it is natural to define the integral of $f(x)$ over the x-axis as the difference between their measures. These ideas will be expressed more precisely in what follows.

Definition 54. Let $f(P)$ be defined in B; then $f_+(P)$ and $f_-(P)$ are defined in B as follows:

$$f_+(P) = \begin{cases} f(P) & \text{if } f(P) > 0 \\ 0 & \text{otherwise,} \end{cases} \qquad f_-(P) = \begin{cases} -f(P) & \text{if } f(P) < 0 \\ 0 & \text{otherwise.} \end{cases}$$

Theorem 195. *Let $f(P)$ be measurable in B; then $f_+(P)$ and $f_-(P)$ are non-negative and measurable in B.*

Proof. $f_+(P) = \max(f(P), 0)$ & $f_-(P) = -\min(f(P), 0)$; hence $f_+(P)$ and $f_-(P)$ are non-negative in B. Also, arguing as in th. 152, it follows that $f_+(P)$ and $f_-(P)$ are measurable in B.

Definition 55. Let $f(P)$ be measurable in B; the Lebesgue integrals of $f_+(P)$ and $f_-(P)$ being defined by def. 52 (in virtue of th. 195), the Lebesgue integral of $f(P)$ over B, denoted by $\int\limits_B f(P) \, dP$, is defined by

$$\int\limits_B f(P) \, dP = \int\limits_B f_+(P) \, dP - \int\limits_B f_-(P) \, dP,$$

provided at least one of the integrals on the right-hand side is finite. If $\int\limits_B f(P) \, dP$ is finite, i.e. if $f_+(P)$ and $f_-(P)$ are both summable over B, then $f(P)$ is said to be summable over B. The conventions governing the use of the symbol $\int\limits_a^b f(x) \, dx$ remain as given in def. 53.

Theorem 196. *Let $f(P)$ be measurable in B; then*

(1) $$\int_B |f(P)| \, dP = \int_B f_+(P) \, dP + \int_B f_-(P) \, dP.$$

Proof. Let

$$B_+ = B.\mathscr{S}(P; f(P) \geqslant 0) \quad \& \quad B_- = B.\mathscr{S}(P; f(P) < 0).$$

By th. 150 $\qquad\qquad B_+ \in \mathscr{L} \quad \& \quad B_- \in \mathscr{L}.$

Since $P \in B_-$ implies $f_+(P) = 0$, and since $B = B_+ + B_-$, we have, by ths. 195, 177, and 182,

(2) $$\int_B f_+(P) \, dP = \int_{B_+} f_+(P) \, dP = \int_{B_+} |f(P)| \, dP,$$

and similarly

(3) $$\int_B f_-(P) \, dP = \int_{B_-} f_-(P) \, dP = \int_{B_-} |f(P)| \, dP;$$

and so, since $B = B_+ + B_-$, (1) follows from (2) and (3) by th. 177.

The next two theorems are of fundamental importance for the general theory of summable functions.

Theorem 197. *Let $f(P)$ be summable over B; then*

(i) $\qquad\qquad |f(P)|$ *is summable over B*

and

(ii) $$\left| \int_B f(P) \, dP \right| \leqslant \int_B |f(P)| \, dP.$$

Proof. By def. 55

$$0 \leqslant \int_B f_+(P) \, dP < \infty \quad \& \quad 0 \leqslant \int_B f_-(P) \, dP < \infty;$$

hence, by th. 196,

$$\infty > \int_B |f(P)| \, dP \geqslant \left| \int_B f_+(P) \, dP - \int_B f_-(P) \, dP \right| = \left| \int_B f(P) \, dP \right|.$$

Theorem 198. *If $|f(P)|$ is summable over B and $f(P)$ is measurable in B, then $f(P)$ is summable over B.*

Proof. By th. 196 and def. 55.

The reader should note that the summability of $|f(P)|$ over B does not imply the measurability of $f(P)$ in B; for example, let N be a linear non-measurable set contained in $(0,1)$, and let

$$f(x) = \begin{cases} 1 & \text{if } x \in N \\ -1 & \text{otherwise;} \end{cases}$$

then $|f(x)|$ is clearly summable over $(0,1)$; but the set of the points x of $(0,1)$ at which $f(x)$ is positive, being N, is non-measurable, and therefore $f(x)$ is not measurable in $(0,1)$.

Theorem 199. *If $f(P)$ is summable over B, then $f(P)$ is finite almost everywhere in B.*

Proof. By ths. 197 (i) and 184.

Theorem 200. *Let $f(x)$ be integrable-R over a closed interval J; then $f(x)$ is summable over J, and its Riemann and Lebesgue integrals over J are equal.*

Proof. Since $f(x) = f_+(x) - f_-(x)$, it follows (th. 61) that it is sufficient to show that

$$(1) \quad \int_a^b f_+(x)\,dx = (R)\int_a^b f_+(x)\,dx \quad \& \quad \int_a^b f_-(x)\,dx = (R)\int_a^b f_-(x)\,dx.$$

Since $f(x)$ is bounded in J, $f_+(x) = \frac{1}{2}\{|f(x)|+f(x)\}$, from which it follows that $f_+(x)$, like $f(x)$, is continuous almost everywhere in J (th. 53). Moreover $f_+(x)$, like $f(x)$, is bounded in J; hence (th. 55) $f_+(x)$ is integrable-R over J, and this, by th. 175, proves one half of (1). A similar argument applied to $f_-(x)$ completes the proof.

Theorem 201. *Let $f(P)$ be measurable in B, and let $g(P)$ be summable over B and such that*

$$P \in B \quad implies \quad |f(P)| \leqslant |g(P)|;$$

then $\qquad f(P)$ *is summable over B.*

Proof. By th. 197, $|g(P)|$ is summable over B; hence (ths. 159 and 179) $|f(P)|$ is summable over B, and, since $f(P)$ is measurable in B, the required result follows from th. 198.

Example. $e^{-x}\dfrac{\sin x}{x}$ is summable over $(0,\infty)$.

Proof. $e^{-x}\dfrac{\sin x}{x}$ is continuous and therefore measurable in $(0,\infty)$, and its modulus is less than e^{-x} in $(0,\infty)$. Since e^{-x} is summable over $(0,\infty)$ (example (i) following th. 178), the required result follows from th. 201.

Theorem 202. *Let $f(P)$ be measurable in B, and let $\phi(P)$ and $\psi(P)$ be summable over B and such that*

$$P \in B \quad implies \quad \phi(P) \leqslant f(P) \leqslant \psi(P);$$

then $\qquad f(P)$ *is summable over B.*

Proof.

$P \in B$ implies $f_+(P) \leqslant \psi_+(P)$ & $f_-(P) \leqslant \phi_-(P)$.

Hence, by ths. 195 and 179, $f_+(P)$ and $f_-(P)$ are summable over B.

Theorem 203. *Let $f(P)$ be bounded and measurable in B, and suppose $mB < \infty$; then*

$$f(P) \text{ is summable over } B \quad \& \quad \left| \int_B f(P)\, dP \right| \leqslant |B|\, M(|f|; B).$$

Proof. By th. 182

$$\int_B M(|f|; B)\, dP = |B|\, M(|f|; B),$$

and so (th. 201) $f(P)$ is summable over B, and by ths. 197 and 179 we have

$$\left| \int_B f(P)\, dP \right| \leqslant \int_B |f(P)|\, dP \leqslant \int_B M(|f|; B)\, dP,$$

which completes the proof.

Theorem 204. $\displaystyle \int_B -f(P)\, dP = - \int_B f(P)\, dP$ *if either side exists.*

Proof. Put $g(P) = -f(P)$; then $g_+(P) = f_-(P)$ & $g_-(P) = f_+(P)$, and the required result follows at once from def. 55.

Theorem 205. *Let $f(P)$ and $g(P)$ be measurable in B; suppose*

(1) $\qquad\qquad P \in B \quad \text{implies} \quad f(P) \leqslant g(P),$

and

(2) $\qquad\qquad \displaystyle \int_B f(P)\, dP > -\infty;$

then $\qquad\qquad \displaystyle \int_B f(P)\, dP \leqslant \int_B g(P)\, dP.$

Proof. By (1) $P \in B$ implies $f_+(P) \leqslant g_+(P)$ & $f_-(P) \geqslant g_-(P)$. Hence, by (2) and ths. 195 and 179,

$$\int_B f_+(P)\, dP \leqslant \int_B g_+(P)\, dP \quad \& \quad \infty > \int_B f_-(P)\, dP \geqslant \int_B g_-(P)\, dP,$$

and so

$$\int_B f(P)\, dP = \int_B f_+(P)\, dP - \int_B f_-(P)\, dP$$

$$\leqslant \int_B g_+(P)\, dP - \int_B g_-(P)\, dP = \int_B g(P)\, dP.$$

Theorem 206. *Suppose* $\int\limits_{B} f(P)\,dP$ *is defined, and B_1 is a measurable subset of B; then $\int\limits_{B_1} f(P)\,dP$ exists, and is finite if $f(P)$ is summable over B.*

Proof. By ths. 195 and 176

$$\int\limits_{B_1} f_+(P)\,dP \leqslant \int\limits_{B} f_+(P)\,dP \quad \& \quad \int\limits_{B_1} f_-(P)\,dP \leqslant \int\limits_{B} f_-(P)\,dP,$$

and the result follows from def. 55.

Theorem 207. *Let $f(P)$ be defined in B, and suppose $|B - B_1| = 0$; then*

$$\int\limits_{B} f(P)\,dP = \int\limits_{B_1} f(P)\,dP \quad \text{if either side exists.}$$

Proof. By ths. 119, 181, and 177

$$\int\limits_{B} f_+(P)\,dP = \int\limits_{B_1} f_+(P)\,dP \quad \text{if either side exists,}$$

and $\quad \int\limits_{B} f_-(P)\,dP = \int\limits_{B_1} f_-(P)\,dP \quad$ if either side exists.

The result now follows at once from def. 55.

Theorem 208. *Let $f(P)$ be defined in a null set B; then*

$$\int\limits_{B} f(P)\,dP = 0.$$

Proof. By th. 181 $\quad \int\limits_{B} f_+(P)\,dP = \int\limits_{B} f_-(P)\,dP = 0.$

Theorem 209. *Let $B = \sum\limits_{r=1}^{k} B_r$, and let $f(P)$ be summable over each of the sets $B_1, B_2, ..., B_k$; then*

$$f(P) \text{ is summable over } B \quad \& \quad \int\limits_{B} f(P)\,dP = \sum\limits_{r=1}^{k} \int\limits_{B_r} f(P)\,dP.$$

Proof. By hypothesis and ths. 195 and 177

$$\int\limits_{B} f_+(P)\,dP = \sum\limits_{r=1}^{k} \int\limits_{B_r} f_+(P)\,dP < \infty \quad \&$$

$$\int\limits_{B} f_-(P)\,dP = \sum\limits_{r=1}^{k} \int\limits_{B_r} f_-(P)\,dP < \infty.$$

Hence $f(P)$ is summable over B, and

$$\int\limits_{B} f(P)\,dP = \sum\limits_{r=1}^{k} \left\{ \int\limits_{B_r} f_+(P)\,dP - \int\limits_{B_r} f_-(P)\,dP \right\} = \sum\limits_{r=1}^{k} \int\limits_{B_r} f(P)\,dP.$$

Theorem 209.1. *Suppose $f(x)$ is summable over (a, b); then*

(i) $a < c < b$ *implies* $\displaystyle\int_a^c f(x)\, dx + \int_c^b f(x)\, dx = \int_a^b f(x)\, dx;$

(ii) *if* $F(x) = \displaystyle\int_a^x f(t)\, dt$, *then*

$a \leqslant \lambda \leqslant b$ & $a \leqslant \mu \leqslant b$ *implies* $\displaystyle\int_\lambda^\mu f(t)\, dt = F(\mu) - F(\lambda).$

Proof. By th. 206, $f(x)$ is summable over (a, c) and over (c, b), and since the sum of these two sets differs from (a, b) by a single point, (i) follows from ths. 207 and 209. To prove (ii) suppose $a \leqslant \lambda < \mu \leqslant b$; by (i) it follows that

$$F(\mu) = F(\lambda) + \int_\lambda^\mu f(x)\, dx,$$

and, since $F(\mu)$ and $F(\lambda)$ are finite, this gives $F(\mu) - F(\lambda) = \int_\lambda^\mu f(x)\, dx.$ If $a \leqslant \mu < \lambda \leqslant b$, then the reasoning above gives

$$\int_\mu^\lambda f(x)\, dx = F(\lambda) - F(\mu),$$

and so, by def. 53, (ii) is proved in all cases.

It may be left to the reader to prove that (i) of th. 209.1 is true whenever $\int_a^b f(x)\, dx$ is defined, even though $f(x)$ is not summable over (a, b).

Theorem 210. *Let $f(P)$ be summable over B, and let $\{B_r\}$ be a sequence of measurable sets such that $B = \sum\limits_{r=1}^{\infty} B_r$; then*

$$\int_B f(P)\, dP = \sum_{r=1}^{\infty} \int_{B_r} f(P)\, dP.$$

Proof. By ths. 195, 148, and 177,

$$\sum_{r=1}^{\infty} \int_{B_r} f_+(P)\, dP = \int_B f_+(P)\, dP < \infty \quad \&$$

$$\sum_{r=1}^{\infty} \int_{B_r} f_-(P)\, dP = \int_B f_-(P)\, dP < \infty;$$

hence

$$\int_B f(P)\, dP = \sum_{r=1}^{\infty} \left\{ \int_{B_r} f_+(P)\, dP - \int_{B_r} f_-(P)\, dP \right\} = \sum_{r=1}^{\infty} \int_{B_r} f(P)\, dP.$$

The reader should note in what respects the enunciation of th. 210 differs from that of th. 177 (ii); the difference is emphasized by the next theorem.

Theorem 211. *Let* $B = \sum_{r=1}^{\infty} B_r$, *and let* $f(P)$ *be measurable in each of the sets* $B_1, B_2,...$; *then* $f(P)$ *is summable over* B *if and only if*

$$\sum_{r=1}^{\infty} \int_{B_r} |f(P)|\, dP < \infty.$$

Proof. Since $|f(P)|$ is measurable in each of the sets $B_1, B_2,...$ (th. 159), it follows by th. 177 that

$$(1) \qquad \int_B |f(P)|\, dP = \sum_{r=1}^{\infty} \int_{B_r} |f(P)|\, dP;$$

moreover $f(P)$ is measurable in B (th. 149), and so, by ths. 197 and 198, $f(P)$ is summable over B if and only if $\int_B |f(P)|\, dP < \infty$; hence the result follows from (1).

Example. Let

$$f(x) = \frac{(-1)^r}{r} \quad \text{if} \quad r-1 \leqslant x < r;$$

then
$$\int_{r-1}^{r} f(x)\, dx = \frac{(-1)^r}{r} \quad (r = 1, 2,...),$$

so that $\sum_{r=1}^{\infty} \int_{r-1}^{r} f(x)\, dx$ exists and is finite.

However, $f(x)$ is *not* summable over $(0, \infty)$ since

$$\sum_{r=1}^{\infty} \int_{r-1}^{r} |f(x)|\, dx = \sum_{r=1}^{\infty} \frac{1}{r} = \infty.$$

Theorem 211.1. *Suppose* $f(x)$ *is summable over* (a, b); *then*

$$(i) \qquad \lim_{\alpha \to a+0} \int_a^{\alpha} f(x)\, dx = \lim_{\beta \to b-0} \int_{\beta}^{b} f(x)\, dx = 0;$$

(ii) *if* α *and* β *tend independently to* $a+0$ *and* $b-0$ *respectively, then*

$$\int_{\alpha}^{\beta} f(x)\, dx \quad \text{tends to} \quad \int_a^b f(x)\, dx.$$

Proof. Since $f(x)$ is summable over (a, b), it follows (th. 176) that

$$a \leqslant \alpha < \beta \leqslant b \quad \text{implies} \quad 0 \leqslant \int_{\alpha}^{\beta} f_+(x)\, dx \leqslant \int_a^b f_+(x)\, dx < \infty.$$

Hence, by ths. 178 and 177, as α tends to $a+0$ and β to $b-0$,

$$\int_\alpha^\beta f_+(x)\,dx \quad \text{tends to} \quad \int_a^b f_+(x)\,dx,$$

and $\qquad \left\{ \int_a^\alpha f_+(x)\,dx + \int_\beta^b f_+(x)\,dx \right\} \quad$ tends to $\quad 0$.

Since $f_+(x)$ is non-negative, it now follows that (i) is satisfied when $f(x)$ is replaced by $f_+(x)$, and similarly when $f(x)$ is replaced by $f_-(x)$; this proves (i), and since

$$\int_a^b f(x)\,dx = \int_a^\alpha f(x)\,dx + \int_\alpha^\beta f(x)\,dx + \int_\beta^b f(x)\,dx,$$

we have (ii).

Theorem 211.2. *Suppose*

(1) $\qquad\qquad f(x)$ *is integrable-CR over* (a,b),

and

(2) $\qquad\qquad f(x)$ *is summable over* (a,b);

then $\qquad \displaystyle\int_a^b f(x)\,dx = (CR)\int_a^b f(x)\,dx.$

Proof. It follows from (1) and def. 37.1 that

$f(x)$ is integrable-R over (α,β) whenever $a < \alpha < \beta < b$,

and so, by th. 200,

$$a < \alpha < \beta < b \quad \text{implies} \quad \int_\alpha^\beta f(x)\,dx = (R)\int_\alpha^\beta f(x)\,dx;$$

hence the result follows from (1), def. 37.1, (2), and th. 211.1.

It should be observed that the conditions (1) and (2) of th. 211.2 are independent; the reader may verify that $f(x)$, defined in the example following th. 211, is integrable-CR over $(0,\infty)$ without being summable over $(0,\infty)$. A more interesting example is the following:

Example. For $x > 0$ let

$$f(x) = \frac{d}{dx}\left(x^2 \sin\frac{\pi}{x^2}\right) = 2x\sin\frac{\pi}{x^2} - \frac{2\pi}{x}\cos\frac{\pi}{x^2}.$$

By th. 66,

$$(R)\int_\epsilon^1 f(x)\,dx = -\epsilon^2 \sin\frac{\pi}{\epsilon^2}, \quad \text{and hence} \quad (CR)\int_0^1 f(x)\,dx = 0.$$

However, $f(x)$ is not summable over $(0,1)$: since $2x\sin\pi/x^2$ is bounded and continuous in $(0,1)$, it is summable over $(0,1)$; hence it will be sufficient to show that $1/x\cos\pi/x^2$ is not summable over $(0,1)$; this will be proved by showing (th. 197) that

$$\int_0^1 \frac{1}{x}\left|\cos\frac{\pi}{x^2}\right|\,dx = \infty.$$

Let $a_n = (n+\tfrac{1}{3})^{-\frac{1}{2}}$ and $b_n = (n-\tfrac{1}{3})^{-\frac{1}{2}}$; then $a_n \leqslant x \leqslant b_n$ implies $n\pi-\tfrac{1}{3}\pi \leqslant \pi/x^2 \leqslant n\pi+\tfrac{1}{3}\pi$, and consequently $|\cos\pi/x^2| \geqslant \tfrac{1}{2}$. Hence, by ths. 176 and 177,

$$\int_0^1 \left|\frac{1}{x}\cos\frac{\pi}{x^2}\right|\,dx \geqslant \sum_{n=1}^{\infty} \int_{a_n}^{b_n} \frac{1}{x}\left|\cos\frac{\pi}{x^2}\right|\,dx$$

$$\geqslant \frac{1}{2}\sum_{n=1}^{\infty}\int_{a_n}^{b_n}\frac{dx}{x} = \frac{1}{4}\sum_{n=1}^{\infty}\log\left(\frac{3n+1}{3n-1}\right) = \infty,$$

since $\qquad \log\left(\dfrac{3n+1}{3n-1}\right) = \displaystyle\int_1^{1+2/(3n-1)}\frac{dx}{x} \geqslant \dfrac{\dfrac{2}{3n-1}}{1+\dfrac{2}{3n-1}} = \dfrac{2}{3n+1}.$

Theorem 212. *Suppose* $f^{(1)}(P), f^{(2)}(P),\ldots$ *are measurable in* B, *and*

(1) $\qquad\qquad P \in B \quad implies \quad f^{(1)}(P) \leqslant f^{(2)}(P) \leqslant \cdots,$

and

(2) $\qquad\qquad \displaystyle\int_B f^{(1)}(P)\,dP > -\infty;$

then

(3) $\qquad -\infty < \displaystyle\int_B \lim_{n\to\infty} f^{(n)}(P)\,dP = \lim_{n\to\infty}\int_B f^{(n)}(P)\,dP.$

Proof. Let $f(P) = \displaystyle\lim_{n\to\infty} f^{(n)}(P)$; by (1) $P \in B$ implies

(4)
$$f^{(1)}_+(P) \leqslant f^{(2)}_+(P) \leqslant \cdots \quad \& \quad f_+(P) = \lim_{n\to\infty} f^{(n)}_+(P),$$
$$f^{(1)}_-(P) \geqslant f^{(2)}_-(P) \geqslant \cdots \quad \& \quad f_-(P) = \lim_{n\to\infty} f^{(n)}_-(P).$$

Now, by (2), $\qquad\qquad \displaystyle\int_B f^{(1)}_-(P)\,dP < \infty.$

Hence, by (4) and ths. 195, 186, and 187,

$$\int_B f_+(P)\,dP = \lim_{n\to\infty}\int_B f^{(n)}_+(P)\,dP \quad \& \quad \int_B f_-(P)\,dP = \lim_{n\to\infty}\int_B f^{(n)}_-(P)\,dP,$$

and so, by th. 179,

$$-\infty < \int_B f(P)\, dP = \lim_{n\to\infty} \int_B f_+^{(n)}(P)\, dP -\lim_{n\to\infty} \int_B f_-^{(n)}(P)\, dP$$

$$= \lim_{n\to\infty}\left\{\int_B f_+^{(n)}(P)\, dP - \int_B f_-^{(n)}(P)\, dP\right\},$$

which gives (3).

Theorem 213. *Suppose* $f_1(P), f_2(P),\dots$ *are measurable in* B, *and* $P \in B$ *implies* $f_1(P) \geqslant f_2(P) \geqslant \dots$; *suppose also that*

$$\int_B f_1(P)\, dP < \infty; \quad then \quad \infty > \int_B \lim_{n\to\infty} f_n(P)\, dP = \lim_{n\to\infty} \int_B f_n(P)\, dP.$$

Proof. Apply th. 212 to the sequence $\{-f_n(P)\}$, and the required result follows by th. 204.

The fundamental theorem on the integration of functions defined as limits of summable functions is the following:

Theorem 214. *Let* $F(P), f_1(P), f_2(P),\dots$ *be summable over* B, *and such that*

$$\lim_{n\to\infty} f_n(P) \text{ exists for every point } P \text{ of } B$$

and $\quad P \in B \quad implies \quad |f_n(P)| \leqslant F(P) \quad (n = 1, 2,\dots);$ *then* $\lim_{n\to\infty} f_n(P)$ *is summable over* B, *and*

$$\int_B \lim_{n\to\infty} f_n(P)\, dP = \lim_{n\to\infty} \int_B f_n(P)\, dP.$$

Proof. Either by an argument similar to that of th. 212, but based on th. 194, or else by a combination of the following two theorems.

Theorem 215. *Let* $F(P), f_1(P), f_2(P),\dots$ *be summable over* B, *and such that*

$$P \in B \quad implies \quad f_r(P) \leqslant F(P) \quad (r = 1, 2,\dots)$$

and $\quad \int_B f_r(P)\, dP$ *does not tend to* $-\infty$ *as* r *tends to* ∞; *then* $\varlimsup_{r\to\infty} f_r(P)$ *is summable over* B, *and*

$$\int_B \varlimsup_{r\to\infty} f_r(P)\, dP \geqslant \varlimsup_{r\to\infty} \int_B f_r(P)\, dP.$$

Proof. Using the notation of the parallel theorem for non-negative functions (th. 193), we have

$$F(P) \geqslant g_r(P) \geqslant f_n(P) \text{ in } B \quad (n = r, r+1,\dots).$$

Hence, by th. 202, $g_r(P)$ is summable over B, and, by th. 205,

$$(1) \qquad \infty > \int_B g_r(P)\, dP \geqslant \int_B f_n(P)\, dP \quad (n = r, r+1, \ldots).$$

By (1) and the terms of the hypothesis there is a number k such that

$$(2) \quad \infty > \int_B g_r(P)\, dP \geqslant \varlimsup_{n \to \infty} \int_B f_n(P)\, dP > k > -\infty \quad (r = 1, 2, \ldots).$$

Moreover, $P \in B$ implies

$$g_1(P) \geqslant g_2(P) \geqslant \ldots \quad \& \quad \lim_{n \to \infty} g_n(P) = \varlimsup_{r \to \infty} f_r(P);$$

and hence the required result follows from (2) and th. 213.

Theorem 216. *Let* $F(P), f_1(P), f_2(P), \ldots$ *be summable over* B, *and such that*

$$P \in B \quad \text{implies} \quad F(P) \leqslant f_r(P) \quad (r = 1, 2, \ldots)$$

and $\int_B f_r(P)\, dP$ *does not tend to* ∞ *as* r *tends to* ∞;

then $\lim\limits_{r \to \infty} f_r(P)$ *is summable over* B, *and*

$$\int_B \varliminf_{r \to \infty} f_r(P)\, dP \leqslant \varliminf_{r \to \infty} \int_B f_r(P)\, dP.$$

Proof. By applying th. 215 to the sequence $\{-f_r(P)\}$, and then using ths. 204 and 154.

Example. $\qquad \lim\limits_{n \to \infty} \displaystyle\int_0^\infty \frac{\log(x+n)}{n} e^{-x} \cos x\, dx = 0.$

Proof. For $n = 1, 2, \ldots$ & $x > 0$ we have (Hardy, § 197)

$$\frac{\log(x+n)}{n} < \frac{x+n}{n} \leqslant 1+x,$$

and so, if we put

$$f_n(x) = \frac{\log(x+n)}{n} e^{-x} \cos x \quad \& \quad F(x) = \begin{cases} 2xe^{-x} & \text{if } x \geqslant 1 \\ 2e^{-x} & \text{if } x < 1, \end{cases}$$

it follows that

$$(1) \qquad x > 0 \quad \text{implies} \quad |f_n(x)| < F(x) \quad (n = 1, 2, \ldots).$$

Since xe^{-x} and e^{-x} are summable over $(0, \infty)$ (examples following ths. 178 and 180), it follows that $F(x)$ is summable over $(0, 1)$ and over $(1, \infty)$, and consequently over $(0, \infty)$. Also, each of the functions $f_n(x)$ is continuous and therefore measurable in $(0, \infty)$; hence, by (1) and th. 201, each of the functions $f_n(x)$ is summable over $(0,\infty)$, and (th. 214)

$$\lim_{n\to\infty} \int_0^\infty f_n(x)\, dx = \int_0^\infty \lim_{n\to\infty} f_n(x)\, dx$$

if $\lim_{n\to\infty} f_n(x)$ is defined in $(0,\infty)$. Since (Hardy, § 199)

$$x > 0 \quad \text{implies} \quad \lim_{n\to\infty} \frac{\log(x+n)}{n} = 0,$$

the result now follows at once from th. 182.

In some of the theorems which follow, we are concerned with the properties of

$$f(P)+g(P), \qquad f(P)-g(P), \qquad f(P)g(P),$$

where $f(P)$ and $g(P)$ are summable over B. By ths. 199 and 86, these functions are defined almost everywhere in B, but there may be a non-empty null set in which they are not defined. For the sake of uniformity in enunciations, it is convenient on this account to use the symbol $\int_B f(P)\, dP$ in an extended sense described in def. 57. To establish the consistency of this definition, we require a few simple theorems.

Theorem 217. *Suppose $f(P)$ and $g(P)$ are defined in B, and*

$$f(P) = g(P) \text{ p.p. in } B;$$

then $\qquad \int_B f(P)\, dP = \int_B g(P)\, dP$ *if either side exists.*

Proof. Let $\qquad B_1 = B.\mathscr{S}(P;f(P)=g(P));$

by hypothesis $\qquad |B-B_1| = 0.$

Suppose $\qquad \int_B f(P)\, dP$ exists;

then, by th. 207,

$$\int_B f(P)\, dP = \int_{B_1} f(P)\, dP = \int_{B_1} g(P)\, dP = \int_B g(P)\, dP.$$

Definition 56. The functions $f(P)$ and $g(P)$ are said to be *equivalent in B* if the equation $f(P) = g(P)$ is true for almost all points P of B (there may be points P of B for which $f(P)$ or $g(P)$ is not even defined). The relation between f and g is symbolized by

$$f(P) \sim g(P) \text{ in } B.$$

Confusion of this use of the symbol $\sim$ with that of def. 10 will be excluded by the context.

Example. $\lim\limits_{m\to\infty} \lim\limits_{n\to\infty} \cos^n(m!\,\pi x) \sim 0$ in $(-\infty, \infty)$ (cf. example following th. 77).

Theorem 218. *If* $f(P) \sim g(P)$ *in* B & $g(P) \sim h(P)$ *in* B, *then*
$$f(P) \sim h(P) \text{ in } B.$$

Proof. The proof, which is a simple exercise on th. 86, is left to the reader.

Definition 57. If

$\int\limits_B g(P)\,dP$ exists (in the sense of def. 55)   & $f(P) \sim g(P)$ in B,

then the Lebesgue integral of $f(P)$ over B, denoted by $\int\limits_B f(P)\,dP$, is defined by
$$\int\limits_B f(P)\,dP = \int\limits_B g(P)\,dP.$$

If $g(P)$ is summable over B, then $f(P)$ is said to be *equivalent in B to a summable function.*

The uniqueness of $\int\limits_B f(P)\,dP$, when it exists in this generalized sense, is guaranteed by ths. 217 and 218.

Theorem 219. *If* $f(P) \sim g(P)$ *in* B, *then*
$$\int\limits_B f(P)\,dP = \int\limits_B g(P)\,dP \text{ if either side exists.}$$

Proof. By th. 218 and def. 57.

Theorem 220. *Suppose* $\int\limits_{B_1} f(P)\,dP$ *exists (in the sense of def. 57), and that*
$$|B - B_1| = 0;$$
then
$$(1) \qquad \int\limits_B f(P)\,dP = \int\limits_{B_1} f(P)\,dP.$$

Proof. By hypothesis, there is a function $g(P)$ defined in B_1, such that
$$g(P) \sim f(P) \text{ in } B_1 \quad \& \quad \int\limits_{B_1} g(P)\,dP \text{ exists in the sense of def. 55.}$$

Let $\qquad h(P) = \begin{cases} g(P) & \text{if } P \in B_1 \\ 0 & \text{otherwise;} \end{cases}$

since $|B-B_1| = 0$, $h(P) \sim f(P)$ in B, and, by th. 207,

$$\int_B h(P)\, dP = \int_{B_1} g(P)\, dP = \int_{B_1} f(P)\, dP,$$

which implies (1).

Theorem 221. *Let $f(P)$ be equivalent in B to a summable function; then*
$f(P)$ *is equivalent in B to a* finite *function summable over B.*

Proof. By hypothesis there exists a function $g(P)$ summable over B and such that $f(P) \sim g(P)$ in B.

Let
$$h(P) = \begin{cases} g(P) & \text{if} \quad |g(P)| < \infty \\ 0 & \text{otherwise.} \end{cases}$$

Then $h(P)$ is finite in B, and, by th. 199, $h(P) \sim g(P)$ in B. Hence $h(P)$ is summable over B (th. 217), and $h(P) \sim f(P)$ in B (th. 218).

Theorem 222. *Let $f(P)$ be equivalent in B to a summable function, and let B be the sum of a sequence of measurable sets, $\{B_r\}$; then*

$$\int_B f(P)\, dP = \sum_{r=1}^{\infty} \int_{B_r} f(P)\, dP.$$

Proof. By hypothesis there is a function $g(P)$ such that

(1) $g(P)$ is summable over B & $f(P) \sim g(P)$ in B.

Since $f(P) \sim g(P)$ in B_r $(r = 1, 2,...)$,

it follows by (1) and th. 210 that

$$\int_B f(P)\, dP = \int_B g(P)\, dP = \sum_{r=1}^{\infty} \int_{B_r} g(P)\, dP = \sum_{r=1}^{\infty} \int_{B_r} f(P)\, dP.$$

Theorem 223. *Let $f_1(P), f_2(P),...$ be equivalent in B to summable functions; suppose $f(P) \sim \lim_{n\to\infty} f_n(P)$ in B, and*

$$|f_r(P)| \leqslant F(P)\ p.p.\ in\ B \quad (r = 1, 2,...),$$

where $F(P)$ is equivalent in B to a summable function; then $f(P)$ is equivalent in B to a summable function, and

$$\int_B f(P)\, dP = \lim_{n\to\infty} \int_B f_n(P)\, dP.$$

Proof. To every positive integer r there will be a set B_r consisting of all those points P of B for which either $f_r(P)$ or $F(P)$ is not defined, or else the statement $|f_r(P)| \leqslant F(P)$ is false; and $|B_r| = 0$ by th. 86 and def. 57. Let Z be the set of the points P of B for which the statement $f(P) = \lim\limits_{n\to\infty} f_n(P)$ is false; then $|Z| = 0$. If

$$B_0 = Z \dotplus \sum_{r=1}^{\infty}{}^* B_r,$$

then B_0 is null (th. 86), and the conditions of th. 214 are satisfied when B is replaced by $B - B_0$. The required result is then an immediate deduction from th. 220.

Theorem 224. *Let $f(P)$ be equivalent in B to a summable function, and let a be any finite real number; then*

$$\int\limits_B a f(P)\, dP = a \int\limits_B f(P)\, dP.$$

Proof. Let $g(P)$ be a finite function summable over B and such that

$$f(P) \sim g(P) \text{ in } B \text{ (th. 221)},$$

and let

$$h(P) = a g(P) \text{ in } B.$$

Then $a = 0$ implies $h(P) = 0$, and so (th. 182)

$$\int\limits_B h(P)\, dP = 0 = 0 \int\limits_B f(P)\, dP.$$

If $0 < a < \infty$, then

$$h_+(P) = a g_+(P) \quad \& \quad h_-(P) = a g_-(P),$$

and so (th. 180)

$$\int\limits_B h_+(P)\, dP - \int\limits_B h_-(P)\, dP$$

$$= a \int\limits_B g_+(P)\, dP - a \int\limits_B g_-(P)\, dP = a \int\limits_B g(P)\, dP = a \int\limits_B f(P)\, dP.$$

Since $a f(P) \sim a g(P)$ in B, it now follows that

$$0 \leqslant a < \infty \quad \text{implies} \quad \int\limits_B a f(P)\, dP = a \int\limits_B f(P)\, dP.$$

The proof is now easily completed by applying th. 204.

The following two theorems are simple exercises on th. 86, and their proof is left to the reader.

Theorem 225. *If $f_r(P) \sim g_r(P)$ in B $(r = 1, 2, ...)$, then*

$$h(P) \sim \lim_{r\to\infty} g_r(P) \text{ in } B \quad \text{implies} \quad h(P) \sim \lim_{r\to\infty} f_r(P) \text{ in } B.$$

Theorem 226.

(i) *If $f_r(P) \sim g_r(P)$ in B $(r = 1, 2, ..., k)$, then*

$$h(P) \sim \sum_{r=1}^{k} g_r(P) \text{ in } B \quad \text{implies} \quad h(P) \sim \sum_{r=1}^{k} f_r(P) \text{ in } B.$$

(ii) *If $f_r(P) \sim g_r(P)$ in B $(r = 1, 2, ...)$, then*

$$h(P) \sim \sum_{r=1}^{\infty} g_r(P) \text{ in } B \quad \text{implies} \quad h(P) \sim \sum_{r=1}^{\infty} f_r(P) \text{ in } B.$$

Theorem 227. *Let $f(P)$ and $g(P)$ be each equivalent in B to a summable function, and let λ and μ be any finite real numbers; then $\{\lambda f(P) + \mu g(P)\}$ is equivalent in B to a summable function, and*

$$\int_B \{\lambda f(P) + \mu g(P)\} \, dP = \lambda \int_B f(P) \, dP + \mu \int_B g(P) \, dP.$$

Proof. After th. 224 it is sufficient to prove the result for the special case $\lambda = \mu = 1$. By th. 221 $\phi(P)$ and $\psi(P)$ exist such that

(1) $\phi(P)$ is finite and summable over B & $f(P) \sim \phi(P)$ in B,

(2) $\psi(P)$ is finite and summable over B & $g(P) \sim \psi(P)$ in B.

Put

(3) $$h(P) = \phi(P) + \psi(P).$$

Then $h(P)$ is finite and measurable in B (th. 156), and since

$$|h(P)| \leqslant |\phi(P)| + |\psi(P)|,$$

it follows by ths. 197, 189, and 201 that $h(P)$ is summable over B; hence, by th. 226, $\{f(P) + g(P)\}$ is equivalent in B to a summable function, and

(4) $$\int_B \{f(P) + g(P)\} \, dP = \int_B h(P) \, dP = \int_B h_+(P) \, dP - \int_B h_-(P) \, dP.$$

Since all the functions in question are finite, (3) implies

$$h_+(P) + \phi_-(P) + \psi_-(P) = h_-(P) + \phi_+(P) + \psi_+(P),$$

whence, by th. 190,

$$\int_B h_+(P) \, dP + \int_B \phi_-(P) \, dP + \int_B \psi_-(P) \, dP$$
$$= \int_B h_-(P) \, dP + \int_B \phi_+(P) \, dP + \int_B \psi_+(P) \, dP;$$

since all the integrals in question are finite, this implies

$$\int_B h_+(P)\,dP - \int_B h_-(P)\,dP$$

$$= \int_B \phi_+(P)\,dP - \int_B \phi_-(P)\,dP + \int_B \psi_+(P)\,dP - \int_B \psi_-(P)\,dP.$$

Hence, by (4), (1), and (2),

$$\int_B \{f(P)+g(P)\}\,dP = \int_B f(P)\,dP + \int_B g(P)\,dP.$$

Theorem 228. *Let $f_1(P), f_2(P),..., f_k(P)$ be each equivalent in B to a summable function; then $\sum_{r=1}^{k} f_r(P)$ is equivalent in B to a summable function, and*

$$\int_B \sum_{r=1}^{k} f_r(P)\,dP = \sum_{r=1}^{k} \int_B f_r(P)\,dP.$$

Proof By induction from th. 227.

The following is one of the most frequently used theorems for the integration of functions defined as sums of infinite series.

Theorem 229. *Let $\{f_r(P)\}$ be a sequence of functions measurable in B, and such that*

(1)
$$\sum_{r=1}^{\infty} \int_B |f_r(P)|\,dP < \infty;$$

then $\sum_{r=1}^{\infty} f_r(P)$ is equivalent in B to a summable function, and

(2)
$$\int_B \sum_{r=1}^{\infty} f_r(P)\,dP = \sum_{r=1}^{\infty} \int_B f_r(P)\,dP.$$

Proof. Put $F(P) = \sum_{r=1}^{\infty} |f_r(P)|$; by (1) and ths. 159 and 191

(3)
$$F(P) \text{ is summable over } B.$$

Put
$$S_n(P) = \sum_{r=1}^{n} f_r(P) \quad (n = 1, 2,...);$$
by (3) and th. 184

$$\sum_{r=1}^{\infty} f_r(P) \text{ converges absolutely p.p. in } B.$$

Hence

(4)
$$\sum_{r=1}^{\infty} f_r(P) \sim \lim_{n\to\infty} S_n(P) \text{ in } B,$$

and

(5)
$$|S_n(P)| \leqslant F(P) \text{ p.p. in } B \quad (n = 1, 2,...).$$

Also, $|f_r(P)| \leqslant F(P)$, so that, by (3) and th. 201, $f_r(P)$ is summable over B $(r = 1, 2,...)$; hence (th. 228) $S_n(P)$ is equivalent in B to a summable function, and

$$(6) \qquad \int\limits_B S_n(P)\,dP = \sum_{r=1}^{n} \int\limits_B f_r(P)\,dP \quad (n = 1, 2,\ldots).$$

By (3), (4), (5), (6), and th. 223, $\sum\limits_{r=1}^{\infty} f_r(P)$ is equivalent in B to a summable function, and

$$\int\limits_B \sum_{r=1}^{\infty} f_r(P)\,dP = \lim_{n\to\infty} \int\limits_B S_n(P)\,dP = \lim_{n\to\infty} \sum_{r=1}^{n} \int\limits_B f_r(P)\,dP,$$

which means (2).

Example (i).

$$\int\limits_0^\infty e^{-x} \cos\sqrt{x}\,dx = 1 - \frac{1}{2} + \frac{2!}{4!} - \frac{3!}{6!} + \frac{4!}{8!} - \cdots.$$

Proof. We have (Hardy, § 217)

$$(1) \qquad e^{-x} \cos\sqrt{x} = \sum_{n=0}^{\infty} (-1)^n \frac{x^n e^{-x}}{(2n!)} \quad (0! = 1).$$

Now, by the example to th. 180,

$$\int\limits_0^\infty x^n e^{-x}\,dx = n! \quad (n = 0, 1, 2,\ldots),$$

and so

$$\sum_{n=0}^{\infty} \int\limits_0^\infty \frac{e^{-x} x^n}{(2n)!}\,dx = \sum_{n=0}^{\infty} \frac{n!}{(2n)!} < \sum_{n=0}^{\infty} 2^{-n} < \infty;$$

it now follows by (1) and th. 229 that

$$\int\limits_0^\infty e^{-x} \cos\sqrt{x}\,dx = \sum_{n=0}^{\infty} (-1)^n \frac{n!}{(2n)!},$$

which is the required result.

Example (ii). Suppose $f(x)$ is finite and summable over (a, b), and let r be a fixed number such that $0 < r < 1$; then

$$\int\limits_a^b f(x) \frac{\sin x}{1 - 2r\cos x + r^2}\,dx = \sum_{n=1}^{\infty} r^{n-1} \int\limits_a^b f(x)\sin nx\,dx.$$

Proof. For every positive integer n

$$(1) \qquad f(x)r^{n-1}\sin nx \quad \text{is measurable in } (a, b)$$

and

$$\int\limits_a^b |f(x)r^{n-1}\sin nx|\,dx \leqslant r^{n-1} \int\limits_a^b |f(x)|\,dx;$$

hence $\quad \sum_{n=1}^{\infty} \int_a^b |f(x)r^{n-1}\sin nx|\, dx \leqslant \dfrac{1}{1-r} \int_a^b |f(x)|\, dx < \infty,$

and so, by (1) and th. 229, it remains only to prove that

$$(2) \qquad\qquad \sum_{n=1}^{\infty} r^{n-1}\sin nx = \frac{\sin x}{1-2r\cos x + r^2}.$$

Put $z = r\cos x + ir\sin x$; since $|z| < 1$, we have

$$\sum_{n=1}^{\infty} r^n(\cos nx + i\sin nx) = \sum_{n=1}^{\infty} z^n = \frac{z}{1-z} = \frac{r\cos x - r^2 + ir\sin x}{1-2r\cos x + r^2},$$

from which (2) follows on comparing imaginary parts.

It is easy to give examples in which

$$\int_B \sum_{n=1}^{\infty} f_n(P)\, dP \neq \sum_{n=1}^{\infty} \int_B f_n(P)\, dP$$

although both sides exist and are finite; as the following shows, the functions $f_n(P)$ may be of the most elementary character.

Example. Let

$$f_n(x) = nx^{n-1} - (n+1)x^n \quad (n = 1, 2, \ldots).$$

Clearly

$$0 < x < 1 \quad \text{implies} \quad \sum_{n=1}^{\infty} f_n(x) = 1, \quad \text{and so} \quad \int_0^1 \sum_{n=1}^{\infty} f_n(x)\, dx = 1;$$

on the other hand, by ths. 200 and 66,

$$\int_0^1 f_n(x)\, dx = 0 \quad (n = 1, 2, \ldots), \quad \text{and so} \quad \sum_{n=1}^{\infty} \int_0^1 f_n(x)\, dx = 0.$$

It follows from th. 229 that this can only happen if

$$\sum_{n=1}^{\infty} \int_0^1 |f_n(x)|\, dx = \infty,$$

and it is easy to verify this directly. Let n be any positive integer; since $0 < x < n/(n+1)$ implies $f_n(x) > 0$, we have

$$\int_0^1 |f_n(x)|\, dx \geqslant \int_0^{n/(n+1)} f_n(x)\, dx$$

$$= \left(\frac{n}{n+1}\right)^n - \left(\frac{n}{n+1}\right)^{n+1} = \left(1+\frac{1}{n}\right)^{-n}\left(\frac{1}{n+1}\right),$$

and since $(1+1/n)^n < 3$ (Hardy, § 73), we have

$$\sum_{n=1}^{\infty} \int_0^1 |f_n(x)|\, dx \geqslant \frac{1}{3} \sum_{n=1}^{\infty} \frac{1}{n+1} = \infty.$$

Theorem 230. *Let $f(P)$ be bounded and measurable in B, and let $g(P)$ be equivalent in B to a summable function; then $f(P)g(P)$ is equivalent in B to a summable function, and*

(1) $$\left| \int_B f(P)g(P)\, dP \right| \leqslant M(|f|; B) \int_B |g(P)|\, dP.$$

Proof. By th. 221 there is a finite function $h(P)$ summable over B and equivalent to $g(P)$ in B. By th. 165

(2) $f(P)h(P) \sim f(P)g(P)$ in B & $f(P)h(P)$ is measurable in B.

Put $\lambda = M(|f|; B)$; then $P \in B$ implies $|f(P)h(P)| \leqslant \lambda |h(P)|$, and so, by (2) and ths. 219, 201, 197, and 180,

$$\left| \int_B f(P)g(P)\, dP \right| = \left| \int_B f(P)h(P)\, dP \right| \leqslant \lambda \int_B |h(P)|\, dP = \lambda \int_B |g(P)|\, dP,$$

which implies (1).

The reader should note that, in th. 230, the summability of $f(P)$ over B cannot replace the assumption that $f(P)$ is bounded and measurable in B; for example, if $f(x) = g(x) = x^{-\frac{1}{2}}$ in $(0, 1)$, then $f(x)$ and $g(x)$ are both summable over $(0, 1)$, but $f(x)g(x)$ is not (example (iii) following th. 178).

Definition 58. Let $\{f_r(P)\}$ be a sequence of functions defined in B and satisfying the following conditions:

(i) there is a finite constant k such that, if P is any point of B and n is any positive integer, then

$$\left| \sum_{r=1}^{n} f_r(P) \right| < k;$$

(ii) $\sum_{r=1}^{\infty} f_r(P)$ exists for every point P of B;

the series $\sum_{r=1}^{\infty} f_r(P)$ will then be said to *converge boundedly* in B.

(The reader should note that the existence of $\sum_{r=1}^{\infty} f_r(P)$ as a function bounded in B gives no indication of the behaviour of its partial sums, and therefore does not imply that $\sum_{r=1}^{\infty} f_r(P)$ converges boundedly in B; this is emphasized in example (ii).)

Examples.

(i) Let $\{P_r\}$ be a sequence consisting of all the rational points of R_n (th. 8), and for every positive integer r let $f_r(P)$ be defined to be zero except at P_r, where its value is unity; then $\sum_{r=1}^{\infty} f_r(P)$ converges boundedly in R_n.

(ii) For every positive integer n

let $\qquad g_n(x) = \begin{cases} n\sin \pi nx & \text{if} \quad 0 \leqslant x \leqslant 1/n \\ 0 & \text{if} \quad 1/n < x \leqslant 1, \end{cases}$

and let $g_0(x) = 0$ in $[0,1]$;

let $\qquad f_n(x) = g_n(x) - g_{n-1}(x) \quad (n = 1, 2, ...)$,

Then $\qquad \sum_{r=1}^{\infty} f_r(x) = \lim_{n\to\infty} g_n(x) = 0$ in $[0,1]$,

but the series $\sum_{r=1}^{\infty} f_r(x)$ does not converge boundedly in $[0,1]$, since for every positive integer n

$$\sum_{r=1}^{n} f_r\left(\frac{1}{2n}\right) = g_n\left(\frac{1}{2n}\right) = n.$$

(iii) The series $\sum_{r=1}^{\infty} 1/r \sin rx$, which converges for all x (Hardy, § 189), converges boundedly in $(-\infty, \infty)$; this follows at once from the following theorem.

Theorem 230.1. *Let n be any chosen positive integer; then for every real number x*

(1) $$\left| \sum_{r=1}^{n} \frac{1}{r}\sin rx \right| < 2\sqrt{\pi}.$$

Proof. Suppose x freely chosen so that

(2) $$0 < x < \pi;$$

since $\qquad |\sin rx| < rx \quad (r = 1, 2, ..., n)$,

(1) is obvious if $nx \leqslant \sqrt{\pi}$. Suppose then that $n > (1/x)\sqrt{\pi}$, and let $q = [(1/x)\sqrt{\pi}]$; on using the same inequality as before, we have

$$\left| \sum_{r=1}^{n} \frac{1}{r}\sin rx - \sum_{r=q+1}^{n} \frac{1}{r}\sin rx \right| < \sqrt{\pi},$$

and so, to prove (1), it is sufficient to show that

(3) $$\left| \sum_{r=q+1}^{n} \frac{1}{r}\sin rx \right| < \sqrt{\pi}.$$

Now

$$\left| 2 \sin \tfrac12 x \sum_{r=q+1}^{n} \frac{1}{r} \sin rx \right| = \left| \sum_{r=q+1}^{n} \frac{1}{r} \cos(r-\tfrac12)x - \sum_{r=q+1}^{n} \frac{1}{r} \cos(r+\tfrac12)x \right|$$

$$= \left| \frac{1}{q+1} \cos(q+\tfrac12)x - \frac{1}{n} \cos(n+\tfrac12)x + \sum_{r=q+1}^{n-1} \left(\frac{1}{r+1} - \frac{1}{r} \right) \cos(r+\tfrac12)x \right|,$$

and so

(4)
$$\left| 2 \sin \tfrac12 x \sum_{r=q+1}^{n} \frac{1}{r} \sin rx \right| \leqslant \frac{1}{q+1} + \frac{1}{n} + \sum_{r=q+1}^{n-1} \left(\frac{1}{r} - \frac{1}{r+1} \right) = \frac{2}{q+1} < \frac{2x}{\sqrt{\pi}};$$

now, by (2) and a well-known theorem of elementary trigonometry,

$$|x \operatorname{cosec} \tfrac12 x| < \pi,$$

and hence (3) follows from (4). The truth of (1) for all x is now easily derived from the case when $0 < x < \pi$ in virtue of the fact that $\sum_{r=1}^{n} 1/r \sin rx$ is an odd function of x with period 2π which vanishes for $x = 0$.

Theorem 231. *Let $g(P)$ be summable over B, and let $\{f_n(P)\}$ be a sequence of functions measurable in B whose sum converges boundedly in B; then $g(P) \sum_{r=1}^{\infty} f_r(P)$ is equivalent in B to a summable function, and*

$$\int_B g(P) \sum_{r=1}^{\infty} f_r(P) \, dP = \sum_{r=1}^{\infty} \int_B g(P) f_r(P) \, dP.$$

Proof. By hypothesis there is a finite number k such that

(1) $P \in B$ implies $\left| \sum_{r=1}^{n} f_r(P) \right| < k$ $(n = 1, 2, ...)$,

and

(2) $\sum_{r=1}^{\infty} f_r(P)$ exists for every point P of B.

Since $g(P)$ is finite p.p. in B (th. 199), it follows by (1) and (2) that

(3) $g(P) \sum_{r=1}^{\infty} f_r(P) \sim \lim_{n\to\infty} \sum_{r=1}^{n} g(P) f_r(P)$ in B.

By ths. 230 and 228,

(4) $\int_B \sum_{r=1}^{n} g(P) f_r(P) \, dP = \sum_{r=1}^{n} \int_B g(P) f_r(P) \, dP$ $(n = 1, 2, ...)$.

Also, by (1),

(5) $\left| \sum_{r=1}^{n} g(P) f_r(P) \right| \leqslant k|g(P)|$ p.p. in B $(n = 1, 2, ...)$.

Now $k|g(P)|$ is summable over B (ths. 197 and 180), and so by (3), (4), (5), and ths. 219 and 223

$$\int_B g(P) \sum_{r=1}^{\infty} f_r(P)\,dP = \lim_{n\to\infty} \sum_{r=1}^{n} \int_B g(P)f_r(P)\,dP,$$

which is the required result.

The reader will recognize the following theorem as a generalization of th. 57 (i).

Theorem 232. *Let $f(P)$ be summable over B, and let $g(P)$ be defined and bounded in B and continuous almost everywhere in B. A sequence of numbers S_n is defined as follows:*

to every positive integer n, let B be represented as the sum of a sequence of non-empty measurable sets, namely

(1) $B = \sum_{r=1}^{\infty} B_n^{(r)}$ & $B_n^{(r)}$ *is contained in a sphere of radius $1/n$; let $P_n^{(r)}$ be freely chosen from $B_n^{(r)}$, and put*

(2) $$S_n = \sum_{r=1}^{\infty} g(P_n^{(r)}) \int_{B_n^{(r)}} f(P)\,dP;$$

then

(3) $$\lim_{n\to\infty} S_n = \int_B f(P)g(P)\,dP.$$

Proof. Let n be any chosen positive integer, and define $h_n(P)$ in B so that
$$h_n(P) = g(P_n^{(r)}) \text{ in } B_n^{(r)};$$
by ths. 160 and 149,

(4) $h_n(P)$ is measurable in B & $P \in B$ implies $|h_n(P)| \leqslant M(|g|; B)$.

By (4) and th. 230 $f(P)h_n(P)$ is equivalent in B to a summable function, and so by ths. 222 and 224, (1), and (2)

(5) $$\int_B f(P)h_n(P)\,dP = \sum_{r=1}^{\infty} \int_{B_n^{(r)}} f(P)h_n(P)\,dP = S_n.$$

Now, if $g(P)$ is continuous at P_0, then, by (1),
$$\lim_{n\to\infty} h_n(P_0) = g(P_0);$$
hence, by hypothesis,

(6) $$\lim_{n\to\infty} h_n(P) \sim g(P) \text{ in } B.$$

But $|h_n(P)f(P)| \leqslant |f(P)| M(|g|; B)$ p.p. in B,

and, by ths. 197 and 180,

$$|f(P)|\, M(|g|; B) \text{ is summable over } B.$$

Hence, by (6), (4), and th. 223,

$$\lim_{n\to\infty} \int_B f(P)h_n(P)\, dP = \int_B f(P)g(P)\, dP,$$

which, by (5), gives (3).

Corollary. Th. 232 is true if $\sum_{r=1}^{\infty}$ is replaced throughout by $\sum_{r=1}^{k}$, where k is a positive integer, i.e. if the numbers S_n are formed by representing B as the sum of a *finite* number of sets.

Example. Let B be the plane set

$$\mathscr{S}((x,y); 0 < x \leqslant 1 \ \& \ 0 < y \leqslant 1);$$

it is required to evaluate $\int_B xy\, d(x,y)$.

Let n be any chosen positive integer, and put

$$B(r,s) = \mathscr{S}\Big((x,y); \frac{r-1}{n} < x \leqslant \frac{r}{n} \ \& \ \frac{s-1}{n} < y \leqslant \frac{s}{n}\Big);$$

clearly

$$B = \sum_{r=1}^{n}\sum_{s=1}^{n} B(r,s), \qquad mB(r,s) = \frac{1}{n^2},$$

and rs/n^2 is one of the values assumed by xy in $B(r,s)$; hence, by ths. 232 and 182,

$$\int_B xy\, d(x,y) = \lim_{n\to\infty} \sum_{r=1}^{n}\sum_{s=1}^{n} \frac{rs}{n^2} \int_{B(r,s)} d(x,y) = \lim_{n\to\infty}\Big\{\frac{1}{n^4}\sum_{r=1}^{n} r \sum_{s=1}^{n} s\Big\} = \frac{1}{4}.$$

Theorem 233. *Let $f(P)$ be measurable in B and $f^2(P)$ summable over B, and suppose $mB < \infty$; then $f(P)$ is summable over B.*

Proof. $P \in B$ implies $|f(P)| \leqslant 1+f^2(P)$; hence, by th. 201, it is sufficient to show that $\{1+f^2(P)\}$ is summable over B, and this follows at once from ths. 188 and 182 since

$$\int_B \{1+f^2(P)\}\, dP = \int_B 1\, dP + \int_B f^2(P)\, dP = mB + \int_B f^2(P)\, dP < \infty.$$

The reader should note that the restriction $mB < \infty$ is essential to th. 233; for example, x^{-2} is summable over $(1,\infty)$ but x^{-1} is not (example (ii) following th. 178).

We have already seen (example to th. 230) that the product of two functions summable over B is not necessarily equivalent in B to a summable function. The next theorem, however, gives conditions in which the product *is* equivalent in B to a summable function.

Theorem 234 (Schwarz's inequality for integrals). *Let $f(P)$ and $g(P)$ be measurable in B and such that $f^2(P)$ and $g^2(P)$ are both summable over B; then $f(P)g(P)$ is equivalent in B to a summable function, and*

(1)
$$\left| \int_B f(P)g(P)\, dP \right| \leqslant \int_B |f(P)g(P)|\, dP \leqslant \sqrt{\left\{ \int_B f^2(P)\, dP \int_B g^2(P)\, dP \right\}}.$$

Proof. By th. 184 $f^2(P)$ and $g^2(P)$ are finite p.p. in B, and so, by th. 86, there is a set B_1 such that

(2) $|B-B_1| = 0$,   and $P \in B_1$ implies $|f(P)| < \infty$ & $|g(P)| < \infty$.

By (2) and th. 119 (ii) $B_1 \in \mathscr{L}$, and so (ths. 148 and 165)

(3) $f(P)g(P)$ is measurable in B_1.

By th. 207 there are non-negative numbers a and b such that

(4) $$\int_B f^2(P)\, dP = \int_{B_1} f^2(P)\, dP = a^2 < \infty$$

$$\& \quad \int_B g^2(P)\, dP = \int_{B_1} g^2(P)\, dP = b^2 < \infty.$$

If $a = 0$, then (th. 185) $f^2(P) \sim 0$ in B_1, and so $f(P)g(P) \sim 0$ in B_1, which, by def. 57, means

$$\int_B |f(P)g(P)|\, dP = 0 = \int_B f^2(P)\, dP \int_B g^2(P)\, dP,$$

thus verifying (1).

Suppose $a > 0$ & $b > 0$; then $P \in B_1$ implies

$$\frac{2}{ab} |f(P)g(P)| = \frac{f^2(P)}{a^2} + \frac{g^2(P)}{b^2} - \left(\frac{|f(P)|}{a} - \frac{|g(P)|}{b} \right)^2.$$

Hence, by (3), ths. 159, 179, and 227, and (4),

$$\frac{2}{ab} \int_{B_1} |f(P)g(P)|\, dP \leqslant \int_{B_1} \left\{ \frac{f^2(P)}{a^2} + \frac{g^2(P)}{b^2} \right\} dP$$

$$= \frac{1}{a^2} \int_{B_1} f^2(P)\, dP + \frac{1}{b^2} \int_{B_1} g^2(P)\, dP = 2,$$

and thus $$\int_{B_1} |f(P)g(P)|\, dP \leqslant ab.$$

By (3) and ths. 207, 198, and 197

$$\left| \int\limits_B f(P)g(P)\,dP \right| = \left| \int\limits_{B_1} f(P)g(P)\,dP \right| \leqslant \int\limits_{B_1} |f(P)g(P)|\,dP \leqslant ab,$$

which means (1).

Corollary. If $f(P)$ is measurable in B and $f^2(P)$ is summable over B, then

$$\left| \int\limits_B f(P)\,dP \right| \leqslant \int\limits_B |f(P)|\,dP \leqslant \sqrt{\left\{ mB \int\limits_B f^2(P)\,dP \right\}} \quad \text{if } mB < \infty.$$

Example. The crudest approximation to $\int\limits_0^\pi x^{-\frac{1}{2}} \sin x\,dx$ is $\int\limits_0^\pi x^{-\frac{1}{2}}\,dx$, i.e. $4\pi^{\frac{1}{2}}/3$; using Schwarz's inequality, we have

$$\left| \int\limits_0^\pi x^{-\frac{1}{2}} \sin x\,dx \right|^2 \leqslant \int\limits_0^\pi x^{-\frac{1}{2}}\,dx \int\limits_0^\pi \sin^2 x\,dx = \int\limits_0^\pi \tfrac{1}{2}x^{-\frac{1}{2}}\,dx \int\limits_0^\pi (1-\cos 2x)\,dx,$$

which gives

$$\left| \int\limits_0^\pi x^{-\frac{1}{2}} \sin x\,dx \right| \leqslant \pi^{\frac{3}{4}}.$$

Theorem 235. *Let $f(P)$ be summable over B, and let*

$$f_n(P) = \begin{cases} f(P) & \text{if } |f(P)| < n \\ 0 & \text{otherwise;} \end{cases}$$

then

(i) $$\lim_{n\to\infty} \int\limits_B f_n(P)\,dP = \int\limits_B f(P)\,dP,$$

(ii) $$\lim_{n\to\infty} \int\limits_B |f(P)-f_n(P)|\,dP = 0.$$

Proof. By th. 161 $f_n(P)$ is measurable in B, and $P \in B$ implies

(1) $|f_n(P)| \leqslant |f(P)|$ & $|f(P)-f_n(P)| \leqslant |f(P)|$ $(n = 1, 2, \dots)$.

Hence, by ths. 201, 227, and 197,

(2) $f_n(P)$ and $|f(P)-f_n(P)|$ are summable over B $(n = 1, 2, \dots)$.

Moreover, by th. 199, $|f(P)| < \infty$ p.p. in B, and so

(3) $f(P) \sim \lim\limits_{n\to\infty} f_n(P)$ in B & $\lim\limits_{n\to\infty} |f(P)-f_n(P)| \sim 0$ in B.

Applying ths. 197 and 223 to (1), (2), and (3), we have (i) and (ii).

Theorem 236. *Let $f(P)$ be summable over B; then to every ϵ there is a δ such that*

$$E \subset B \quad \& \quad mE < \delta \quad implies \quad \left| \int_E f(P)\, dP \right| < \epsilon.$$

Proof. Choose ϵ freely; by ths. 206 and 197 it suffices to show that δ exists such that

(1) $\qquad E \subset B \quad \& \quad mE < \delta \quad$ implies $\quad \int_E |f(P)|\, dP < \epsilon.$

By th. 235 there is a positive integer n and a function $f_n(P)$ such that

(2) $f_n(P)$ is summable over B $\quad \& \quad P \in B \quad$ implies $\quad |f_n(P)| < n,$

and

(3) $\qquad \int_B |f(P) - f_n(P)|\, dP < \tfrac{1}{2}\epsilon.$

Put $\delta = \tfrac{1}{2}\epsilon/n$, and let E be any measurable subset of B with $mE < \delta$. By (3) and th. 176

(4) $\qquad \int_E |f(P) - f_n(P)|\, dP < \tfrac{1}{2}\epsilon,$

and, by (2) and ths. 203 and 197,

(5) $\qquad \int_E |f_n(P)|\, dP \leqslant n\,mE < n\delta = \tfrac{1}{2}\epsilon.$

Now $|f(P)| \leqslant |f(P) - f_n(P)| + |f_n(P)|$; hence, by (4), (5), and th. 189, $\int_E |f(P)|\, dP < \epsilon$, which shows that δ satisfies (1).

Corollary. Theorem 236 remains true when the assumption '$f(P)$ is summable over B' is replaced by the assumption '$f(P)$ is equivalent in B to a summable function'.

Theorem 237. *Suppose $f(P)$ is summable over B, and let S be a measurable set in B satisfying the following conditions:*

(1) $\qquad\qquad\qquad mS < \infty,$

(2) *if $P \in S$, then every sphere about P contains a closed cube K (closed interval K if $n = 1$) such that*

$$K \subset B, \quad P \in K, \quad and \quad \int_K f(P)\, dP \geqslant 0;$$

then $\qquad\qquad\qquad f(P) \geqslant 0 \ p.p. \ in \ S.$

Proof. Let ν be any chosen positive integer, and let

$$E = S.\mathscr{S}(P; f(P) < -1/\nu);$$

clearly, by th. 86, it is sufficient to show that

(3) E is null.

Let α be the aggregate of all the closed cubes K in B such that $\int_K f(P)\,dP \geqslant 0$. By (1) and (2), α and E satisfy the conditions of th. 125, and so, if ϵ is freely chosen, there is a finite number of mutually exclusive closed cubes, say $K_1, K_2,..., K_N$, such that, if $C = \sum_{r=1}^{N} K_r$, then

(4)   • $mC - \epsilon \leqslant mE \leqslant |CE| + \epsilon,$

and

(5) $K_r \subset B$ & $\infty > \int_{K_r} f(P)\,dP \geqslant 0$ $(r = 1, 2,..., N).$

Since $E \in \mathcal{L}$ (ths. 150 and 148) and $C \in \mathcal{L}$, we have $CE \in \mathcal{L}$ & $C\overline{E} \in \mathcal{L}$ (ths. 90 and 95), and so, by (5) and ths. 206 and 209,

$$0 \leqslant \sum_{r=1}^{N} \int_{K_r} f(P)\,dP = \int_C f(P)\,dP = \int_{CE} f(P)\,dP + \int_{C\overline{E}} f(P)\,dP < \infty,$$

and hence, by ths. 205 and 182,

$$\int_{C\overline{E}} f(P)\,dP \geqslant - \int_{CE} f(P)\,dP \geqslant \int_{CE} \frac{1}{\nu}\,dP = \frac{1}{\nu}\,mCE,$$

which, by (4), implies

(6) $\dfrac{1}{\nu}mE \leqslant \displaystyle\int_{C\overline{E}} f(P)\,dP + \dfrac{\epsilon}{\nu}.$

Since $E \in \mathcal{L}$, $mC = mCE + mC\overline{E}$; and so, by (4), $mC\overline{E} \leqslant 2\epsilon$ while $C\overline{E} \subset B$; hence, if ϵ is taken small enough, it follows from th. 236 that $\int_{C\overline{E}} f(P)\,dP$ can be made arbitrarily small, and this, by (6), means

$$\frac{1}{\nu}mE = 0, \text{ which implies (3).}$$

Theorem 238.   *Let $f(x)$ be defined in an interval (a,b) so that*

(1) $\displaystyle\int_{\alpha}^{\beta} f(t)\,dt = 0$ *if* $a \leqslant \alpha < \beta \leqslant b;$

then $f(x) \sim 0$ *in* $(a,b).$

Proof. Let ν be any chosen positive integer; put

$$E = \mathcal{S}\left(x; a < x < b \ \& \ f(x) < -\frac{1}{\nu}\right),$$

and let H be freely chosen so that

(2) $(E+H)$ is an open subset of (a, b).

By (1), (2), and th. 206, $f(x)$ is summable over $(E+H)$ and, since $(E+H)$ is the sum of a sequence or of a finite number of sub-intervals of (a, b) (th. 19), it follows from (1) and ths. 209 and 210 that

$$\int_{E+H} f(x) \, dx \geqslant 0;$$

Since $H \in \mathscr{L}$ & $E \in \mathscr{L}$ it now follows from ths. 206 and 209 that

$$0 \leqslant \int_{E+H} f(x) \, dx = \int_{E} f(x) \, dx + \int_{H} f(x) \, dx,$$

and hence, by ths. 205 and 182, that

$$\int_{H} f(x) \, dx \geqslant \int_{E} -f(x) \, dx \geqslant \frac{1}{\nu} mE.$$

E being measurable, H can be chosen so that mH is arbitrarily small (th. 110 (i)), and so it follows, as in th. 237, that $mE = 0$ and consequently $f(P) \geqslant 0$ p.p. in (a, b). Since (1) remains true when $f(x)$ is replaced by $-f(x)$, it now follows that $-f(x) \geqslant 0$, i.e. $f(x) \leqslant 0$ p.p. in (a, b). Combining the two results, we now have (th. 86) $f(x) = 0$ p.p. in (a, b), which is the required result.

§ 2. Integration of Complex Functions

The reader will be familiar with the notion of a complex function of a real variable (Hardy, Chapters III and X) and will know that the definitions of differentiation and integration can be extended to such functions. The remainder of this chapter is devoted to an outline of the application of Lebesgue integration to complex functions.

In the first place we generalize the idea of a function defined in a set of points B and say that

(1) $f(P) = g(P) + ih(P)$

is a complex function of P defined in B if the functions $g(P)$ and $h(P)$ are defined (as real functions) and finite in B. $f(P)$ is measurable in B if both $g(P)$ and $h(P)$ are measurable in B, and, similarly, $f(P)$ is continuous at Q if both $g(P)$ and $h(P)$ are continuous at Q. If $f(t)$ is a complex function of a real variable t, then

$$\lim_{h \to 0} \frac{f(t+h) - f(t)}{h}, \quad \text{i.e.} \quad f'(t),$$

exists if and only if $g'(t)$ and $h'(t)$ exist and are finite, and then we have
$$f'(t) = g'(t) + ih'(t).$$

The rules for differentiation are those for real functions; in particular (Hardy, § 239), if $f'(t)$ exists, then

(2) $$\frac{d}{dt} e^{f(t)} = f'(t) e^{f(t)};$$

also, if z is a complex number and t^z is defined as $e^{z \log t}$ for $t > 0$, then

(3) $$t > 0 \quad \text{implies} \quad \frac{d}{dt} t^z = z t^{z-1}.$$

Definition 59. If $f(P)$ is given by (1), and $g(P)$ and $h(P)$ are summable over B, then $f(P)$ is said to be summable over B and we define
$$\int_B f(P) \, dP = \int_B g(P) \, dP + i \int_B h(P) \, dP.$$

If $f(P)$ is summable over B, then $|f(P)|$ is measurable in B (th. 164) and $|f(P)| \leqslant |g(P)| + |h(P)|$; hence it follows (ths. 197, 190, and 179) that $|f(P)|$ is summable over B. Conversely, if $|f(P)|$ is summable over B and $f(P)$ is measurable in B, then, since
$$|g(P)| \leqslant |f(P)| \quad \& \quad |h(P)| \leqslant |f(P)|,$$
it follows (th. 201) that $g(P)$ and $h(P)$, and consequently $f(P)$, are summable over B. The further result, that
$$\left| \int_B f(P) \, dP \right| \leqslant \int_B |f(P)| \, dP,$$
which plays such an important part in the theory of real functions, requires more careful consideration; however, once we have established the truth of ths. 197 and 198 for complex functions, it follows easily that all the subsequent theorems, except those whose enunciations become meaningless (ths. 202, 205, 212, 213, 215, 216), remain valid for complex functions. Schwarz's inequality is valid if $f^2(P)$ and $g^2(P)$ are replaced by their moduli.

Theorem 239. *Suppose the complex function* $f(P)$ *is summable over* B; *then*
$$\left| \int_B f(P) \, dP \right| \leqslant \int_B |f(P)| \, dP.$$

Proof. Suppose $\quad f(P) = g(P) + ih(P),$

and $\quad \displaystyle\int_B f(P) \, dP = r \cos\theta + ir \sin\theta \quad (0 \leqslant r < \infty).$

Then $\quad \int\limits_B g(P)\,dP = r\cos\theta \quad$ and $\quad \int\limits_B h(P)\,dP = r\sin\theta,$

and so, by th. 227,

(1) $\qquad \int\limits_B \{g(P)\cos\theta + h(P)\sin\theta\}\,dP = r.$

But $\{g(P)\cos\theta + h(P)\sin\theta\}$ is the real part of $f(P)e^{-i\theta}$, and so

$$g(P)\cos\theta + h(P)\sin\theta \leqslant |f(P)e^{-i\theta}| = |f(P)| \text{ in } B;$$

hence, by (1) and th. 205, since $|f(P)|$ is measurable in B,

$$\left|\int\limits_B f(P)\,dP\right| = r = \int\limits_B \{g(P)\cos\theta + h(P)\sin\theta\}\,dP \leqslant \int\limits_B |f(P)|\,dP.$$

(I am indebted to Dr. T. Estermann for this elegant proof of th. 239.)

Integrals of the elementary complex functions of a real variable are evaluated by finding their primitives; it follows easily that, if $f(t) = g(t)+ih(t)$ and $f'(t)$ is continuous throughout a closed interval $[a,b]$, then

$$\int\limits_a^b f'(t)\,dt = \int\limits_a^b g'(t)\,dt + i\int\limits_a^b h'(t)\,dt = f(b)-f(a).$$

In particular, if z is a complex number, then, by (3), p. 157, $\dfrac{d}{dt}t^z = zt^{z-1}$,

and zt^{z-1} is continuous throughout every *closed* sub-interval of $(0,\infty)$; hence, it now follows that

$$\int\limits_\alpha^\beta t^{z-1}\,dt = \frac{1}{z}(\beta^z-\alpha^z) \quad \text{if} \quad 0 < \alpha < \beta < \infty \quad \& \quad z \neq 0.$$

Arguing as in th. 211.1, we find that

$$\int\limits_1^\infty \frac{dt}{t^{1+z}} = \int\limits_0^1 t^{z-1}\,dt = \frac{1}{z} \quad \text{if the real part of } z \text{ is positive.}$$

Similarly, by (2), p. 157, if z is a complex number, then $\dfrac{d}{dt}e^{zt} = ze^{zt}$,

and ze^{zt} is continuous in every interval; hence, if α and β are finite real numbers and $z \neq 0$, then

$$\int\limits_\alpha^\beta e^{zt}\,dt = \frac{1}{z}(e^{z\beta}-e^{z\alpha}),$$

and again, arguing as in th. 211.1, we have

(1) $\displaystyle\int_0^\infty e^{-zt}\,dt = \frac{1}{z}$ if the real part of z is positive.

Example. If $x > 0$, then

$$\int_0^\infty e^{-xt}\cos yt\,dt = \frac{x}{x^2+y^2}\quad\text{and}\quad \int_0^\infty e^{-xt}\sin yt\,dt = \frac{y}{x^2+y^2}.$$

Proof. Put $f(t) = e^{(-x+iy)t}$; by (1) above

$$\int_0^\infty e^{-xt}\cos yt\,dt + i\int_0^\infty e^{-xt}\sin yt\,dt = \int_0^\infty f(t)\,dt = (x-iy)^{-1} = \frac{x+iy}{x^2+y^2}$$

from which the required results follow immediately.

Example. Suppose $z = x+iy$ and $x > 0$; then $\Gamma(z) = \displaystyle\int_0^\infty e^{-t}t^{z-1}\,dt$
is defined and finite, and

$$\Gamma(z) = \lim_{n\to\infty}\frac{n!\,n^z}{z(z+1)(z+2)\ldots(z+n)}$$

(this is known as Gauss's formula for the gamma function).

Proof. Put $f(t) = e^{-t}t^{z-1}$; then $f(t)$ is continuous and therefore
measurable in $(0,\infty)$, and $|f(t)| = e^{-t}t^{x-1}$. Since $|f(t)|$ is summable
over $(0,\infty)$ (example following th. 180), it now follows by th. 198 (for
complex functions) that $f(t)$ is summable over $(0,\infty)$. Now, if n is any
positive integer, we have (ths. 179 and 182) for $0 < t < n$

$$\int_{1-t/n}^1 \frac{du}{u} \geqslant \int_{1-t/n}^1 du = \frac{t}{n},$$

whence $\log(1-t/n) \leqslant -t/n$ and therefore $(1-t/n)^n \leqslant e^{-t}$. So, if we
define
$$f_n(t) = \begin{cases} (1-t/n)^n t^{z-1} & \text{if } 0 < t < n \\ 0 & \text{if } t \geqslant n, \end{cases}$$

it follows that $f_n(t)$ is continuous and therefore measurable in $(0,\infty)$;
also (since $\lim_{n\to\infty}(1-t/n)^n = e^{-t}$)

$$|f_n(t)| \leqslant |f(t)| \quad (n = 1, 2,\ldots) \quad \&\quad \lim_{n\to\infty}f_n(t) = f(t) \text{ in } (0,\infty).$$

Since we have shown that $f(t)$ is summable over $(0,\infty)$, it now follows by ths. 201 and 214 (interpreted for complex functions) and ths. 177 and 182 that

$$\int_0^\infty f(t)\,dt = \lim_{n\to\infty} \int_0^\infty f_n(t)\,dt = \lim_{n\to\infty} \int_0^n f_n(t)\,dt = \lim_{n\to\infty} \int_0^n \left(1-\frac{t}{n}\right)^n t^{z-1}\,dt,$$

and so Gauss's formula is proved if we show that

$$(1) \qquad \int_0^n \left(1-\frac{t}{n}\right)^n t^{z-1}\,dt = \frac{n!\,n^z}{z(z+1)(z+2)\ldots(z+n)} \qquad (n = 1, 2,\ldots).$$

Now $\int_0^n f_n(t)\,dt$ may be evaluated as a Cauchy-Riemann integral for complex functions; on substituting $v = t/n$, its value is seen to be $n^z \int_0^1 (1-v)^n v^{z-1}\,dv$, and, on integrating by parts n times successively, (1) follows immediately.

VII

FUNCTIONS OF A SINGLE VARIABLE

§ 1. Miscellaneous Theorems

Theorem 240. *Suppose $f(x)$ is summable over (a, b); then $\int_a^x f(t)\, dt$ is a continuous function of x bounded in (a, b) and is continuous throughout $[a, b]$ if both a and b are finite.*

Proof. Suppose $a < \xi < b$; then $f(x)$ is summable over (a, ξ) (th. 206), and by ths. 197 and 176 we have

$$\left| \int_a^\xi f(x)\, dx \right| \leqslant \int_a^\xi |f(x)|\, dx \leqslant \int_a^b |f(x)|\, dx < \infty,$$

and this proves that $\int_a^x f(t)\, dt$ is bounded in (a, b). Again, since $f(x)$ is summable over (a, ξ) and over (ξ, b) (th. 206), it follows from th. 211.1 (i) that

$$\lim_{\beta \to \xi - 0} \int_\beta^\xi f(x)\, dx = \lim_{\alpha \to \xi + 0} \int_\xi^\alpha f(x)\, dx = 0,$$

and this, by th. 209.1, proves that $\int_a^x f(t)\, dt$ is continuous in (a, b); the proof is now completed by th. 211.1 (i).

Theorem 241. *Suppose $f(x)$ is defined in (a, b), and that $\int_a^b f(x)\, dx$ exists. Let k be any finite real number; then*

(i) $$\int_a^b f(x)\, dx = \int_{a+k}^{b+k} f(x-k)\, dx;$$

(ii) $$\int_a^b f(x)\, dx = \frac{1}{k} \int_{ka}^{kb} f\left(\frac{x}{k}\right) dx \quad if \quad k \neq 0.$$

Proof. By def. 55 it is sufficient to consider the case in which $f(x)$ is non-negative, for if the theorem holds for $f_+(x)$ and $f_-(x)$ separately, it also holds for $f(x)$. To prove (i) let

(1) $$S = \Omega_0(f; (a, b)) = \mathscr{S}((x, y); a < x < b \ \& \ 0 < y < f(x)).$$

By (1) and def. 52,

(2) $$mS = \int_a^b f(x)\, dx.$$

Let the transformation F be defined by $F((x,y)) = (x+k,y)$; then

$$F(S) = \mathscr{S}((z,y); a+k < z < b+k \ \& \ 0 < y < f(z-k)),$$

and so, by (2), ths. 128 and 127, and def. 52, we have

$$\int_a^b f(x)\,dx = mS = mF(S) = \int_{a+k}^{b+k} f(z-k)\,dz,$$

which proves (i). To prove (ii) suppose first that $k > 0$, and let $G((x,y)) = (kx,y)$; then

$$G(S) = \mathscr{S}\left\{(z,y); ka < z < kb \ \& \ 0 < y < f\left(\frac{z}{k}\right)\right\},$$

and so, by the same theorems as before,

$$k\int_a^b f(x)\,dx = kmS = mF(S) = \int_{ka}^{kb} f\left(\frac{z}{k}\right)dz.$$

Finally, to prove (ii) generally it is now sufficient to show

(3) $$\int_a^b f(x)\,dx = -\int_{-a}^{-b} f(-x)\,dx.$$

Let $H((x,y)) = (-x,y)$; then

$$H(S) = \mathscr{S}((z,y); -b < z < -a \ \& \ 0 < y < f(-z)),$$

and so, as before,

$$\int_a^b f(x)\,dx = mS = mH(S) = \int_{-b}^{-a} f(-z)\,dz,$$

and this, by def. 53, gives (3).

Theorem 242. (Integration by parts.) *Suppose $f(x)$ and $g(x)$ are summable over (a,b); let λ and μ be any chosen finite real numbers, and let*

$$F(t) = \int_a^t f(x)\,dx + \lambda \quad and \quad G(t) = \int_a^t g(x)\,dx + \mu \quad if \quad a \leqslant t \leqslant b;$$

then

(1) $$\int_a^b f(x)G(x)\,dx + \int_a^b g(x)F(x)\,dx = F(b)G(b) - F(a)G(a).$$

Proof. Suppose α and β are *finite* and satisfy

$$a \leqslant \alpha < \beta \leqslant b;$$

choose $x_0, x_1,..., x_n$ freely, so that $\alpha = x_0 < x_1 < ... < x_n = \beta$. By th. 209.1 (ii),

$$(2) \quad \sum_{r=1}^{n} G(x_r) \int_{x_{r-1}}^{x_r} f(x)\,dx + \sum_{r=1}^{n} F(x_{r-1}) \int_{x_{r-1}}^{x_r} g(x)\,dx$$

$$= \sum_{r=1}^{n} G(x_r)\{F(x_r)-F(x_{r-1})\} + \sum_{r=1}^{n} F(x_{r-1})\{G(x_r)-G(x_{r-1})\}$$

$$= G(\beta)F(\beta) - G(\alpha)F(\alpha).$$

Now $G(x)$ and $F(x)$ are continuous and bounded in (a,b) and therefore in (α,β) (th. 240), and so, by (2) and th. 232, we have

$$(3) \quad \int_{\alpha}^{\beta} f(x)G(x)\,dx + \int_{\alpha}^{\beta} g(x)F(x)\,dx = F(\beta)G(\beta) - F(\alpha)G(\alpha).$$

Since $F(x)$ is continuous and bounded in (a,b), it follows that $F(x)g(x)$ is equivalent in (a,b) to a summable function (ths. 163 and 230), and hence, applying th. 211.1 (ii) (extended slightly so as to apply to functions *equivalent* in (a,b) to a summable function), it follows that, as α and β tend independently to $a+0$ and $b-0$ respectively,

$$\int_{\alpha}^{\beta} F(x)g(x)\,dx \quad \text{tends to} \quad \int_{a}^{b} F(x)g(x)\,dx;$$

at the same time,

$$\int_{\alpha}^{\beta} G(x)f(x)\,dx \quad \text{tends to} \quad \int_{a}^{b} G(x)f(x)\,dx$$

for similar reasons.

Hence, by (3), as α tends to $a+0$ and β to $b-0$,

$$F(\beta)G(\beta) - F(\alpha)G(\alpha) \quad \text{tends to} \quad \int_{a}^{b} F(x)g(x)\,dx + \int_{a}^{b} G(x)f(x)\,dx,$$

and this, in virtue of th. 211.1, gives (1).

Theorem 243. *Let $f(x)$ be finite and non-decreasing in (a,b); then D, the set of the points x of (a,b) for which $f(x)$ is discontinuous, is finite or enumerable.*

Proof. By th. 7 there is a sequence $x_1, x_2,...$ consisting of all the rational numbers. Suppose $\xi \in D$; since $f(x)$ is non-decreasing in (a,b), we may define $n(\xi)$ to be the least integer n such that

$$f(\xi-0) < x_n < f(\xi+0).$$

If $\xi' \in D$ & $\xi' > \xi$, then $f(\xi'-0) \geqslant f(\xi+0)$ and hence $n(\xi) \neq n(\xi')$. It follows that D is equivalent to an aggregate of positive integers and is therefore finite or enumerable (th. 3).

Theorem 244. *Suppose $f(x)$ is summable over J, a closed interval $[a,b]$, and let $g(x)$ be finite, non-negative, and non-decreasing in J; let*

$$F(x) = \int_x^b f(t)\, dt \text{ in } J; \text{ then}$$

(i) $$g(b)m(F; J) \leqslant \int_a^b f(x)g(x)\, dx \leqslant g(b)M(F; J);$$

(ii) *there is a point ξ of $[a,b]$ such that*

$$\int_a^b f(x)g(x)\, dx = g(b) \int_\xi^b f(x)\, dx.$$

Proof. Let $h(x) = g(x)$ if $a < x \leqslant b$, and $h(a) = 0$; suppose

$$a = x_0 < x_1 < \ldots < x_n = b;$$

then

$$\sum_{r=1}^n \{h(x_r)-h(x_{r-1})\} = h(b) \quad \& \quad h(x_r) \geqslant h(x_{r-1}) \quad (r = 1, 2, \ldots, n).$$

Hence

(1) $$h(b)m(F; J) \leqslant \sum_{r=1}^n F(x_r)\{h(x_r)-h(x_{r-1})\} \leqslant h(b)M(F; J).$$

Since $h(x_0) = 0$ & $F(x_n) = 0$, we have

$$\sum_{r=1}^n h(x_r)F(x_r) = \sum_{r=1}^n h(x_{r-1})F(x_{r-1}),$$

and hence, by (1),

$$h(b)m(F; J) \leqslant \sum_{r=1}^n h(x_{r-1})\{F(x_{r-1})-F(x_r)\} \leqslant h(b)M(F; J),$$

which, by th. 209.1 (ii), means

(2) $$h(b)m(F; J) \leqslant \sum_{r=1}^n h(x_{r-1}) \int_{x_{r-1}}^{x_r} f(x)\, dx \leqslant h(b)M(F; J).$$

Now $h(x)$ is bounded in J, and $h(x)$ is continuous p.p. in J by ths. 243 and 83 (or ths. 53 and 50); since $h(x) = g(x)$ for $a < x \leqslant b$, (i) now follows from (2) and th. 232.

Now $$F(x) = F(a) - \int_a^x f(t)\, dt,$$

and so, by th. 240, $F(x)$ is continuous throughout $[a, b]$; hence, by (i) (Hardy, §§ 100 and 102), there is a point ξ of $[a, b]$ such that

$$\int_a^b f(x)g(x)\,dx = g(b)F(\xi),$$

which proves (ii).

Example. Suppose $g(x)$ is finite, non-negative and non-decreasing in $[a, b]$; then

$$\left| \int_a^b g(x)\cos nx\,dx \right| \leqslant \frac{2}{n}g(b) \quad (n = 1, 2, \ldots).$$

Proof. With the notation of th. 244, $x \in J$ implies

$$F(x) = \int_x^b \cos nt\,dt = \frac{1}{n}\{\sin nb - \sin nx\}, \quad \text{and so} \quad |F(x)| \leqslant \frac{2}{n};$$

the result now follows from (i) of th. 244.

Theorem 245. (Second mean-value theorem.) *Suppose $f(x)$ is summable over (a, b), and let $g(x)$ be bounded and non-decreasing in (a, b); let λ and μ be freely chosen so that*

$$-\infty < \lambda \leqslant \lim_{x \to a+0} g(x) \leqslant \lim_{x \to b-0} g(x) \leqslant \mu < \infty;$$

then ξ exists such that

$$\int_a^b f(x)g(x)\,dx = \lambda \int_a^\xi f(x)\,dx + \mu \int_\xi^b f(x)\,dx \quad \& \quad a \leqslant \xi \leqslant b.$$

Proof. Let α and β be any *finite* numbers satisfying

$$a \leqslant \alpha < \beta \leqslant b.$$

Let $g^*(x) = g(x)$ if $\alpha \leqslant x < \beta$, and $g^*(\beta) = \mu$. Since $g^*(x) - \lambda$ is finite, non-negative and non-decreasing in $[\alpha, \beta]$, it follows from th. 244 (ii) that ξ exists such that

$$\int_\alpha^\beta \{g^*(x) - \lambda\}f(x)\,dx = (\mu - \lambda)\int_\xi^\beta f(x)\,dx \quad \& \quad \alpha \leqslant \xi \leqslant \beta,$$

and, since $g^*(x) = g(x)$ in (α, β), it follows easily that this means

$$(1) \qquad \int_\alpha^\beta f(x)g(x)\,dx = \lambda \int_\alpha^\beta f(x)\,dx + (\mu - \lambda)\int_\xi^\beta f(x)\,dx.$$

Now let $\{a_n\}$ and $\{b_n\}$ be sequences such that

$$a_1 > a_2 > \ldots \quad \& \quad \lim_{n \to \infty} a_n = a$$

and

$$a_1 < b_1 < b_2 < \ldots \quad \& \quad \lim_{n \to \infty} b_n = b.$$

If we define $F(x) = \int\limits_a^x f(t) \, dt$, we have (th. 209.1 (ii)), as the analogue of (1), that for every positive integer n there is a point ξ_n of (a, b) such that

$$(2) \qquad \int\limits_{a_n}^{b_n} f(x)g(x) \, dx = \lambda \int\limits_{a_n}^{b_n} f(x) \, dx + (\mu - \lambda)\{F(b_n) - F(\xi_n)\}.$$

It follows, as in th. 244, that $f(x)g(x)$ is equivalent in (a, b) to a summable function, and, arguing now as from (3) of th. 242, it follows from (2) of this theorem that

$$(3) \qquad \int\limits_a^b f(x)g(x) \, dx = \lambda F(b) + (\mu - \lambda)\{F(b) - \lim_{n \to \infty} F(\xi_n)\}.$$

If $\{\xi_n\}$ contains a bounded sub-sequence, then (th. 32) it must contain a sub-sequence $\{\xi_{n_r}\}$ such that

$$(4) \qquad \lim_{r \to \infty} \xi_{n_r} = \xi \quad \text{for some } \xi \text{ satisfying } a \leqslant \xi \leqslant b;$$

otherwise there is a sub-sequence $\{\xi_{n_r}\}$ of $\{\xi_n\}$ such that

$$(5) \qquad \lim_{r \to \infty} \xi_{n_r} = \xi, \quad \text{where} \quad \xi = a \text{ or } \xi = b.$$

Whether (4) is true or (5) is true, it follows from (3) and th. 211.1 that

$$\int\limits_a^b f(x)g(x) \, dx = \lambda F(b) + (\mu - \lambda)\{F(b) - F(\xi)\},$$

and this, by th. 209.1, gives

$$\int\limits_a^b f(x)g(x) \, dx = \lambda \int\limits_a^\xi f(x) \, dx + \mu \int\limits_\xi^b f(x) \, dx,$$

while, by (4) and (5), $a \leqslant \xi \leqslant b$.

Theorem 246. *Let $f(x)$ be summable over R_1, and let ϵ be freely chosen; then there is a function $g(x)$ continuous and bounded in R_1 and such that*

$$(1) \qquad \int\limits_{-\infty}^{\infty} |f(x) - g(x)| \, dx < \epsilon.$$

Proof. By th. 235 there is a positive integer n and a function $f_n(x)$ such that

$$(2) \qquad |f_n(x)| \leqslant n \quad \& \quad f_n(x) \text{ is measurable in } R_1,$$

and

$$(3) \qquad \int\limits_{-\infty}^{\infty} |f(x) - f_n(x)| \, dx < \tfrac{1}{2}\epsilon.$$

By (2) and th. 173 there is a linear set E and a function $g(x)$ satisfying

(4) $$|g(x)| \leqslant n \quad \& \quad g(x) \text{ is continuous in } R_1,$$

and

(5) $$x \in \bar{E} \quad \text{implies} \quad f_n(x) = g(x), \quad \text{and} \quad mE < \frac{\epsilon}{4n}.$$

From (2), (4), and ths. 163 and 158 we have

$$|f_n(x) - g(x)| \leqslant 2n \quad \& \quad f_n(x) - g(x) \text{ is measurable in } R_1,$$

and hence, by (5) and ths. 182 and 203,

$$\int_{\bar{E}} |f_n(x) - g(x)|\, dx = 0 \quad \& \quad \int_E |f_n(x) - g(x)|\, dx \leqslant 2n\, mE < \tfrac{1}{2}\epsilon;$$

so, by th. 177,

(6) $$\int_{R_1} |f_n(x) - g(x)|\, dx < \tfrac{1}{2}\epsilon.$$

Since $$|f(x) - g(x)| \leqslant |f(x) - f_n(x)| + |f_n(x) - g(x)|,$$

(1) now follows from (3) and (6) in virtue of ths. 179 and 189.

Theorem 247. *Suppose $a < b$ and $X = (a, b)$; let I be an interval $(-\delta, \delta)$, and let $\psi(x, h)$ be a function of two variables such that*

(1) *if $h \in I$, then $\psi(x, h)$ is summable over X,*

(2) *there is a function $\theta(x)$ summable over X such that*

$$h \in I \quad \& \quad x \in X \quad \text{implies} \quad |\psi(x, h)| \leqslant |\theta(x)|$$

(this is so, in particular, if X is bounded and $\psi(x, h)$ is bounded in $\mathscr{S}((x, h); x \in X \ \& \ h \in I))$,

and

(3) $$\phi(x) \sim \lim_{h \to 0} \psi(x, h) \text{ in } X;$$

then

(4) $$\int_a^b \phi(x)\, dx = \lim_{h \to 0} \int_a^b \psi(x, h)\, dx.$$

Proof. By (3), $$\phi(x) \sim \lim_{n \to \infty} \psi\left(x, \frac{1}{n}\right);$$

hence, by (1), (2), and th. 223, $\phi(x)$ is equivalent in X to a summable function, and so, if (4) is false, there is an ϵ and a sequence of numbers, $\{h_n\}$, such that $h_n \neq 0$, $\lim\limits_{n \to \infty} h_n = 0$, and

(5) $$\left| \int_a^b \psi(x, h_n)\, dx - \int_a^b \phi(x)\, dx \right| > \epsilon \quad (n = 1, 2, \ldots).$$

However, by (3), since $\lim\limits_{n\to\infty} h_n = 0$,

$$\phi(x) \sim \lim_{n\to\infty} \psi(x, h_n) \text{ in } X,$$

and so, by (1), (2), and th. 223,

$$\lim_{n\to\infty}\left\{ \int_a^b \psi(x, h_n)\, dx - \int_a^b \phi(x)\, dx \right\} = 0,$$

which contradicts (5). Hence (4) is true.

Theorem 248. *Suppose*

(1) $\qquad\qquad\qquad f(x)$ *is summable over* R_1;

then

(2) $\qquad\qquad \lim\limits_{h\to0} \int\limits_{-\infty}^{\infty} |f(x+h)-f(x)|\, dx = 0.$

Proof. Choose ϵ freely; if we show that δ exists such that

(3) $\qquad 0 < |h| < \delta$ implies $\int\limits_0^{\infty} |f(x+h)-f(x)|\, dx < \epsilon,$

it follows easily from ths. 209.1 (i) and 241 that (2) is true. By (1) and th. 241, for every finite number h,

(4) $\qquad\qquad -\infty < \int\limits_{-\infty}^{\infty} f(x+h)\, dx = \int\limits_{-\infty}^{\infty} f(x)\, dx < \infty,$

from which it follows (ths. 227 and 197) that $|f(x+h)-f(x)|$ is equivalent in R_1 to a summable function; hence if

$$F(h) = \int_0^{\infty} |f(x+h)-f(x)|\, dx,$$

then

(5) $\quad \infty > F(h) = \int\limits_0^{N} |f(x+h)-f(x)|\, dx + \int\limits_N^{\infty} |f(x+h)-f(x)|\, dx$

for every positive integer N. Also, by ths. 179 and 189,

(6) $\quad \int\limits_N^{\infty} |f(x+h)-f(x)|\, dx \leqslant \int\limits_N^{\infty} |f(x+h)|\, dx + \int\limits_N^{\infty} |f(x)|\, dx.$

Now, by (1) and th. 211.1 (i), N may be chosen so that

$$\int_{N-1}^{\infty} |f(x)|\, dx < \tfrac{1}{8}\epsilon,$$

in which case (ths. 176 and 241) $\int_N^\infty |f(x)|\,dx < \frac{1}{8}\epsilon$, and $|h| < 1$ implies

$$\int_N^\infty |f(x+h)|\,dx = \int_{N+h}^\infty |f(x)|\,dx \leqslant \int_{N-1}^\infty |f(x)|\,dx < \tfrac{1}{8}\epsilon;$$

hence, by (6) and (5),

(7) $|h| < 1$ implies $0 \leqslant F(h) - \int_0^N |f(x+h)-f(x)|\,dx < \tfrac{1}{4}\epsilon.$

By th. 246, $g(x)$ exists such that

(8) $g(x)$ is continuous and bounded in R_1,

and

(9) $\int_{-\infty}^\infty |f(x)-g(x)|\,dx < \tfrac{1}{4}\epsilon.$

From (9) and ths. 241 and 176, the integrals of $|g(x)-f(x)|$ and $|f(x+h)-g(x+h)|$ over $(0, N)$ are both less than $\frac{1}{4}\epsilon$, and hence that of $|f(x+h)-f(x)+g(x)-g(x+h)|$ is less than $\frac{1}{2}\epsilon$ (ths. 179 and 189); hence, by (7), (3) is proved if we show that

(10) $\lim_{h\to 0} \int_0^N |g(x+h)-g(x)|\,dx = 0.$

If we put $\psi(x, h) = |g(x+h)-g(x)|$, then, by (8), the conditions of th. 247 are satisfied if $\phi(x) = 0$ in $[0, N]$; hence, as a result of ths. 247 and 182, we have (10), and this completes the proof.

Theorem 249. *Suppose $f(x)$ is summable over R_1, and*

(1) $\phi(x)$ *is bounded and measurable in R_1,*

and

(2)   *there is a constant λ such that*

$$\phi(x+\lambda) = -\phi(x) \textit{ for every } x \textit{ in } R_1;$$

then

(3) $\lim_{k\to\infty} \int_{-\infty}^\infty f(x)\phi(kx)\,dx = 0.$

Proof. Let k be any finite real number, $k \neq 0$; by (1) and ths. 168 and 230, $f(x)\phi(kx)$ is equivalent in R_1 to a summable function; let

(4) $I(k) = \int_{-\infty}^\infty f(x)\phi(kx)\,dx.$

It follows from th. 241 and (2) that

$$I(k) = \int_{-\infty}^{\infty} f\left(x+\frac{\lambda}{k}\right)\phi(kx+\lambda)\,dx = \int_{-\infty}^{\infty} -f\left(x+\frac{\lambda}{k}\right)\phi(kx)\,dx,$$

and so, by (4) and th. 227,

$$2I(k) = \int_{-\infty}^{\infty} \left\{f(x)-f\left(x+\frac{\lambda}{k}\right)\right\}\phi(kx)\,dx;$$

hence (th. 230)

$$2|I(k)| \leqslant M(|\phi|;R_1) \int_{-\infty}^{\infty} \left|f(x)-f\left(x+\frac{\lambda}{k}\right)\right|dx,$$

which, by (1) and th. 248, implies (3).

Example. Let $g(x)$ be summable over a linear set S; then

$$\lim_{k\to\infty} \int_S g(x)\cos kx\,dx = 0.$$

Proof. Put
$$f(x) = \begin{cases} g(x) & \text{if } x \in S \\ 0 & \text{if } x \in \bar{S}; \end{cases}$$

since $S \in \mathscr{L}$, we have (th. 182)

$$\int_{\bar{S}} f(x)\,dx = 0 \quad \& \quad \int_S f(x)\,dx = \int_S g(x)\,dx;$$

hence (th. 209) $f(x)$ is summable over R_1, and (th. 249)

$$\lim_{k\to\infty} \int_S g(x)\cos kx\,dx = \lim_{k\to\infty} \int_{-\infty}^{\infty} f(x)\cos kx\,dx = 0.$$

Theorem 250. *Suppose $a < b$ and $X = (a,b)$. Let $f(x,t)$ be a function of two variables defined and finite when $x \in X$ and t belongs to some interval T centre t_0, and such that*

(1)   *for every t of T, $f(x,t)$ is summable over X,*

and

(2)   *there is a function $F(x)$ summable over X, and*

$$\left|\frac{\partial}{\partial t}f(x,t)\right| \leqslant F(x) \quad \text{whenever } t \in T \text{ and } x \in X;$$

then

(3) $$\frac{d}{dt}\int_a^b f(x,t_0)\,dx = \int_a^b \frac{\partial}{\partial t}f(x,t_0)\,dx.$$

(The left-hand side of (3) denotes the value of $\dfrac{d}{dt}\displaystyle\int_a^b f(x,t)\,dx$ when $t = t_0$, and $\dfrac{\partial}{\partial t}f(x,t_0)$ denotes the value of $\dfrac{\partial}{\partial t}f(x,t)$ when $t = t_0$.)

Proof. Let t_1 be any point of T other than t_0; by (1) and th. 227

$$(4) \qquad \int_a^b f(x,t_1)\,dx - \int_a^b f(x,t_0)\,dx = \int_a^b \{f(x,t_1)-f(x,t_0)\}\,dx.$$

Let ξ be any point of X; by (2) and the first mean-value theorem of the differential calculus (Hardy, § 125) there is a point t' of T such that

$$(5) \qquad \left|\frac{f(\xi,t_1)-f(\xi,t_0)}{t_1-t_0}\right| = \left|\frac{\partial}{\partial t}f(\xi,t')\right| \leqslant F(\xi).$$

Since $\quad \displaystyle\lim_{t_1\to t_0}\frac{f(x,t_1)-f(x,t_0)}{t_1-t_0} = \frac{\partial}{\partial t}f(x,t_0)$ for every x of X,

it follows from (4), (5), and th. 247 that

$$\lim_{t_1\to t_0}\frac{1}{t_1-t_0}\left\{\int_a^b f(x,t_1)\,dx - \int_a^b f(x,t_0)\,dx\right\} = \int_a^b \frac{\partial}{\partial t}f(x,t_0)\,dx,$$

which means (3).

Example. $\quad I(t) = \displaystyle\int_0^\infty e^{-x}\frac{\sin tx}{x}\,dx = \arctan t.$

Proof.

$$\left|e^{-x}\frac{\sin tx}{x}\right| \leqslant |t|e^{-x} \quad\&\quad \left|\frac{\partial}{\partial t}e^{-x}\frac{\sin tx}{x}\right| = |e^{-x}\cos tx| \leqslant e^{-x};$$

since e^{-x} is summable over $(0,\infty)$, it now follows from ths. 201 and 250 that

$$\frac{d}{dt}I(t) = \int_0^\infty e^{-x}\cos tx\,dx,$$

and hence, by the example on p. 159, that

$$\frac{d}{dt}I(t) = (1+t^2)^{-1};$$

from this, and the fact that $I(0) = 0$, it follows easily from th. 64 that $I(t) = \arctan t$.

§ 2. Derivative of a Lebesgue Integral

Definition 60. Let $f(x)$ be defined and finite in an interval including x_0. To every sufficiently small ϵ let $\lambda(x_0; \epsilon)$ be the lower bound and $\mu(x_0; \epsilon)$ the upper bound of the aggregate of the values

$$\frac{f(x)-f(x_0)}{x-x_0} \quad \text{when} \quad 0 < |x-x_0| < \epsilon;$$

then, as ϵ decreases,

$$\lambda(x_0; \epsilon) \text{ increases (or remains constant),}$$

and $\mu(x_0; \epsilon)$ decreases (or remains constant);

hence we may define

$$\underline{D}f(x_0) = \lim_{\epsilon \to 0} \lambda(x_0; \epsilon) \quad \text{and} \quad \overline{D}f(x_0) = \lim_{\epsilon \to 0} \mu(x_0; \epsilon).$$

$\underline{D}f(x_0)$ is called the *lower derivate* of $f(x)$ at x_0, and $\overline{D}f(x_0)$ is called the *upper derivate* of $f(x)$ at x_0; clearly

$$\underline{D}f(x_0) \leqslant \overline{D}f(x_0).$$

If and only if $\underline{D}f(x_0) = \overline{D}f(x_0)$, their common value is denoted by $f'(x_0)$ or by $\frac{d}{dx}f(x_0)$.

(In analogy with def. 51 we may denote

$$\lim_{\epsilon \to 0} \mu(x_0; \epsilon) \text{ by } \overline{\lim_{x \to x_0}} \frac{f(x)-f(x_0)}{x-x_0} \quad \text{and} \quad \lim_{\epsilon \to 0} \lambda(x_0; \epsilon) \text{ by } \underline{\lim_{x \to x_0}} \frac{f(x)-f(x_0)}{x-x_0}.$$

It is also useful to denote the upper and the lower limits of

$$\frac{f(x_0+\epsilon)-f(x_0)}{\epsilon}$$

as $\epsilon \to 0$ by $D^+f(x_0)$ and $D_+f(x_0)$ respectively, and the upper and lower limits of

$$\frac{f(x_0-\epsilon)-f(x_0)}{-\epsilon}$$

as $\epsilon \to 0$ by $D^-f(x_0)$ and $D_-f(x_0)$ respectively.)

Corollary. $\underline{D}f(x) = -\overline{D}\{-f(x)\}.$

Example. Let

$$f(x) = \begin{cases} x \sin 1/x & \text{if } x = 0 \\ 0 & \text{if } x = 0; \end{cases}$$

then $x \neq 0$ implies $\dfrac{f(x)-f(0)}{x} = \sin\dfrac{1}{x},$

and so $\underline{D}f(0) = -1$ and $\overline{D}f(0) = 1.$

Theorem 251. *Let $f(x)$ be continuous in an interval I; then $\underline{D}f(x)$ and $\overline{D}f(x)$ are measurable in I.*

Proof. With the notation of def. 60, $\overline{D}f(x) = \lim_{n\to\infty} \mu(x; 1/n)$, and so, to prove the measurability of $\overline{D}f(x)$ in I, it is sufficient (th. 155) to prove that $\mu(x; \epsilon)$ is measurable in I for every ϵ. Choose ϵ, and let $\{r_n\}$ be a sequence consisting of all the rational numbers in $(-\epsilon, \epsilon)$ except 0 (th. 9). Since $f(x)$ is continuous in I, it follows that, if $x_0 \in I$, then $\mu(x_0; \epsilon)$ is the upper bound of the aggregate of the numbers

$$\frac{f(x_0+r_n)-f(x_0)}{r_n} \quad (n = 1, 2, ...).$$

Now each of the functions

$$\frac{f(x+r_n)-f(x)}{r_n} \quad (n = 1, 2, ...)$$

is continuous and therefore measurable in I, it being assumed that $f(x)$ is defined outside I so that $f(x)$ is continuous in $(-\infty, \infty)$. Hence, by th. 152, $\mu(x; \epsilon)$ is measurable in I, and this completes the proof that $\overline{D}f(x)$ is measurable in I. The measurability of $\underline{D}f(x)$ in I is proved similarly, or by considering $\overline{D}\{-f(x)\}$.

Theorem 252. *Let $f(x)$ be summable over (a, b), and let*

$$F(x) = \int_a^x f(t)\, dt;$$

let ξ be a point of (a, b) for which $f(x)$ is continuous; then

$$F'(\xi) = f(\xi).$$

Proof. Choose ϵ freely, and then h_0 so that

$$|h| < h_0 \quad \text{implies} \quad a < \xi \mid h < b \quad \& \quad |f(\xi+h)-f(\xi)| < \epsilon.$$

By ths. 209.1, 227, 224, and 203, $|h| < h_0$ implies

$$|F(\xi+h)-F(\xi)-hf(\xi)| = \left| \int_\xi^{\xi+h} \{f(x)-f(\xi)\}\, dx \right| \leqslant \epsilon|h|,$$

and this gives the required result.

The reader will recognize the following theorem as a generalization of th. 63.

Theorem 253. *Suppose $f(x)$ is summable over an interval (a, b); then*

$$\frac{d}{dx} \int_a^x f(t)\, dt \sim f(x) \text{ in } (a, b).$$

Proof. Let I denote (a,b), and $F(x) = \int_a^x f(t)\,dt$. Let $\{r_n\}$ be a sequence consisting of all the rational numbers (th. 7), and for every positive integer n let

$$A_n = I \cdot \mathscr{S}(x; \bar{D}F(x) > r_n).$$

Since

$$\frac{d}{dx}\int_a^x r_n\,dt = r_n,$$

it follows easily that

$$x \in A_n \quad \text{implies} \quad \bar{D}\left\{\int_a^x \{f(t)-r_n\}\,dt\right\} > 0,$$

and since $A_n \in \mathscr{L}$ (th. 251), it now follows from def. 60 and th. 237 that $f(x)-r_n \geqslant 0$ p.p. in A_n, i.e.

(1) $I \cdot \mathscr{S}(x; \bar{D}F(x) > r_n > f(x))$ is null $(n = 1, 2,...)$.

Now if x is a point of I for which $\bar{D}F(x) > f(x)$, then there must be a positive integer m such that $\bar{D}F(x) > r_m > f(x)$; hence, by (1) and th. 86,

(2) $I \cdot \mathscr{S}(x; \bar{D}F(x) > f(x))$ is null.

Since

$$-F(x) = \int_a^x -f(t)\,dt,$$

we have, as an analogue of (2), since $\bar{D}\{-F(x)\} = -\underline{D}F(x)$, that

(3) $I \cdot \mathscr{S}(x; \underline{D}F(x) < f(x))$ is null.

By (2), (3), and th. 86

$$\bar{D}F(x) \leqslant f(x) \leqslant \underline{D}F(x) \text{ p.p. in } I,$$

and since $\bar{D}F(x) \geqslant \underline{D}F(x)$,

this means $F'(x) \sim f(x)$ in I.

§3. Summability of Derivatives

The result of th. 253 suggests the problem of finding conditions in which

(1) $$\int_a^b F'(x)\,dx = F(b)-F(a),$$

$F(x)$ being a function which is continuous throughout a closed interval $[a,b]$. The equation (1) might be false for several reasons:

(i) $F'(x)$ might be undefined in a subset of (a,b) which is not null,

(ii) $F'(x)$ might not be equivalent in (a,b) to a summable function, or finally,

(iii) the integral of $F'(x)$ over (a,b) might exist and differ from $F(b)-F(a)$.

Each of these possibilities can, in fact, be realized.

Example. Let
$$F(x) = \begin{cases} 0 & \text{if } x = 0 \\ x^2 \sin \pi/x^2 & \text{if } x \neq 0; \end{cases}$$
then $F'(x)$ exists and is *finite* for every x in $(0,1)$, but $F'(x)$ is not summable over $(0,1)$ (example following th. 211.2); this illustrates (ii).

We shall now show that, if $F(x)$ is bounded and non-decreasing in $[a,b]$, then $F'(x)$ is equivalent in (a,b) to a summable function, although (th. 263) the integral of $F'(x)$ over (a,b) may differ from $F(b)-F(a)$.

Theorem 254. *Let $f(x)$ be non-decreasing in $[a,b]$; suppose $S \subset (a,b)$, and $x \in S$ implies $\overline{D}f(x) > k$; then*
$$f(b)-f(a) \geqslant k|S|.$$

Proof. By def. 60 every point of S belongs to arbitrarily small closed intervals $[\lambda,\mu]$ contained in $[a,b]$ and such that
$$f(\mu)-f(\lambda) > k(\mu-\lambda).$$
Choose ϵ freely; it then follows from th. 125 that there is a finite number of points, $x_1, x_2,..., x_n, y_1, y_2,..., y_n$, such that
$$a \leqslant x_1 < y_1 < x_2 < y_2 < ... < x_n < y_n \leqslant b,$$
(1) $$|S| \leqslant \epsilon + \left| \sum_{r=1}^{n} S[x_r, y_r] \right|,$$
and $$f(y_r)-f(x_r) > k(y_r-x_r) \quad (r = 1, 2,..., n).$$
Since $f(x)$ is non-decreasing in $[a,b]$, this implies (th. 93)
$$f(b)-f(a) \geqslant \sum_{r=1}^{n} \{f(y_r)-f(x_r)\} > \sum_{r=1}^{n} k(y_r-x_r) = k\left| \sum_{r=1}^{n} [x_r, y_r] \right|,$$
and hence, by (1) and th. 81, $f(b)-f(a) > k\{|S|-\epsilon\}$ for every ϵ, which means $f(b)-f(a) \geqslant k|S|$. (See also th. 277.1.)

Theorem 255. *Let $f(x)$ be bounded and non-decreasing in $[a,b]$, and let S be a subset of (a,b) such that*
(1) $$x \in S \quad \text{implies} \quad \underline{D}f(x) < \alpha < \beta < \overline{D}f(x),$$
α *and* β *being fixed numbers; then S is null.*

Proof. By (1) every point of S belongs to arbitrarily small closed intervals $[\lambda,\mu]$ such that
$$[\lambda,\mu] \subset (a,b) \quad \& \quad f(\mu)-f(\lambda) < \alpha(\mu-\lambda).$$

Choose ϵ freely; it then follows, by ths. 125 and 85, that there is a finite number of points, $x_1,\ x_2,...,\ x_n,\ y_1,\ y_2,...,\ y_n$, satisfying

$$a \leqslant x_1 < y_1 < x_2 < y_2 < ... < x_n < y_n \leqslant b,$$

(2) $$\sum_{r=1}^{n}(y_r - x_r) - \epsilon < |S| < \sum_{r=1}^{n}|S(x_r, y_r)| + \epsilon,$$

and

(3) $$f(y_r) - f(x_r) < \alpha(y_r - x_r) \quad (r = 1, 2,..., n).$$

By (3) and (2), since $\alpha \geqslant 0$,

(4) $$\sum_{r=1}^{n}\{f(y_r) - f(x_r)\} - \alpha\epsilon < \alpha|S|,$$

and, by (2) and a repeated application of th. 254, since $\beta \geqslant 0$,

(5) $$\beta|S| < \sum_{r=1}^{n}\{f(y_r) - f(x_r)\} + \beta\epsilon.$$

By (4) and (5) $\quad (\beta - \alpha)|S| \leqslant (\alpha + \beta)\epsilon \quad$ for every ϵ,

and this means that S is null.

Theorem 256. *Let $f(x)$ be bounded and non-decreasing in $[a, b]$; then $f'(x)$ exists and is finite almost everywhere in $[a, b]$.*

Proof. Let $I = (a, b)$, and let $A = I . \mathscr{S}(x; \underline{D}f(x) < \overline{D}f(x))$. Let $\{r_n\}$ be a sequence consisting of all positive rational numbers (th. 9), and for every pair of positive integers m and n let

$$A_{m,n} = I . \mathscr{S}(x; \underline{D}f(x) < r_m < r_n < \overline{D}f(x))$$

(which is taken to mean $A_{m,n} = 0$ if $r_m \geqslant r_n$); then, since $f(x)$ is non-decreasing in I, we have $A = \sum_{m=1}^{\infty *} \sum_{n=1}^{\infty *} A_{m,n}$. It now follows from ths. 255 and 86 that A is null, and hence $f'(x)$ exists at almost all points x of I. If $Z = I . \mathscr{S}(x; f'(x) = \infty)$, it remains only to prove that Z is null. By th. 254, $f(b) - f(a) \geqslant k|Z|$ for every finite real number k, and, since $f(x)$ is bounded in $[a, b]$, this means $|Z| = 0$.

A more elementary, though somewhat longer, proof of th. 256 is given in § 6 of this chapter.

An interesting consequence of th. 256 is

Theorem 257 (FUBINI). *Suppose*

(1) $f_1(x), f_2(x),...$ *are non-decreasing in J, a closed interval $[a, b]$,* and

(2) $$\sum_{r=1}^{\infty} f_r(x) \text{ converges to } f_0(x) \text{ for every } x \text{ in } J;$$

then

$$(3) \qquad f_0'(x) \sim \sum_{r=1}^{\infty} f_r'(x) \ in \ J.$$

Proof. By (1) and (2), $f_0(x)$ is finite and non-decreasing in J, and so, by (1) and th. 256, if $r = 0, 1, 2,...$, then Z_r, the set of the points x of J for which $f_r'(x)$ is undefined or is infinite, is null; so, if

$$Z = \sum_{r=0}^{\infty}{}^* Z_r,$$

we have, by (1) and th. 86,

$$(4) \qquad x \in J\bar{Z} \quad \text{implies} \quad 0 \leqslant f_r'(x) < \infty \quad (r = 0, 1, 2,...),$$

and $\qquad\qquad\qquad\qquad Z$ is null.

Let $S_n(x) = \sum_{r=1}^{n} f_r(x)$; by (4) and (1),

$$x \in J\bar{Z} \quad \text{implies} \quad S_n'(x) \leqslant f_0'(x) \quad (n = 1, 2,...),$$

which, since Z is null, implies

$$(5) \qquad \sum_{r=1}^{\infty} f_r'(x) \text{ converges p.p. in } J \text{ to } \lim_{n \to \infty} S_n'(x).$$

It follows from (5) that (3) will be proved if there is an increasing sequence of integers $n_1, n_2,...$ such that

$$(6) \qquad \lim_{r \to \infty} \frac{d}{dx}\{f_0(x) - S_{n_r}(x)\} \sim 0 \text{ in } J.$$

Now, by (1) and (2), for $n = 1, 2,...$,

$$(7) \qquad f_0(x) - S_n(x) \text{ is finite and non-decreasing in } J;$$

by (7) and (2) there is an increasing sequence of integers $n_1, n_2,...$ such that, for every x in J

$$|f_0(x) - S_{n_r}(x)| < 2^{-r} \quad (r = 1, 2,...),$$

and this implies that

$$\sum_{r=1}^{\infty}\{f_0(x) - S_{n_r}(x)\} \text{ converges for every } x \text{ in } J;$$

hence, by (7), we have, as an analogue of (5),

$$\sum_{r=1}^{\infty} \frac{d}{dx}\{f_0(x) - S_{n_r}(x)\} \text{ converges p.p. in } J,$$

and this implies (6).

Theorem 258. *Let $F(x)$ be bounded and non-decreasing in J, a closed interval $[a, b]$; then $F'(x)$ is equivalent in J to a summable function, and*

$$(1) \qquad \int_a^b F'(x)\, dx \leqslant F(b) - F(a).$$

Proof. Let

$$(2) \qquad F(x) = \begin{cases} F(a) & \text{if } x < a \\ F(b) & \text{if } x > b, \end{cases}$$

and let $\qquad F_r(x) = r\{F(x+1/r) - F(x)\} \quad (r = 1, 2, \dots).$

Since $F(x)$ is non-decreasing in R_1, it follows, by ths. 166, 164, and 192, that

$$(3) \qquad 0 \leqslant \int_a^b \lim_{r\to\infty} F_r(x)\, dx \leqslant \lim_{r\to\infty} r \int_a^b \{F(x+1/r) - F(x)\}\, dx.$$

Since $F(x)$ is bounded and measurable in R_1, we have (ths. 168 and 203) that $F(x+1/r)$ and $F(x)$ are summable over J; hence, by ths. 241, 227, and 209.1,

$$(4) \qquad \int_a^b \{F(x+1/r) - F(x)\}\, dx = \int_b^{b+1/r} F(x)\, dx - \int_a^{a+1/r} F(x)\, dx$$

$$(r = 1, 2, \dots).$$

Now, by (2) and ths. 182 and 205,

$$r \int_b^{b+1/r} F(x)\, dx = F(b) \quad \& \quad r \int_a^{a+1/r} F(x)\, dx \geqslant F(a) \quad (r = 1, 2, \dots),$$

and so, by (4) and (3),

$$0 \leqslant \int_a^b \lim_{r\to\infty} F_r(x)\, dx \leqslant F(b) - F(a);$$

since $F'(x)$ exists almost everywhere in J (th. 256), and since $F(b) - F(a) < \infty$, this means that $F'(x)$ is equivalent in J to a summable function and that (1) is true.

The sign $\leqslant$ in th. 258 cannot be replaced by $=$ even when $F(x)$ is continuous throughout J, as the following theorem shows.

Theorem 259. *There is a function $\theta(x)$ which is continuous and non-decreasing in J, the closed interval $[0, 1]$, and which is such that*

$$\int_0^1 \theta'(x)\, dx < \theta(1) - \theta(0).$$

Proof. Following the method of th. 123, we first construct a sequence of intervals, $\{I_r\}$, whose sum, U, together with a perfect null set K, composes J. More precisely, we take I_1 to be concentric with J and of length $\frac{1}{3}$; I_2 and I_3 are obtained by selecting from each of the closed intervals which compose $J - I_1$ a concentric interval of length $\frac{1}{9}$. At the next stage four more intervals are defined, and, more generally, at the nth stage we define I_r for $r = 2^{n-1}, 2^{n-1}+1,..., 2^n-1$, the order being determined among the 2^{n-1} intervals by the rule that (a, b) precedes (c, d) if $a < c$. We now set up a 1–1 correspondence between the intervals I_r and the aggregate α which consists of all the numbers $s/2^n$, where n is any positive integer and s any odd positive integer less than 2^n; the procedure is modelled on the method used in constructing the intervals I_r. We assign $\frac{1}{2}$ to I_1, $\frac{1}{4}$ and $\frac{3}{4}$ to I_2 and I_3 respectively; $\frac{1}{8}, \frac{3}{8}, \frac{5}{8}, \frac{7}{8}$ to I_4, I_5, I_6, I_7 respectively. The intervals are thus considered as they are formed (i.e. in groups, the nth group consisting of 2^{n-1} members), and to the rth member of the nth group (the order in the group being determined as above) we assign the number $(2r-1)/2^n$. $\theta(x)$ is now defined in I_r as being constant and equal to the member of α assigned to I_r; it is easily seen that, after the nth stage, $\theta(x)$ is defined in $\sum_{r=1}^{2^n-1} I_r$ so as to be constant in each of the constituent intervals I_r, and so that

$$x_1 < x_2 \quad \text{implies} \quad \theta(x_1) \leqslant \theta(x_2);$$

also, $\theta(x)$ assumes each one of the values $1/2^n, 2/2^n, 3/2^n,..., (2^n-1)/2^n$. The function $\theta(x)$ thus defined in U has the following properties:

(1) $\theta(x)$ is constant in every interval contained in U,

(2) if $x_1 \in U$ & $x_2 \in U$, then $x_1 < x_2$ implies $\theta(x_1) \leqslant \theta(x_2)$, and

(3) if $\lambda \in \alpha$, then there is a point x of U such that $\theta(x) = \lambda$.

Having defined $\theta(x)$ in U, we now define it in $\bar{U}$ by the formula

$$\theta(x) = \begin{cases} 0 & \text{if} \quad x \leqslant 0 \\ M(\theta; U(0, x)) & \text{if} \quad x > 0. \end{cases}$$

By (2) $\theta(x)$ is non-decreasing, and from (3) it follows that

$$\theta(1) - \theta(0) = 1.$$

Now, if $\theta(x)$ is discontinuous for some value of x, then, since $\theta(x)$ is non-decreasing, it follows that there is a sub-interval Δ of $(0, 1)$ consisting of numbers which are not values of $\theta(x)$ for any x; but, since Δ must include members of α, this clearly contradicts (3), and so $\theta(x)$ must be continuous for every x. Since $x \in U$ implies $\theta'(x) = 0$, by (1), and since K is null (th. 123), it follows that

$$\theta'(x) \sim 0 \text{ in } J, \text{ and hence } \int_0^1 \theta'(x)\, dx = 0 < 1 = \theta(1) - \theta(0).$$

Theorem 260. *Let $f(x)$ be defined in $[a, b]$, and let there be a finite real number k such that*

(1) $\qquad a \leqslant x < y \leqslant b \quad \text{implies} \quad |f(y) - f(x)| \leqslant k(y - x);$

then $\qquad \int_a^b f'(x)\, dx = f(b) - f(a).$

Proof. Let $g(x) = f(x) + kx$ in $[a, b]$; by (1) $g(x)$ is bounded and non-decreasing in $[a, b]$, and so, by th. 258,

$$0 \leqslant \int_a^b g'(x)\, dx \leqslant g(b) - g(a);$$

since $g'(x) = k + f'(x)$ whenever $g'(x)$ exists, it now follows from ths. 227 and 182 that

$$g(b) - g(a) \geqslant \int_a^b \{k + f'(x)\}\, dx = \int_a^b f'(x)\, dx + k(b - a),$$

and hence

(2) $\qquad f(b) - f(a) \geqslant \int_a^b f'(x)\, dx.$

Since (1) remains true when $f(x)$ is replaced by $-f(x)$, we have, as an analogue of (2),

$$f(a) - f(b) \geqslant \int_a^b -f'(x)\, dx,$$

which, together with (2) and th. 204, proves the theorem.

Theorem 261. *Let $f(x)$ be continuous throughout $[a, b]$, and let $f'(x)$ be defined and bounded in (a, b); then*

$$\int_a^b f'(x)\, dx = f(b) - f(a).$$

Proof. By hypothesis and the first mean-value theorem there is a finite number k such that

$$a \leqslant x < y \leqslant b \quad \text{implies} \quad |f(y) - f(x)| \leqslant k(y - x),$$

and so the result follows from th. 260.

When $f'(x)$ is finite but unbounded in $[a, b]$, $f'(x)$ need not be summable over $[a, b]$ (example, p. 175); however, as th. 264 shows, if $f'(x)$ is finite *and* summable over $[a, b]$, then

$$\int_a^b f'(x)\, dx = f(b) - f(a).$$

Theorem 262 (ZYGMUND). *Suppose $f(x)$ is continuous throughout J, a closed interval $[a, b]$, and suppose that E, the set of the points x of J for which $\underline{D}f(x) \leqslant 0$, satisfies the condition (def. 45)*

(1)   *$f(E)$ contains no interval*

(this is so, in particular, if E is finite or enumerable); then $f(x)$ is non-decreasing in J.

Proof. Suppose, if possible, that α and β exist such that

(2) $a \leqslant \alpha < \beta \leqslant b$ & $f(\alpha) > f(\beta)$.

By (1) there must be a number λ such that

(3) $f(\alpha) > \lambda > f(\beta)$,

and

(4) $x \in J$ & $f(x) = \lambda$ implies $\underline{D}f(x) > 0$.

Since $f(x)$ is continuous throughout $[\alpha, \beta]$, it follows (Hardy, § 100) from (3) that $[\alpha, \beta]\mathscr{S}(x; f(x) = \lambda)$ is not empty and also that ξ, its upper bound, satisfies the conditions

$\alpha < \xi < \beta$, $f(\xi) = \lambda$,   and $f(x) < \lambda$ if $\xi < x < \beta$;

but this contradicts (4), and hence (2) is false.

Theorem 263. *Suppose $f(x)$ is continuous throughout J, a closed interval $[a, b]$, and is such that*

(1)   *the set of the points x of J for which $\underline{D}f(x) = -\infty$ is finite or enumerable, and*

(2)   *Z, the set of the points x of J for which $\underline{D}f(x) < 0$, is null;*

then $f(b) \geqslant f(a)$.

Proof. Choose ϵ freely; by th. 106 there is to every positive integer r an open set Z_r containing Z and such that

(3) $|Z_r| < \epsilon 2^{-r}$.

If we put $Z_r(x) = |(a, x)Z_r|$, then $Z_r(x)$ is a non-decreasing function of x, and (th. 81)

(4) $Z_r(b) - Z_r(a) \leqslant |Z_r|$ $(r = 1, 2, \ldots)$

Since Z_r is open,

$$x \in Z_r \quad \text{implies} \quad Z_r(x+h) - Z_r(x) = h$$

provided $|h|$ is small enough, and since $Z \subset Z_r$, it now follows that

$$x \in Z \quad \text{implies} \quad Z_r'(x) = 1 \quad (r = 1, 2, ...).$$

Hence, by (3) and (4), if $Z(x) = \sum\limits_{r=1}^{\infty} Z_r(x)$, we have

(5) $\hspace{3cm} Z(x)$ is non-decreasing in J,

(6) $\hspace{3cm} Z(b) - Z(a) < \epsilon,$

and

(7) $\quad x \in Z \quad$ implies $\quad \underline{D}Z(x) \geqslant \underline{D} \sum\limits_{r=1}^{n} Z_r(x) = n \quad (n = 1, 2, ...),$

i.e. $Z'(x) = \infty$.

Put $\hspace{3cm} \theta(x) = f(x) + Z(x) + \epsilon x;$

by (7) $\quad x \in JZ \quad \& \quad \underline{D}f(x) > -\infty \quad$ implies $\quad \underline{D}\theta(x) = \infty,$

and by (5) $\hspace{1.5cm} x \in J\bar{Z} \quad$ implies $\quad \underline{D}\theta(x) \geqslant \epsilon;$

hence, if $\theta(x)$ is continuous throughout J, it follows from (1) and th. 262 that $\theta(b) \geqslant \theta(a)$, and so, by (6),

(8) $\quad f(b) - f(a) \geqslant Z(a) - Z(b) - \epsilon(b-a) \geqslant -\epsilon - \epsilon(b-a).$

To prove that $\theta(x)$ is continuous throughout J it is clearly sufficient to show that $Z(x)$ is continuous throughout J. Let δ be a freely chosen positive number. By (3) n exists so that

(9) $\hspace{3cm} \sum\limits_{r=n+1}^{\infty} |Z_r| < \tfrac{1}{2}\delta.$

Now, by th. 103, $a \leqslant x < y \leqslant b$ implies

$$|(a, x)Z_r| + |(x, y)Z_r| = |(a, y)Z_r| \quad (r = 1, 2, ...),$$

and hence, by (5),

(10) $\hspace{2cm} 0 \leqslant Z(y) - Z(x) = \sum\limits_{r=1}^{\infty} |(x, y)Z_r|.$

By th. 81,

$$|(x, y)Z_r| \leqslant (y-x) \quad \& \quad |(x, y)Z_r| \leqslant |Z_r|,$$

and so, by (9) and (10),

$$0 \leqslant Z(y) - Z(x) \leqslant n(y-x) + \tfrac{1}{2}\delta,$$

which means that $|Z(y) - Z(x)| < \delta$ provided $(y-x)$ is small enough; hence $Z(x)$ is continuous throughout J, and (8) is true for every ϵ, which means $f(b) \geqslant f(a)$.

Theorem 264. *Suppose $f(x)$ is continuous throughout J, a closed interval $[a, b]$, and that*

(1) *$f'(x)$ is defined and finite in J except at the points of a set E which is finite or enumerable,*

and

(2)   *$f'(x)$ is equivalent in J to a summable function;*

then $\int_a^b f'(x)\, dx = f(b) - f(a).$

Proof. Let n be any positive integer, and

(3) $g_n(x) = \min(n, \overline{D}f(x))$ in (a, b).

Arguing as in th. 152, we have from th. 251,

(4) $g_n(x)$ is measurable in J;

also

(5) $x \in J\overline{E}$ implies $|g_n(x)| \leqslant |f'(x)|$ & $\lim\limits_{n\to\infty} g_n(x) = f'(x)$.

Since E is null (th. 52), it follows from (2), (4), (5), and ths. 201 and 223 that

(6) $\int_a^b f'(x)\, dx = \lim\limits_{n\to\infty} \int_a^b g_n(x)\, dx.$

Choose n freely, and put $G_n(x) = \int_a^x g_n(t)\, dt$; if x and $x+h$ belong to J, then (th. 209.1)

$$G_n(x+h) - G_n(x) = \int_x^{x+h} g_n(t)\, dt,$$

and so, if $h \neq 0$, we have (ths. 205 and 182)

$$\frac{G_n(x+h) - G_n(x)}{h} \leqslant n.$$

Hence, if $\theta_n(x) = f(x) - G_n(x)$,

$x \in \overline{E}J$ implies $\underline{D}\theta_n(x) = f'(x) + \underline{D}\{-G_n(x)\} \geqslant f'(x) - n > -\infty$;

also, since $G'_n(x) \sim g_n(x)$ in J (th. 253), and $|E| = 0$, it follows that for almost all x of J

$$\underline{D}\theta_n(x) = f'(x) - g_n(x) \geqslant 0.$$

Thus we have shown that $J \cdot \mathscr{S}(x; \underline{D}\theta_n(x) = -\infty)$ is finite or enumerable, and $J \cdot \mathscr{S}(x; \underline{D}\theta_n(x) < 0)$ is null; by hypothesis and th. 240 $\theta_n(x)$ is continuous throughout J, and so it now follows from th. 263

that $\theta_n(b) \geqslant \theta_n(a)$, i.e.

$$f(b) - \int_a^b g_n(x)\,dx \geqslant f(a) \quad (n = 1, 2, ...);$$

hence, by (6),

(7) $$f(b) - f(a) \geqslant \int_a^b f'(x)\,dx.$$

Since the conditions of the theorem are satisfied when $f(x)$ is replaced by $-f(x)$, we have, as an analogue of (7),

$$f(a) - f(b) \geqslant \int_a^b -f'(x)\,dx,$$

and this, together with th. 204 and (7), gives the required result.

§ 4. Bounded Variation and Absolute Continuity

Suppose $F(x)$ is continuous throughout $[a, b]$, $F(a) = 0$, and $F'(x)$ is equivalent in $[a, b]$ to a summable function; let

$$G(x) = \int_a^x F'(t)\,dt \quad a \leqslant x \leqslant b;$$

we have seen (th. 264) that $G(x)$ and $F(x)$ are identical if $F'(x)$ is *finite* in (a, b), but (th. 259) that in general $F(x)$ and $G(x)$ are not identical. Thus, given a function $f(x)$ defined in (a, b), the problem of finding a function $F(x)$ satisfying the conditions

(i) $F(a) = 0$, and $F(x)$ is continuous throughout $[a, b]$, and

(ii) $F'(x) \sim f(x)$ in $[a, b]$

does not admit of a *unique* solution. There will certainly be *a* solution if $f(x)$ is summable over (a, b), for then $\int_a^x f(t)\,dt$ satisfies the conditions for $F(x)$, and it follows easily from th. 251 that there will be *no* solution if $f(x)$ is not measurable in $[a, b]$; but the function $\theta(x)$ defined in th. 259 enables us to assert that, if there is one solution, then there are infinitely many; for, if $F_1(x)$ satisfies (i) and (ii), and $\theta(x)$ (th. 259) is such that $\theta(0) = 0$, $\theta(1) = 1$, and $\theta(x)$ is continuous throughout $[0, 1]$, while $\theta'(x) = 0$ p.p. in $[0, 1]$, then clearly $F(x)$, given by

$$F(x) = F_1(x) + \lambda\theta\!\left(\frac{x-a}{b-a}\right),$$

satisfies (i) and (ii) for every finite number λ.

We are therefore presented with the following two related problems:

(1) Suppose $f(x)$ is summable over $[a,b]$; what distinguishes $\int_a^x f(t)\,dt$ from all the other functions $F(x)$ which satisfy (i) and (ii)?

(2) If $F(x)$ is continuous throughout $[a,b]$, what conditions are necessary and sufficient in order that

$$F(x)-F(a) = \int_a^x F'(t)\,dt \quad a \leqslant x \leqslant b\,?$$

Before discussing the solution of these problems we consider a new class of functions $F(x)$ for which $\int_a^b F'(x)\,dx$ is finite.

Definition 61. Let $f(x)$ be defined and finite in J, a closed interval $[a,b]$. Then $T_+(f;J)$, the *positive variation* of f over J, and $T_-(f;J)$, the *negative variation* of f over J, are respectively the upper and the lower bounds of a certain aggregate α of real numbers, where $u \in \alpha$ if and only if there is a finite number of points $x_1, x_2,..., x_n, y_1, y_2,..., y_n$ such that

$$a \leqslant x_1 \leqslant y_1 \leqslant x_2 \leqslant y_2 \leqslant ... \leqslant x_n \leqslant y_n \leqslant b,$$

and
$$u = \sum_{r=1}^n \{f(y_r)-f(x_r)\}.$$

Clearly $T_+(f;J) \geqslant 0$, $T_-(f;J) \leqslant 0$, and so we may define $T(f;J)$, the *total variation* of f over J, by the equation

$$T(f;J) = T_+(f;J)-T_-(f;J).$$

If $T(f;J) < \infty$, f is said to be of *bounded variation* in J.

Examples.

(i) Let $f(x)$ be bounded and non-decreasing in $[a,b]$; then $f(x)$ is of bounded variation in $[a,b]$; for, with the notation of def. 61,

$$0 \leqslant \sum_{r=1}^n \{f(y_r)-f(x_r)\} \leqslant f(b)-f(a).$$

(ii) Let
$$f(x) = \begin{cases} x\sin \pi/x & \text{if } x \neq 0 \\ 0 & \text{if } x = 0; \end{cases}$$

then $f(x)$ is continuous throughout $[0,1]$, but $f(x)$ is not of bounded variation in $[0,1]$, for

$$f\left(\frac{1}{2n}\right) = 0 \quad \text{and} \quad f\left(\frac{1}{2n+\frac{1}{2}}\right) = \frac{1}{2n+\frac{1}{2}} \quad (n = 1, 2,...),$$

and so
$$\sum_{n=1}^{\infty} \left\{ f\left(\frac{1}{2n}\right) - f\left(\frac{1}{2n+\frac{1}{2}}\right) \right\} = \sum_{n=1}^{\infty} \frac{-1}{2n+\frac{1}{2}} = -\infty,$$
which implies $T_-(f; [0, 1]) = -\infty$.

Theorem 265. *Suppose $f(x)$ and $g(x)$ are of bounded variation in $[a, b]$, and let λ and μ be any finite real numbers; then $\lambda f(x) + \mu g(x)$ is of bounded variation in $[a, b]$.*

Proof. Put $h(x) = \lambda f(x) + \mu g(x)$; with the notation of def. 61,
$$\sum_{r=1}^{n} \{h(y_r) - h(x_r)\} = \lambda \sum_{r=1}^{n} \{f(y_r) - f(x_r)\} + \mu \sum_{r=1}^{n} \{g(y_r) - g(x_r)\},$$
from which it follows easily that
$$T_+(h; J) \leqslant |\lambda| T(f; J) + |\mu| T(g; J);$$
a similar argument proves that $T_-(h; J)$ is finite, and this completes the proof.

Corollary. If $f(x)$ and $g(x)$ are finite and non-decreasing in $[a, b]$, then $f(x) - g(x)$ is of bounded variation in $[a, b]$; this follows at once from example (i) following def. 61 and th. 265.

Theorem 266. *Suppose f is of bounded variation in J, a closed interval $[a, b]$; then $f(b) - f(a) = T_+(f; J) + T_-(f; J)$.*

Proof. Suppose
$$a = y_0 \leqslant x_1 \leqslant y_1 \leqslant x_2 \leqslant y_2 \leqslant \dots \leqslant x_n \leqslant y_n \leqslant x_{n+1} = b;$$
then
$$f(b) - f(a) = \sum_{r=1}^{n} \{f(y_r) - f(x_r)\} + \sum_{r=1}^{n+1} \{f(x_r) - f(y_{r-1})\};$$
hence
$$\sum_{r=1}^{n} \{f(y_r) - f(x_r)\} = f(b) - f(a) - \sum_{r=1}^{n+1} \{f(x_r) - f(y_{r-1})\},$$
and since
$$\sum_{r=1}^{n+1} \{f(x_r) - f(y_{r-1})\} \leqslant T_+(f; J),$$
this gives
$$\sum_{r=1}^{n} \{f(y_r) - f(x_r)\} \geqslant f(b) - f(a) - T_+(f; J),$$
which, by def. 61, implies $T_-(f; J) \geqslant f(b) - f(a) - T_+(f; J)$, i.e.
$$(1) \qquad f(b) - f(a) \leqslant T_+(f; J) + T_-(f; J).$$
Now, by def. 61, it follows at once that
$$T_+(-f; J) = -T_-(f; J);$$
hence, by (1),
$$-f(b) + f(a) \leqslant -T_-(f; J) - T_+(f; J),$$
and this, together with (1), gives the required result.

Theorem 267. *Let $f(x)$ be of bounded variation in J, a closed interval $[a,b]$; then there are functions $\theta(x)$ and $\phi(x)$ which are non-negative, non-decreasing, and bounded in J, and such that*

$$f(x) = \theta(x) - \phi(x)$$

for every point x of J.

Proof. Let $P(x)$ and $N(x)$ be defined in J as follows:

(1)
$$P(a) = N(a) = 0, \text{ and, if } a < x \leqslant b, \text{ let}$$
$$P(x) = T_+(f;[a,x]) \text{ and } N(x) = -T_-(f;[a,x]).$$

It follows from def. 61 that $P(x)$ and $N(x)$ are non-negative and non-decreasing in J, and that neither exceeds $T(f;J)$. Also, by (1) and th. 266, $x \in J$ implies

$$f(x) - f(a) = P(x) - N(x), \quad \text{i.e.} \quad f(x) = P(x) + f(a) - N(x);$$

hence, if
$$\theta(x) = \begin{cases} P(x) + f(a) & \text{if } f(a) \geqslant 0 \\ P(x) & \text{if } f(a) < 0, \end{cases}$$

and
$$\phi(x) = \theta(x) - f(x),$$

the conditions of the theorem are satisfied.

The following theorem shows that the definition of $T(f;J)$ given in def. 61 is consistent with another well established definition of the total variation of a function.

Theorem 268. *Let $f(x)$ be defined and finite in J, a closed interval $[a,b]$, and let μ be the upper bound of the aggregate of the numbers u for which there is a finite number of points $x_0, x_1,..., x_n$ such that*

$$a = x_0 < x_1 < ... < x_n = b$$

and
$$u = \sum_{r=1}^{n} |f(x_r) - f(x_{r-1})| \,;$$

then
$$\mu = T(f;J).$$

Proof. It follows at once from def. 61 that none of the numbers u can exceed $T_+(f;J) - T_-(f;J)$, and so we have only to prove

(1)
$$\mu \geqslant T_+(f;J) - T_-(f;J).$$

Now obviously $\quad \mu \geqslant T_+(f;J) \quad \& \quad \mu \geqslant -T_-(f;J),$

and so (1) is certainly satisfied if $T(f;J) = \infty$. Suppose now that $T(f;J) < \infty$, and let $x_1, x_2,..., x_{n+1}, y_0, y_1,..., y_n$ be freely chosen so that $a = y_0 \leqslant x_1 \leqslant y_1 \leqslant ... \leqslant x_n \leqslant y_n \leqslant x_{n+1} = b$; then

$$\mu \geqslant \sum_{r=1}^{n} \{f(y_r) - f(x_r)\} - \sum_{r=1}^{n+1} \{f(x_r) - f(y_{r-1})\}$$
$$= f(b) - f(a) - 2\sum_{r=1}^{n+1} \{f(x_r) - f(y_{r-1})\},$$

and so, by def. 61, $\mu \geqslant f(b)-f(a)-2T_-(f; J)$, from which (1) follows in virtue of th. 266.

Theorem 269. *Let $f(x)$ have bounded variation in $[a, b]$; then $f'(x)$ is equivalent in $[a, b]$ to a summable function.*

Proof. By th. 267 there are functions $\theta(x)$ and $\phi(x)$ which are bounded and non-decreasing in $[a, b]$, and such that

(1) $\qquad a \leqslant x \leqslant b \quad$ implies $\quad f(x) = \theta(x)-\phi(x)$.

By ths. 258 and 227 $\{\theta'(x)-\phi'(x)\}$ is equivalent in $[a, b]$ to a summable function, and hence, by (1), we have the required result.

It does not of course follow that, if $f(x)$ is continuous throughout $[a, b]$ and is of bounded variation in $[a, b]$, then

$$\int_a^b f'(x)\, dx = f(b)-f(a),$$

since this equation is not necessarily true even when $f(x)$ is non-decreasing in $[a, b]$ (th. 259). We shall now define a sub-class of the class of functions $f(x)$ which have bounded variation in $[a, b]$, and we shall show that the above equation is always true for members of this sub-class.

Definition 62. Suppose $a < b$ and X consists of (a, b), or of this set together with the points a and b; let $f(x)$ be defined in X so that to every ϵ there is a δ such that, if $(x_1, y_1), (x_2, y_2),..., (x_n, y_n)$ are mutually exclusive sub-intervals of X, then

$$\sum_{r=1}^{n} (y_r-x_r) < \delta \quad \text{implies} \quad \sum_{r=1}^{n} |f(y_r)-f(x_r)| < \epsilon.$$

In these circumstances $f(x)$ is said to be *absolutely continuous* in X.

Clearly, if $f(x)$ is absolutely continuous in X, it is also continuous in X: for to every ϵ there is a δ such that

$$|h| < \delta \quad \text{implies} \quad |f(x+h)-f(x)| < \epsilon$$

if x and $x+h$ belong to X. The following example not only shows that the converse is false (cf. example (ii) following def. 61), but also shows that a continuous function may have bounded variation in X without being absolutely continuous in X.

Example. Let $\theta(x)$ be the function defined in th. 259. Using the notation of that theorem, $J - \sum_{r=1}^{2^n-1} I_r$ is the sum of 2^n closed intervals, say $[a_1, b_1]$, $[a_2, b_2]$,..., $[a_{2^n}, b_{2^n}]$, each of length 3^{-n}, where

$$0 = a_1 < b_1 < a_2 < b_2 < ... < a_{2^n} < b_{2^n} = 1;$$

since $\theta(x)$ is constant in each of the closed intervals $[b_r, a_{r+1}]$ $(r = 1, 2,..., 2^n - 1)$, it follows that

$$\sum_{r=1}^{2^n} \{\theta(b_r) - \theta(a_r)\} = \theta(1) - \theta(0) = 1,$$

while $$\sum_{r=1}^{2^n} (b_r - a_r) = (\tfrac{2}{3})^n;$$

this being true for arbitrarily large n, $\theta(x)$ cannot be absolutely continuous in J.

Theorem 270. *Let $f(x)$ be summable over $[a, b]$, and let*

$$F(x) = \int_a^x f(t)\, dt;$$

then $F(x)$ is absolutely continuous in $[a, b]$.

Proof. Let $(x_1, y_1), (x_2, y_2),..., (x_n, y_n)$ be a finite number of mutually exclusive sub-intervals of $[a, b]$; by ths. 209.1, 197, and 177

$$(1) \qquad \sum_{r=1}^{n} |F(y_r) - F(x_r)| \leqslant \sum_{r=1}^{n} \int_{x_r}^{y_r} |f(t)|\, dt = \int_S |f(t)|\, dt,$$

where $$S = \sum_{r=1}^{n} (x_r, y_r).$$

Now $|f(x)|$ is summable over $[a, b]$ (th. 197 (i)), and $mS = \sum_{r=1}^{n} (y_r - x_r)$ (th. 93); hence it follows from th. 236 and (1) that $F(x)$ is absolutely continuous in $[a, b]$.

Theorem 271. *Let $F(x)$ be absolutely continuous in $[a, b]$; then $F(x)$ is of bounded variation in $[a, b]$.*

Proof. By hypothesis ϵ can be chosen so that

$$a \leqslant z_1 < z_2 < ... < z_t \leqslant b \quad \& \quad z_t - z_1 < \epsilon \quad \text{implies}$$
$$(1) \qquad \sum_{r=2}^{t} |F(z_r) - F(z_{r-1})| < 1.$$

Let $x_0, x_1,..., x_n$ be chosen so that

(2) $a = x_0 < x_1 < ... < x_n = b$ & $x_r - x_{r-1} < \epsilon$ $(r = 1, 2,..., n)$.

Now let $y_0, y_1,..., y_q$ be any finite set of points such that

$$a = y_0 < y_1 < ... < y_q = b;$$

by th. 268 our theorem is proved if we show

(3) $$\sum_{r=1}^{q} |F(y_r) - F(y_{r-1})| < n.$$

To this end, let $z_0, z_1, ..., z_s$ be the union of the sets of the points x_r and y_r. By (1) and (2), if λ is among $1, 2, ..., n$, then

(4) $$\sum_{r} |F(z_r) - F(z_{r-1})| < 1,$$

the condition of summation being $x_{\lambda-1} \leqslant z_{r-1} < z_r \leqslant x_\lambda$. By (4) and (2)

(5) $$\sum_{r=1}^{s} |F(z_r) - F(z_{r-1})| < n,$$

and from the definition of the points z_r it follows that

$$\sum_{r=1}^{q} |F(y_r) - F(y_{r-1})| \leqslant \sum_{\nu=1}^{s} |F(z_\nu) - F(z_{\nu-1})|;$$

whence, by (5), we have (3), and this completes the proof.

Theorem 272. *Let $f(x)$ and $g(x)$ be absolutely continuous in X, and let λ and μ be any finite real numbers; then $\lambda f(x) + \mu g(x)$ is absolutely continuous in X.*

Proof. Let $\qquad h(x) = \lambda f(x) + \mu g(x)$ in X;

let $(x_1, y_1), (x_2, y_2), ..., (x_n, y_n)$ be a finite number of mutually exclusive sub-intervals of X; then

$$h(y_r) - h(x_r) = \lambda\{f(y_r) - f(x_r)\} + \mu\{g(y_r) - g(x_r)\} \quad (r = 1, 2, ..., n),$$

and hence

$$\sum_{r=1}^{n} |h(y_r) - h(x_r)| \leqslant |\lambda| \sum_{r=1}^{n} |f(y_r) - f(x_r)| + |\mu| \sum_{r=1}^{n} |g(y_r) - g(x_r)|.$$

Since λ and μ are finite, the terms of the hypothesis now imply that if ϵ is freely chosen, then

$$\sum_{r=1}^{n} |h(y_r) - h(x_r)| < \epsilon \text{ provided } \sum_{r=1}^{n} (y_r - x_r) \text{ is small enough,}$$

and this means that $h(x)$ is absolutely continuous in X.

Theorem 273. *Suppose $F(x)$ is absolutely continuous in $[a, b]$, and $F'(x) \sim 0$ in $[a, b]$; then $F(b) = F(a)$.*

Proof. Choose ϵ freely, and let α be the aggregate of closed intervals $[\lambda, \mu]$ such that

(1) $\qquad a \leqslant \lambda < \mu \leqslant b \quad \& \quad |F(\mu) - F(\lambda)| < \epsilon(\mu - \lambda).$

Let $\qquad\qquad S = [a, b] \mathcal{O}(x; F'(x) = 0);$

then every point of S belongs to arbitrarily small members of α, and, by hypothesis, $|S| = |b-a|$; hence, by (1) and th. 125, there is a finite number of points, say $x_1, x_2,..., x_n, y_0, y_1,..., y_{n-1}$ such that

(2)
$$a = y_0 \leqslant x_1 < y_1 < x_2 < y_2 < ... < x_{n-1} < y_{n-1} \leqslant x_n = b,$$
$$b-a \geqslant \sum_{r=1}^{n-1}(y_r - x_r) > b-a-\epsilon,$$

and

(3) $|F(y_r) - F(x_r)| < \epsilon(y_r - x_r)$ $(r = 1, 2,..., n-1)$.

Now $F(b) - F(a) = \sum_{r=1}^{n-1}\{F(y_r) - F(x_r)\} + \sum_{r=1}^{n}\{F(x_r) - F(y_{r-1})\}$,

and so, by (3) and (2),

(4) $|F(b) - F(a)| < \epsilon(b-a) + \sum_{r=1}^{n}|F(x_r) - F(y_{r-1})|$,

while $\sum_{r=1}^{n}|x_r - y_{r-1}| < \epsilon$.

Since ϵ is arbitrary, it follows by (4), (2), and def. 62 that $F(b) = F(a)$.

Theorem 273.1. *Let $F(x)$ and $G(x)$ be absolutely continuous in J, a closed interval $[a, b]$, and such that*

$$F(a) = G(a) \quad \& \quad F'(x) \sim G'(x) \text{ in } J;$$

then $F(x)$ and $G(x)$ are identical in J.

Proof. Let $H(x) = F(x) - G(x)$;

then $H(x)$ is absolutely continuous in J (th. 272), and $H(a) = 0$; hence, by th. 273, it is sufficient to show that $H'(x) \sim 0$ in J. Now $F(x)$ and $G(x)$ are both of bounded variation in J (th. 271), and so (ths. 269 and 221) $F'(x)$ and $G'(x)$ are finite p.p. in J; since, by hypothesis, $F'(x) \sim G'(x)$ in J, it now follows (th. 86) that $F'(x)$ and $G'(x)$ are finite and equal p.p. in J, and hence $H'(x) \sim 0$ in J.

The result of th. 273.1, together with th. 270, enables us to answer the questions which were raised at the beginning of this section. To the question (1), namely, if $f(x)$ is summable over $[a, b]$, 'What distinguishes $\int_a^x f(t)\,dt$ from all the other functions $F(x)$ which vanish at a, are continuous throughout $[a, b]$, and satisfy the condition $F'(x) \sim f(x)$ in $[a, b]$?' the answer is that $\int_a^x f(t)\,dt$ is the only function which satisfies the conditions for $F(x)$ and is at the same time absolutely continuous in $[a, b]$. The answer to the other question is contained in th. 270 and the following theorem.

Theorem 274. *Let $F(x)$ be absolutely continuous in $[a,b]$; then*

$$F(x) - F(a) = \int_a^x F'(t)\, dt \quad a \leqslant x \leqslant b.$$

Proof. By ths. 271 and 269 $F'(x)$ is equivalent in $[a,b]$ to a summable function; let

$$G(x) = \int_a^x F'(t)\, dt \quad a \leqslant x \leqslant b.$$

By hypothesis it follows that $F(x) - F(a)$ is absolutely continuous in $[a,b]$, and its derivative is equivalent in $[a,b]$ to $G'(x)$ (th. 253); since $G(x)$ is absolutely continuous in $[a,b]$ (th. 270) and vanishes for $x = a$, the required result follows at once from th. 273.1.

§ 5. Integration by Substitution

We can now consider the problem of finding conditions in which the formula for integration by substitution (Hardy, § 161) is valid for Lebesgue integrals. It follows from th. 241 that, if $\phi(t)$ is a linear function of t, and $\int_{\phi(t_1)}^{\phi(t_2)} f(x)\, dx$ exists, then

$$\int_{t_1}^{t_2} f\{\phi(t)\}\phi'(t)\, dt = \int_{\phi(t_1)}^{\phi(t_2)} f(x)\, dx.$$

This formula is also valid when the functions $f(x)$, $\phi(t)$, and $\phi'(t)$ are continuous in appropriate intervals, and the elementary argument which proves it is roughly as follows: Put $F(x) = \int_{\phi(t_1)}^x f(u)\, du$; then

(i) $$F\{\phi(t_2)\} - F\{\phi(t_1)\} = \int_{t_1}^{t_2} \frac{d}{dt} F\{\phi(t)\}\, dt,$$

(ii) $$F'(x) = f(x) \quad \text{if} \quad x = \phi(t) \quad \& \quad t_1 < t < t_2,$$

and so $$\frac{d}{dt} F\{\phi(t)\} = f\{\phi(t)\}\phi'(t) \text{ in } (t_1, t_2).$$

Now, in the more general case, it follows from th. 274 that (i) is valid if $F\{\phi(t)\}$ is absolutely continuous in $[t_1, t_2]$. Greater difficulty is found in justifying a suitable analogue of (ii), and the trouble arises from the fact that the equation $F'(x) = f(x)$ may be false for all the points x of a null set X, while the set of the points t for which $\phi(t) \in X$ is *not* null; it will appear, however, that if $\phi(t)$ is absolutely continuous in $[t_1, t_2]$, then $\phi'(t) \sim 0$ in the set of the points t for which $\phi(t) \in X$, and, finally, the governing factor is the absolute continuity of $F\{\phi(t)\}$ in $[t_1, t_2]$.

Theorem 275. *Let $f(x)$ be summable over J, a closed interval $[a, b]$, and let*

$$F(x) = \int_a^x f(u)\, du \quad in \ J;$$

suppose

(1) $\phi(t)$ *is absolutely continuous in a closed interval T such that (def. 45)* $\phi(T) \subset J$.

Then $F\{\phi(t)\}$ is absolutely continuous in T if

(2) $f(x)$ *is bounded in J,*

or if

(3) $\phi(t)$ *is non-decreasing in T.*

Proof. Suppose

$$T = [t_1, t_2], \quad and \quad t_1 \leqslant \lambda_1 < \mu_1 \leqslant \ldots \leqslant \lambda_n < \mu_n \leqslant t_2;$$

by th. 209.1

(4) $$F\{\phi(\mu_r)\} - F\{\phi(\lambda_r)\} = \int_{\phi(\lambda_r)}^{\phi(\mu_r)} f(u)\, du \quad (r = 1, 2, \ldots, n).$$

If (2) is satisfied, then, by (4) and ths. 197 and 203,

$$\sum_{r=1}^n |F\{\phi(\mu_r)\} - F\{\phi(\lambda_r)\}| \leqslant M(|f|; J) \sum_{r=1}^n |\phi(\mu_r) - \phi(\lambda_r)|;$$

and since, by (1), the right-hand side of this inequality tends to zero with $\sum_{r=1}^n (\mu_r - \lambda_r)$, it follows that $F\{\phi(t)\}$ is absolutely continuous in T.

If (3) is satisfied, then

$$\phi(\lambda_1) \leqslant \phi(\mu_1) \leqslant \phi(\lambda_2) \leqslant \ldots \leqslant \phi(\lambda_n) \leqslant \phi(\mu_n);$$

let $S_r = \mathscr{S}(u; \phi(\lambda_r) < u < \phi(\mu_r))$, and $S = \sum_{r=1}^n S_r;$ it then follows from (4) and ths. 197 and 177 that

(5) $$\sum_{r=1}^n |F\{\phi(\mu_r)\} - F\{\phi(\lambda_r)\}| = \sum_{r=1}^n \left| \int_{S_r} f(u)\, du \right| \leqslant \int_S |f(u)|\, du.$$

By th. 93, $mS = \sum_{r=1}^n \{\phi(\mu_r) - \phi(\lambda_r)\}$, and hence, by (1), mS tends to zero with $\sum\limits_{r=1}^{n}(\mu_r-\lambda_r)$; since $|f(u)|$ is summable over J (th. 197), it now follows from (5) and th. 236 that $F\{\phi(t)\}$ is absolutely continuous in T.

Theorem 276. *Let $f(x)$ be absolutely continuous in J, a closed interval $[a,b]$, and let E be any subset of (a,b) for which $|f(E)| = 0$ (def. 45); then $f'(x) \sim 0$ in E.*

Proof. It is convenient first to prove three lemmas.

Lemma 1. Let U be any open subset of J; then

$$|f(U)| \leqslant \int\limits_{U} |f'(x)|\, dx.$$

Proof. Let W be any closed sub-interval of J; since $f(x)$ is continuous throughout W, it follows that $f(W)$ is a closed interval of length $\omega(f; W)$ (def. 27) (or else consists of a single point), and moreover there are points λ and μ belonging to W such that

$$\lambda < \mu \quad \& \quad |f(\mu)-f(\lambda)| = \omega(f; W) = |f(W)|;$$

hence, by ths. 81, 274, 197, and 176,

$$|f(W^\circ)| \leqslant |f(W)| = \left|\int\limits_{\lambda}^{\mu} f'(x)\, dx\right| \leqslant \int\limits_{\lambda}^{\mu} |f'(x)|\, dx \leqslant \int\limits_{W^\circ} |f'(x)|\, dx,$$

and so, if U is the sum of a sequence of intervals, $\{I_r\}$, it follows from ths. 84 and 177 that

$$|f(U)| = \left|\sum\limits_{r=1}^{\infty}\!^{*} f(I_r)\right| \leqslant \sum\limits_{r=1}^{\infty} |f(I_r)| \leqslant \sum\limits_{r=1}^{\infty} \int\limits_{I_r} |f'(x)|\, dx = \int\limits_{U} |f'(x)|\, dx.$$

A similar argument applies when U is the sum of a finite number of intervals, and this, in virtue of th. 19, proves lemma 1.

Lemma 2. Let C be a closed subset of (a,b), and θ a positive number such that for every pair of points x_1, x_2 of C

(1) $x_1 < x_2$ implies $f(x_2)-f(x_1) \geqslant \theta(x_2-x_1)$;

let U be any open subset of J containing C; then $|f(U)| \geqslant \theta\, mC$.

Proof. As in lemma 1, we shall only consider the case where U is the sum of a sequence of intervals $\{(a_r, b_r)\}$. If $C(a_r, b_r)$ is not empty, let α_r and β_r be its bounds ($\alpha_r \leqslant \beta_r$), and put

$$S_r = \mathscr{S}(x; \alpha_r < x < \beta_r);$$

otherwise, let $S_r = 0$. By th. 23, and since $U \supset C$, it follows that

α_1, β_1, α_2, β_2,... are all the points of C which do not belong to $\sum\limits_{r=1}^{\infty} S_r$; these, being finite or enumerable, form a null set (th. 83), and so, by ths. 119, 81, and 94,

$$(2) \qquad mC \leqslant m\Big(\sum_{r=1}^{\infty} S_r\Big) = \sum_{r=1}^{\infty} (\beta_r - \alpha_r).$$

Let $\qquad Y_r = \mathscr{S}(y; f(\alpha_r) < y < f(\beta_r));$

since α_r and β_r belong to C, it follows from (1) that the sets Y_r are mutually exclusive, and that $mY_r \geqslant \theta(\beta_r - \alpha_r)$; hence, by (2) and th. 94,

$$(3) \qquad m\Big(\sum_{r=1}^{\infty} Y_r\Big) = \sum_{r=1}^{\infty} mY_r \geqslant \theta \sum_{r=1}^{\infty} (\beta_r - \alpha_r) \geqslant \theta\, mC.$$

Further, since $f(x)$ is continuous throughout J, it follows, as in lemma 1, that $f(S_r) \supset Y_r$ and consequently

$$f\Big(\sum_{r=1}^{\infty} S_r\Big) \supset \sum_{r=1}^{\infty} Y_r;$$

hence, by (3), since $U \supset \sum\limits_{r=1}^{\infty} S_r$, we have (th. 81)

$$|f(U)| \geqslant \Big|f\Big(\sum_{r=1}^{\infty} S_r\Big)\Big| \geqslant \Big|\sum_{r=1}^{\infty} Y_r\Big| \geqslant \theta\, mC.$$

Lemma 3. Let K be a closed set of positive measure contained in (a, b) and such that $f'(x) > 0$ for every point x of K; then $|f(K)| > 0$.

Proof. For every pair of positive integers m and n let $S_{m,n}$ be the set of all the points x of J such that

$$\frac{f(y) - f(x)}{y - x} \geqslant \frac{1}{m} \quad \text{for all } y \text{ satisfying} \quad 0 < |x - y| < \frac{1}{n}.$$

Clearly $K = \sum\limits_{n=1}^{\infty}{}^{*} \sum\limits_{m=1}^{\infty}{}^{*} KS_{m,n}$, and so, by ths. 6 and 86, since $mK > 0$, there is a pair of positive integers μ and ν such that $|KS_{\mu,\nu}| > 0$, and moreover there is a closed interval Δ such that

$$\Delta \subset (a, b) \quad \& \quad |\Delta K S_{\mu,\nu}| > 0 \quad \& \quad |\Delta| < \frac{1}{\nu}$$

(this follows easily by considering a net N over J for which $g(N) < 1/\nu$). Put $C = \Delta K S_{\mu,\nu}$; then

$$(4) \qquad x \in C \quad \& \quad y \in \Delta \quad \& \quad y \neq x \quad \text{implies} \quad \frac{f(y) - f(x)}{y - x} \geqslant \frac{1}{\mu}.$$

Now $S_{\mu,\nu}$ is closed: for suppose ξ is the limit of a sequence $\{x_n\}$ of points of $S_{\mu,\nu}$; choose y freely so that $0 < |\xi-y| < 1/\nu$; since $\lim\limits_{n\to\infty} x_n = \xi$, it follows that $0 < |y-x_n| < 1/\nu$, and consequently

$$\frac{f(y)-f(x_n)}{y-x_n} \geqslant \frac{1}{\mu}$$

for all large n, and this, since $f(x)$ is continuous throughout J, implies

$$\frac{f(y)-f(\xi)}{y-\xi} \geqslant \frac{1}{\mu} \quad \text{and therefore} \quad \xi \in S_{\mu,\nu}.$$

Since K, Δ, and $S_{\mu,\nu}$ are all closed, so is C (th. 27), and so, by (4) and lemma 2, if U is an open subset of (a,b) containing C, then $|f(U)| \geqslant (1/\mu)mC$. Put $U_1 = U-C$; then U_1 is open (ths. 25 and 17), and so, by lemma 1, $|f(U_1)| \leqslant \int\limits_{U_1} |f'(x)|\, dx$; hence (th. 85)

$$(5) \quad \frac{1}{\mu}mC \leqslant |f(U)| = |f(C)\dotplus f(U_1)|$$

$$\leqslant |f(C)| + |f(U_1)| \leqslant |f(C)| + \int\limits_{U_1} |f'(x)|\, dx.$$

Now $f'(x)$ is equivalent in J to a summable function (th. 274), and so the same is true of $|f'(x)|$ (th. 197); hence, since U may be chosen so that mU_1 is arbitrarily small (th. 110), it now follows from (5) and the cor. to th. 236 that $|f(C)| \geqslant (1/\mu)mC$, and so (th. 81)

$$|f(K)| \geqslant |f(C)| > 0,$$

which proves lemma 3.

Proof. of th. 276. Suppose first that E is measurable. By th. 274, $f'(x)$ is equivalent in J to a summable function, and hence, by ths. 119 and 148,

$$E.\mathscr{S}(x;f'(x) > 0) \text{ is measurable,}$$

and, if it were not null, would contain a closed set of positive measure (ths. 110 and 97); since, by lemma 3, this would imply $|f(E)| > 0$, it follows that $|E.\mathscr{S}(x;f'(x) > 0)| = 0$. Reasoning similarly with $-f(x)$ in place of $f(x)$, we have $|E.\mathscr{S}(x;f'(x) < 0)| = 0$, and hence, since $f'(x)$ is defined almost everywhere in E, we have

$$(6) \qquad\qquad f'(x) \sim 0 \text{ in } E \quad \text{if} \quad E \in \mathscr{L}.$$

Now suppose E is non-measurable, while $|f(E)| = 0$. By th. 106, to every positive integer r there is a set U_r such that

$$(7) \qquad U_r \text{ is open,} \quad f(E) \subset U_r, \quad \text{and} \quad mU_r < \frac{1}{r}.$$

Let $$A_r = (a, b) . \mathscr{S}(x; f(x) \in U_r);$$

then A_r is open; for suppose $\xi \in A_r$: since $f(x)$ is continuous for $x = \xi$, it follows that to every ϵ there is an interval I centre ξ such that $f(I)$ is contained in the linear interval $(f(\xi)-\epsilon, f(\xi)+\epsilon)$. Since U_r is open, ϵ may be chosen so small that the latter interval is contained in U_r, in which case $f(I) \subset U_r$, showing that ξ is interior to A_r.

Put $A = \prod\limits_{r=1}^{\infty} A_r$; by ths. 100 and 104, $A \in \mathscr{L}$; and since

$$f(A) \subset U_r \quad (r = 1, 2, \ldots),$$

it follows from (7) that $|f(A)| = 0$, and so, by (6), $f'(x) \sim 0$ in A. Since $E \subset A_r$ $(r = 1, 2, \ldots)$, we have $E \subset A$, and hence $f'(x) \sim 0$ in E.

Theorem 277. *Suppose $f(x)$ is finite and summable over J, a closed interval $[x_1, x_2]$, and that $F(x) = \int\limits_{x_1}^{x} f(u) \, du$ in J. Suppose*

(1) $\phi(t)$ *is absolutely continuous in T, a closed interval $[t_1, t_2]$, satisfying* $\phi(T) \subset J,$

and

(2) $F\{\phi(t)\}$ *is absolutely continuous in T*

(this is true, in particular, if $f(x)$ is bounded in J or if $\phi(t)$ is non-decreasing in T (th. 275)); then

(3) $\displaystyle \int\limits_{\phi(t_1)}^{\phi(t_2)} f(u) \, du = \int\limits_{t_1}^{t_2} f\{\phi(t)\}\phi'(t) \, dt = F\{\phi(t_2)\} - F\{\phi(t_1)\}.$

Proof. Let T_1 be the set of the points t of T for which $\phi'(t)$ is finite and not zero, and let τ be any point of T_1; then, if $|h|$ is small enough,

(4) $\displaystyle \frac{F\{\phi(\tau+h)\} - F\{\phi(\tau)\}}{h} = \frac{F\{\phi(\tau+h)\} - F\{\phi(\tau)\}}{\phi(\tau+h) - \phi(\tau)} \cdot \frac{\phi(\tau+h) - \phi(\tau)}{h}.$

Let X be the null set of the points x of J for which the equation $F'(x) = f(x)$ is false (th. 253); by th. 276

$$|T_1 . \mathscr{S}(t; \phi(t) \in X)| = 0,$$

and hence, by (4),

(5) $\displaystyle \frac{d}{dt} F\{\phi(t)\} \sim f\{\phi(t)\}\phi'(t)$ in T_1.

If we are also given that $f(x)$ is bounded in J, then, by ths. 209.1 and 203, if t and $t+h$ belong to T, we have

$$|F\{\phi(t+h)\}-F\{\phi(t)\}|$$
$$=\left|\int_{\phi(t)}^{\phi(t+h)} f(u)\,du\right| \leqslant |\phi(t+h)-\phi(t)|\, M(|f|;J)$$

and consequently

(6) $\phi'(t)=0$ implies $\dfrac{d}{dt}F\{\phi(t)\}=0.$

Now, by (1) and ths. 274 and 221, $\phi'(t)$ is defined and finite almost everywhere in T, and so, by (5) and (6),

(7) if $f(x)$ is bounded in J, then $\dfrac{d}{dt}F\{\phi(t)\} \sim f\{\phi(t)\}\phi'(t)$ in T.

By (7) and ths. 275 and 274,

(8) if $f(x)$ is bounded in J, then $F\{\phi(t_2)\}-F\{\phi(t_1)\} = \int_{t_1}^{t_2} f\{\phi(t)\}\phi'(t)\,dt.$

If $f(x)$ is unbounded in J, we proceed as follows: for every positive integer n we define in J

$$f_n(x) = \begin{cases} f(x) & \text{if } |f(x)| < n \\ 0 & \text{otherwise,} \end{cases} \qquad F_n(x) = \int_{x_1}^{x} f_n(u)\,du,$$

and it then follows (th. 235) that

(9) $F\{\phi(t_2)\}-F\{\phi(t_1)\} = \lim_{n\to\infty}(F_n\{\phi(t_2)\}-F_n\{\phi(t_1)\}).$

Since $\phi'(t)$ is equivalent in T to a summable function, it follows that

(10) $T_1 \in \mathscr{L}, \quad T-T_1 \in \mathscr{L}, \quad \text{and} \quad \phi'(t)\sim 0 \text{ in } T-T_1;$

hence, by (8) and ths. 209 and 182,

$$F_n\{\phi(t_2)\}-F_n\{\phi(t_1)\} = \int_{T_1} f_n\{\phi(t)\}\phi'(t)\,dt \quad (n=1,2,\ldots),$$

which, by (9), implies

(11) $F\{\phi(t_2)\}-F\{\phi(t_1)\} = \lim_{n\to\infty}\int_{T_1} f_n\{\phi(t)\}\phi'(t)\,dt.$

Now since $f(x)$ is finite in J, it follows for every point t of T_1 that

$$|f_n\{\phi(t)\}\phi'(t)| \leqslant |f\{\phi(t)\}\phi'(t)| \quad (n=1,2,\ldots),$$

(12) and $f\{\phi(t)\}\phi'(t) = \lim_{n\to\infty} f_n\{\phi(t)\}\phi'(t);$

further, by (2), (5), (10), and ths. 274, 219, and 206, $f\{\phi(t)\}\phi'(t)$ is summable over T_1; hence (ths. 197 and 214), by (12) and (11),

$$(13) \qquad F\{\phi(t_2)\} - F\{\phi(t_1)\} = \int_{T_1} f\{\phi(t)\}\phi'(t)\, dt.$$

By (13), (10), and ths. 209 and 182,

$$F\{\phi(t_2)\} - F\{\phi(t_1)\} = \int_{t_1}^{t_2} f\{\phi(t)\}\phi'(t)\, dt,$$

which proves (3).

§ 6. Appendix to § 3

The use of Vitali's theorem (th. 125) in proving the result of th. 256 may be avoided by a lemma due to F. Riesz.

Lemma. Let $\phi(x)$ be defined and bounded in an interval (a, b), and let U be the set of the points x of (a, b) for which there is a point x' such that

$$(1) \qquad x < x' < b \quad \& \quad \phi(x') > M(\phi; x);$$

then U is open, and, if $(a', b') \subset U$ & $a' \in \bar{U}$ & $b' \in \bar{U}$, then

$$\phi(a' + \epsilon) \leqslant \Phi(b')$$

for all sufficiently small ϵ, where

$$\Phi(x) = \begin{cases} M(\phi; x) & \text{if } x < b \\ \varlimsup_{\epsilon \to 0} \phi(b - \epsilon) & \text{if } x = b. \end{cases}$$

Proof. Suppose $x \in U$ and x' satisfies (1); it follows at once from def. 28 that $\phi(x') > M(\phi; \xi)$ for all ξ sufficiently close to x, and this means that U is open. Now suppose, if possible, that

$$(2) \qquad (a', b') \subset U \quad \& \quad a' \in \bar{U} \quad \& \quad b' \in \bar{U}$$

and that there is a number ξ such that

$$(3) \qquad a' < \xi < b' \quad \& \quad \phi(\xi) > \Phi(b').$$

Let μ be the upper bound of all numbers x satisfying

$$a' < x < b' \quad \& \quad \phi(x) \geqslant \phi(\xi);$$

clearly $\mu \geqslant \xi$ & $\Phi(\mu) \geqslant \phi(\xi)$, and so, by (3), $\mu \neq b'$, which implies $a' < \xi \leqslant \mu < b'$. By (2) this means $\mu \in U$, and so μ' exists satisfying

$$(4) \qquad \mu < \mu' < b \quad \& \quad \phi(\mu') > \Phi(\mu) \geqslant \phi(\xi).$$

Hence, from the definition of μ, $\mu' \geqslant b'$; this being impossible if $b' = b$, it follows from (4) and (3) that

$$b' \leqslant \mu' < b \quad \& \quad \phi(\mu') > \phi(\xi) > \Phi(b').$$

Now the possibility $\mu' = b'$ is excluded by the definition of $\Phi(x)$, and so we have $b' < \mu' < b$ & $\phi(\mu') > \Phi(b')$, which implies $b' \in U$ and therefore contradicts (2). This completes the proof of the lemma.

Theorem 277.1. *Let $f(x)$ be bounded and non-decreasing in the interval (a, b), let K be any finite real number, and* (def. 60)

$$S = (a, b) . \mathscr{S}(x; D^+f(x) > K);$$

then
$$f(b-0) - f(a+0) \geqslant K|S|.$$

Proof. Let $\phi(x) = f(x) - Kx$. If ξ is a point of S for which $f(x)$ is continuous, then ξ' exists such that

$$\xi < \xi' < b \quad \& \quad \phi(\xi') > \phi(\xi) = M(\phi; \xi),$$

and this means that ξ belongs to the set U defined in the lemma. Since $f(x)$ is continuous p.p. in (a, b) (th. 243), it follows that

$$(1) \qquad\qquad |U| \geqslant |US| = |S|.$$

Since $f(x)$ is non-decreasing in (a, b), $\Phi(x)$ of the lemma is given by

$$\Phi(x) = \begin{cases} f(x+0) - Kx & \text{if} \quad x < b \\ f(b-0) - Kb & \text{if} \quad x = b, \end{cases}$$

and so, by the lemma, if $I = (a', b') \subset U$ & $a' \in \bar{U}$ & $b' \in \bar{U}$, then

$$(2)$$
$$\Delta(I) \geqslant K(b' - a'), \quad \text{where} \quad \Delta(I) = \begin{cases} f(b'+0) - f(a'+0) & \text{if} \quad b' < b \\ f(b-0) - f(a'+0) & \text{if} \quad b' = b. \end{cases}$$

Now α, the aggregate of all possible such intervals (a', b'), is finite or enumerable (th. 19); if α is enumerable and consists of $I_1, I_2, \ldots$, then, by (2), since $f(x)$ is non-decreasing in (a, b), we have for every positive integer n

$$f(b-0) - f(a+0) \geqslant \sum_{r=1}^{n} \Delta(I_r) \geqslant K \sum_{r=1}^{n} |I_r|,$$

which, by (1) and th. 94 (ii), gives

$$f(b-0) - f(a+0) \geqslant K \sum_{r=1}^{\infty} |I_r| = K|U| \geqslant K|S|.$$

This completes the proof when α is enumerable; the proof when α is finite is practically the same.

Theorem 277.2. *Let $f(x)$ be bounded and non-decreasing in the interval (a, b), let k and K be finite numbers, $0 < k < K$, and let*

$$S = (a, b) \mathscr{S}(x; D_- f(x) < k < K < D^+f(x));$$

then $|S| = 0$.

Proof. If $\xi \in S$, then $\lim\limits_{\epsilon \to 0} \dfrac{f(\xi-\epsilon)-f(\xi)}{-\epsilon} < k$, which means

$$\overline{\lim_{\epsilon \to 0}} \frac{f(\xi-\epsilon)-f(\xi)}{\epsilon} > -k,$$

so that, if $\phi(x) = f(-x)+kx$, then $D^+\phi(x) > 0$ when $x = -\xi$. Hence, if the transformation $F(x)$ is defined by $F(x) = -x$, it follows from the lemma (as in the proof of th. 277.1) that there is an aggregate α of mutually exclusive intervals whose sum contains almost all the points of $F(S)$, and, if $(-b', -a')$ is any member of α, then (since $f(-x)$ is non-increasing in $(-b, -a)$)

(1) $\phi(-b'+0) \leqslant \phi(-a'-0)$.

It now follows from th. 127 that the sum of all the intervals (a', b'), such that $(-b', -a') \in \alpha$, contains almost all the points of S, and, by (1), if $(-b', -a') \in \alpha$, then $f(b'-0)-kb' \leqslant f(a'+0)-ka'$, i.e.

(2) $f(b'-0)-f(a'+0) \leqslant k(b'-a')$.

By (2) and th. 277.1 it now follows that there is an aggregate β of mutually exclusive sub-intervals of (a, b) whose sum contains almost all the points of S, and, if $I \in \beta$, then

$$K|SI| \leqslant k|I|,$$

and, since β is finite or enumerable, it follows easily from th. 94 that

$$K|S| \leqslant k(b-a).$$

Now the above argument could be used to prove that

$$a \leqslant \lambda < \mu \leqslant b \quad \text{implies} \quad |S(\lambda, \mu)| \leqslant \frac{k}{K}(\mu-\lambda);$$

hence, if $I_1, I_2,\ldots$ are sub-intervals of (a, b) covering S, we have

$$|S| \leqslant \sum_{r=1}^{\infty} |SI_r| \leqslant \frac{k}{K} \sum_{r=1}^{\infty} |I_r|,$$

which implies (def. 40) that

$$|S| \leqslant \frac{k}{K}|S| < \infty,$$

and since $0 < k/K < 1$, this means $|S| = 0$.

Theorem 277.3. *Let $f(x)$ be bounded and non-decreasing in (a, b); then $f'(x)$ exists and is finite almost everywhere in (a, b).*

Proof. Let $\{r_n\}$ be a sequence consisting of all positive rational numbers (th. 9), and for every pair of positive integers m and n let

$$A_{m,n} = (a, b)\mathscr{S}(x; D_-f(x) < r_m < r_n < D^+f(x))$$

(which is taken to mean $A_{m,n} = 0$ if $r_m \geqslant r_n$); then, since $f(x)$ is non-decreasing in (a, b), we have

$$(a,b)\mathscr{S}(x; D_-f(x) < D^+f(x)) = \sum_{m=1}^{\infty}{}^* \sum_{n=1}^{\infty}{}^* A_{m,n},$$

and so it follows from ths. 277.2 and 86 that

(1) $\qquad\qquad D^+f(x) \leqslant D_-f(x)$ p.p. in (a, b).

If we now show

(2) $\qquad\qquad D^-f(x) \leqslant D_+f(x)$ p.p. in (a, b),

it will follow from (1) and (2) that, for almost all x in (a, b),

$$D^+f(x) \leqslant D_-f(x) \leqslant D^-f(x) \leqslant D_+f(x),$$

i.e. $f'(x)$ exists. To this end, put $\phi(x) = -f(-x)$; $\phi(x)$ is non-decreasing in $(-b, -a)$, and so, by an analogue of (1),

$$\mathscr{S}(x; -b < x < -a \ \& \ D^+\phi(x) > D_-\phi(x)) \text{ is null};$$

hence (th. 127) (2) is proved if we show that

(3) $\qquad a < \xi < b \ \ \& \ \ D^-f(\xi) > D_+f(\xi) \quad \text{implies}$
$$D^+\phi(-\xi) > D_-\phi(-\xi).$$

Now (3) implies

$$\varlimsup_{\epsilon\to 0} \frac{f(\xi-\epsilon)-f(\xi)}{-\epsilon} > \varliminf_{\epsilon\to 0}\frac{f(\xi+\epsilon)-f(\xi)}{\epsilon},$$

i.e.
$$\varlimsup_{\epsilon\to 0} \frac{\phi(-\xi+\epsilon)-\phi(-\xi)}{\epsilon} > \varliminf_{\epsilon\to 0}\frac{\phi(-\xi-\epsilon)-\phi(-\xi)}{-\epsilon},$$

i.e.
$$D^+\phi(-\xi) > D_-\phi(-\xi),$$

and this completes the proof of (2). It remains only to prove that if

$$Z = (a,b)\mathscr{S}(x; f'(x) = \infty),$$

then $|Z| = 0$, and this follows at once from th. 277.1, which gives

$$n|Z| \leqslant f(b-0)-f(a+0) \quad (n = 1, 2, ...).$$

VIII

EVALUATION OF DOUBLE INTEGRALS

THE reader will be familiar with the method of evaluating the volume of a solid S (in R_3), which consists in integrating with respect to ξ the function whose value for every real ξ is the area of the section of S by the plane $x = \xi$. The same volume will sometimes be more conveniently evaluated by considering sections of S parallel to one of the other coordinate planes. The validity of this method presupposes

(i) the existence of a number which may be regarded as measuring the volume of S,

(ii) that to every one of the sections of S which are considered there is a number which measures its area,

(iii) that the area function so defined is integrable over an appropriate range,

(iv) that the result is independent of the direction of the planes of section of S.

The Lebesgue theory of measure enables us to state very simple conditions in which this procedure is valid.

Theorem 278 (FUBINI). *Let A be any measurable set in R_3; for every real number ξ put $A(\xi) = \mathscr{S}((y,z);(\xi,y,z) \in A)$; then, for almost all x, $A(x)$ is a plane measurable set, and*

$$mA = \int\limits_{-\infty}^{\infty} |A(x)| \, dx.$$

Proof.

Lemma 1. Let J be an interval in R_3; then $mJ = \int\limits_{-\infty}^{\infty} mJ(x) \, dx$.

Proof. Suppose $J = \mathscr{S}((x,y,z); x \subset X \ \& \ y \in Y \ \& \ z \in Z)$; then $x \in \bar{X}$ implies $J(x) = 0$, and, if $x \in X$, then $J(x)$ is a plane interval and $mJ(x) = |Y||Z| = k$, say. Hence, by ths. 182 and 82,

$$\int\limits_{-\infty}^{\infty} mJ(x) \, dx = \int\limits_{X} k \, dx = k|X| = mJ.$$

Lemma 2. If $e(x) = |A(x)|$, then $|A| \geqslant |\Omega_0(e; R_1)|$.

Proof. Let $\{J_r\}$ be a sequence of intervals covering A, and put $u(x) = \sum\limits_{r=1}^{\infty} |J_r(x)|$. By lemma 1, th. 191, and def. 52,

$$(1) \qquad \sum_{r=1}^{\infty} |J_r| = \int\limits_{-\infty}^{\infty} \sum_{r=1}^{\infty} |J_r(x)| \, dx = \int\limits_{-\infty}^{\infty} u(x) \, dx = |\Omega_0(u; R_1)|;$$

also, by ths. 81 and 84, since $\sum\limits_{r=1}^{\infty}{}^{*} J_r(x) \supset A(x)$, we have $u(x) \geqslant e(x)$ in R_1; hence, by (1) and ths. 132 and 81,

$$\sum_{r=1}^{\infty} |J_r| \geqslant |\Omega_0(e; R_1)|,$$

and since the J_r are only required to cover A, this implies

$$|A| \geqslant |\Omega_0(e; R_1)|.$$

(The reader will note that the measurability of A is irrelevant to this lemma.)

Lemma 3. Let A be bounded and measurable; then

$$mA = \int\limits_{-\infty}^{\infty} |A(x)| \, dx.$$

Proof. Since $mA < \infty$, it follows from lemma 2 and ths. 116 and 117 that

$$m_* \Omega_0(e; R_1) \geqslant mA \quad \text{implies} \quad m\Omega_0(e; R_1) = mA,$$

and so, by def. 52,

(2) $\qquad m_* \Omega_0(e; R_1) \geqslant mA \quad \text{implies} \quad mA = \int\limits_{-\infty}^{\infty} |A(x)| \, dx.$

With the notation of lemma 1, choose J so that $J \supset A$; put

$$i(x) = m_*\{J(x) - A(x)\} \quad \text{and} \quad \beta(x) = |J(x) - A(x)|.$$

Let $B = \mathscr{S}((x, t); x \in X \,\&\, e(x) < t < k)$; then (def. 49)

$$\Omega_1(e; X) + B = \mathscr{C}(k; X);$$

hence, by ths. 115 and 141,

(3) $\qquad m_* \Omega_1(e; X) = k \, mX - |B| = mJ - |B|.$

Let the transformation F be given by $F((x, t)) = (x, k - t)$; then

$$F(B) = \mathscr{S}((x, t); x \in X \,\&\, 0 < t < k - e(x));$$

hence, by ths. 127, 115, 132, and 81,

$$|B| = |F(B)| = |\Omega_0(i; X)| \leqslant |\Omega_0(\beta; X)|,$$

and, by lemma 2, this implies

$$|B| \leqslant |\Omega_0(\beta; R_1)| \leqslant |J - A|;$$

since $A \in \mathscr{L}$, it now follows from (3) and ths. 135 and 97 that

$$m_* \Omega_0(e; R_1) = m_* \Omega_1(e; X) \geqslant mJ - (mJ - mA) = mA,$$

and so the proof of lemma 3 is completed by (2).

Proof. of th. 278. By ths. 109 and 92 there is a sequence of bounded measurable sets, $\{A_r\}$, such that

$$A_1 \subset A_2 \subset \ldots \quad \& \quad A = \sum_{r=1}^{\infty}{}^{*} A_r.$$

Hence, by lemma 3 and ths. 81 and 108, we have for every x

(4) $mA_r = \int\limits_{-\infty}^{\infty} |A_r(x)|\, dx \quad \& \quad |A_r(x)| \leqslant |A_{r+1}(x)| \quad (r = 1, 2, \ldots)$

$$\& \quad \lim_{r \to \infty} |A_r(x)| = |A(x)|.$$

By (4), and ths. 98 and 186,

(5) $mA = \lim\limits_{r \to \infty} mA_r = \lim\limits_{r \to \infty} \int\limits_{-\infty}^{\infty} |A_r(x)|\, dx$

$$= \int\limits_{-\infty}^{\infty} \lim_{r \to \infty} |A_r(x)|\, dx = \int\limits_{-\infty}^{\infty} |A(x)|\, dx.$$

Finally, to show that $mA(x) \sim |A(x)|$ in R_1, let $\{C_r\}$ be a sequence of closed sets such that (th. 111)

(6) $$A = Z + \sum_{r=1}^{\infty}{}^{*} C_r \quad \& \quad |Z| = 0.$$

Now $C_r(x)$ is, for every positive integer r, a closed set; for, if (λ, μ) is a limiting point of $C_r(x)$, then (x, λ, μ) is a limiting point of C_r and therefore belongs to C_r (which is closed); hence $(\lambda, \mu) \in C_r(x)$. It now follows from ths. 105 and 99 that $\sum\limits_{r=1}^{\infty}{}^{*} C_r(x)$ is a plane measurable set for every x, and so, by (6) and th. 119, it will suffice to show that

(7) $Z(x)$ is null for almost all x.

Since Z is null, it is measurable (th. 89); hence, as an analogue of (5), we have

$$\int\limits_{-\infty}^{\infty} |Z(x)|\, dx = 0,$$

which, by th. 185, implies (7).

Theorem 279. *Let $f(x, y)$ be non-negative and measurable in R_2; then*

$$\int\limits_{R_2} f(x, y)\, d(x, y) = \int\limits_{-\infty}^{\infty} dx \int\limits_{-\infty}^{\infty} f(x, y)\, dy = \int\limits_{-\infty}^{\infty} dy \int\limits_{-\infty}^{\infty} f(x, y)\, dx.$$

(The symbol $\int\limits_{-\infty}^{\infty} dx \int\limits_{-\infty}^{\infty} f(x, y)\, dy$ denotes $\int\limits_{-\infty}^{\infty} g(x)\, dx$, where $g(x)$ is defined, for almost all x, as $\int\limits_{-\infty}^{\infty} f(x, y)\, dy$.)

Proof. Let $A = \Omega_0(f; R_2)$; by def. 52

$$(1) \qquad mA = \int_{R_2} f(x, y)\, d(x, y).$$

Now, if ξ is any real number, we have, with the notation of th. 278,

$$A(\xi) = \mathscr{S}((y, z);\ 0 < z < f(\xi, y)),$$

and hence (def. 52)

$$(2) \qquad A(\xi) \in \mathscr{L} \quad \text{implies} \quad mA(\xi) = \int_{-\infty}^{\infty} f(\xi, y)\, dy.$$

Now, by th. 278,

$$|A(x)| \sim mA(x) \text{ in } R_1 \quad \text{and} \quad \int_{-\infty}^{\infty} |A(x)|\, dx = mA.$$

Hence, by (1) and (2),

$$\int_{R_2} f(x, y)\, d(x, y) = \int_{-\infty}^{\infty} dx \int_{-\infty}^{\infty} f(x, y)\, dy.$$

Similar reasoning, in which 'sections of A parallel to the yz-plane' are replaced by 'sections of A parallel to the xz-plane', shows that

$$\int_{R_2} f(x, y)\, d(x, y) = \int_{-\infty}^{\infty} dy \int_{-\infty}^{\infty} f(x, y)\, dx,$$

and this completes the proof.

Theorem 280. *Let $f(x, y)$ be measurable in R_2, and suppose*

$$(1) \qquad \int_{-\infty}^{\infty} dx \int_{-\infty}^{\infty} |f(x, y)|\, dy < \infty;$$

then $\int_{-\infty}^{\infty} dx \int_{-\infty}^{\infty} f(x, y)\, dy = \int_{-\infty}^{\infty} dy \int_{-\infty}^{\infty} f(x, y)\, dx = \int_{R_2} f(x, y)\, d(x, y).$

Proof. By th. 159 $|f(x, y)|$ is measurable in R_2, and hence, by (1) and th. 279, $|f(x, y)|$ is summable over R_2. Since $f(x, y)$ is measurable in R_2, it now follows from th. 198 that $f(x, y)$ is summable over R_2, which means that $f_+(x, y)$ and $f_-(x, y)$ are both summable over R_2. Since both these functions are non-negative, we have, by th. 279,

$$(2) \qquad \infty > \int_{R_2} f_+(x, y)\, d(x, y) = \int_{-\infty}^{\infty} dx \int_{-\infty}^{\infty} f_+(x, y)\, dy,$$

and

$$(3) \qquad \infty > \int_{R_2} f_-(x, y)\, d(x, y) = \int_{-\infty}^{\infty} dx \int_{-\infty}^{\infty} f_-(x, y)\, dy.$$

Let N be the set of all points x for which at least one of the integrals

$$\int_{-\infty}^{\infty} f_+(x,y)\, dy, \qquad \int_{-\infty}^{\infty} f_-(x,y)\, dy$$

is undefined or is infinite. By (2), (3), and ths. 221 and 86, N is null; hence

$$(4)\quad \int_{-\infty}^{\infty} f(x,y)\, dy = \int_{-\infty}^{\infty} f_+(x,y)\, dy - \int_{-\infty}^{\infty} f_-(x,y)\, dy \quad \text{for almost all } x.$$

Now, by (2), (3), and th. 227,

$$\int_{R_2} f(x,y)\, d(x,y) = \int_{-\infty}^{\infty} dx \left\{ \int_{-\infty}^{\infty} f_+(x,y)\, dy - \int_{-\infty}^{\infty} f_-(x,y)\, dy \right\};$$

hence, by (4) and th. 219,

$$\int_{R_2} f(x,y)\, d(x,y) = \int_{-\infty}^{\infty} dx \int_{-\infty}^{\infty} f(x,y)\, dy.$$

Similar reasoning shows that

$$\int_{R_2} f(x,y)\, d(x,y) = \int_{-\infty}^{\infty} dy \int_{-\infty}^{\infty} f(x,y)\, dx.$$

Ths. 279 and 280 are easily modified so as to be applicable to integrals over plane sets not consisting of R_2; the following theorem deals with a case of frequent occurrence.

Theorem 281. *Suppose* $\xi_1 < \xi_2$, $\eta_1 < \eta_2$, *and*
$$S = \mathscr{S}((x,y);\ \xi_1 < x < \xi_2\ \&\ \eta_1 < y < \eta_2).$$
Let $f(x,y)$ *be non-negative and measurable in* S; *then*

$$\int_S f(x,y)\, d(x,y) = \int_{\eta_1}^{\eta_2} dy \int_{\xi_1}^{\xi_2} f(x,y)\, dx = \int_{\xi_1}^{\xi_2} dx \int_{\eta_1}^{\eta_2} f(x,y)\, dy.$$

Proof. Let

$$(1)\qquad g(x,y) = \begin{cases} f(x,y) & \text{if } (x,y) \in S \\ 0 & \text{if } (x,y) \in \overline{S}. \end{cases}$$

Since $S \in \mathscr{L}$, it follows from (1) and ths. 90, 182, and 177 that

$$(2)\qquad \int_S f(x,y)\, d(x,y) = \int_{R_2} g(x,y)\, d(x,y).$$

Now, by th. 182,

$$\int_{-\infty}^{\infty} g(x,y)\, dy = 0 \quad \text{if } x \geqslant \xi_2 \text{ or } x \leqslant \xi_1,$$

and so, by (2) and ths. 279, 209.1, and 182,

$$(3) \qquad \int\limits_{S} f(x,y)\,d(x,y) = \int\limits_{\xi_1}^{\xi_2} dx \int\limits_{-\infty}^{\infty} g(x,y)\,dy.$$

Again, $g(x,y) = 0$ if $y \geqslant \eta_2$ or $y \leqslant \eta_1$, and so, by (3), (1), and ths. 209.1 and 182,

$$\int\limits_{S} f(x,y)\,d(x,y) = \int\limits_{\xi_1}^{\xi_2} dx \int\limits_{\eta_1}^{\eta_2} f(x,y)\,dy,$$

and similar reasoning shows that

$$\int\limits_{S} f(x,y)\,d(x,y) = \int\limits_{\eta_1}^{\eta_2} dy \int\limits_{\xi_1}^{\xi_2} f(x,y)\,dx.$$

Theorem 282. *Let S be defined as in th. 281, and let $f(x,y)$ be measurable in S; then either* both *the integrals*

$$\int\limits_{\xi_1}^{\xi_2} dx \int\limits_{\eta_1}^{\eta_2} |f(x,y)|\,dy, \qquad \int\limits_{\eta_1}^{\eta_2} dy \int\limits_{\xi_1}^{\xi_2} |f(x,y)|\,dx$$

are infinite, in which case $f(x,y)$ is not summable over S, or else $f(x,y)$ is summable over S, and then

$$\int\limits_{S} f(x,y)\,d(x,y) = \int\limits_{\xi_1}^{\xi_2} dx \int\limits_{\eta_1}^{\eta_2} f(x,y)\,dy = \int\limits_{\eta_1}^{\eta_2} dy \int\limits_{\xi_1}^{\xi_2} f(x,y)\,dx.$$

Proof. By ths. 197 and 198, $f(x,y)$ is summable over S if and only if $|f(x,y)|$ is summable over S, and so the first part of the theorem follows from th. 281. The proof of the second part is almost the same as that of th. 281, except that the reference to th. 279 is replaced by a reference to th. 280.

Example. The formula for integration by parts can easily be deduced from th. 282; we have, essentially, to show that, if $f(x)$ and $g(x)$ are summable over (a,b), and if

$$F(t) = \int\limits_{a}^{t} f(x)\,dx \quad \& \quad G(t) = \int\limits_{a}^{t} g(x)\,dx,$$

then

$$(1) \qquad \int\limits_{a}^{b} \{f(x)G(x) + g(x)F(x)\}\,dx = F(b)G(b).$$

Proof. Let $S = \mathscr{S}((x,t); a < x < b \,\&\, a < t < b)$, and let $\gamma(x,t)$ be defined in S by the formula

$$\gamma(x,t) = \begin{cases} g(x) & \text{if} \quad t < x \\ 0 & \text{if} \quad t \geqslant x; \end{cases}$$

then
$$\int_a^b f(x)G(x)\,dx = \int_a^b dx \int_a^b f(x)\gamma(x,t)\,dt.$$

It is left as an exercise to the reader to prove that $f(x)\gamma(x,t)$ is measurable in S, and that $\int_a^b dx \int_a^b |f(x)\gamma(x,t)|\,dt < \infty$. This done, it follows from th. 282 that

$$\int_a^b f(x)G(x)\,dx = \int_a^b dt \int_a^b f(x)\gamma(x,t)\,dx = \int_a^b dt \int_t^b f(x)g(t)\,dx,$$

and hence the left-hand side of (1) equals

$$\int_a^b g(t)\{F(b)-F(t)\}\,dt + \int_a^b g(t)F(t)\,dt, \quad \text{i.e.} \quad F(b)\int_a^b g(t)\,dt,$$

which verifies (1).

In connexion with th. 282 it should be observed that, if $f(x,y)$ is measurable in S, but is not *summable* over S, then it may happen that

$$\int_{\xi_1}^{\xi_2} dx \int_{\eta_1}^{\eta_2} f(x,y)\,dy \quad \text{and} \quad \int_{\eta_1}^{\eta_2} dy \int_{\xi_1}^{\xi_2} f(x,y)\,dx$$

both exist and are different. On the other hand, if it happens that these two integrals are equal and finite, it does not follow that $f(x,y)$ is summable over S. These remarks are illustrated by the following examples.

Example (i) Let I be the interval given by
$$0 < x < 1 \quad \& \quad 0 < y < 1,$$
and let
$$f(x,y) = \frac{x^2-y^2}{(x^2+y^2)^2} \quad \text{if} \quad (x,y) \in I.$$

Clearly $f(x,y)$ is continuous and therefore measurable in I.

Suppose x is fixed, and $0 < x < 1$; then
$$f(x,y) = \frac{\partial}{\partial y}F(x,y), \quad \text{where} \quad F(x,y) = \frac{y}{x^2+y^2},$$

and since $f(x,y)$ is bounded for $0 \leqslant y \leqslant 1$, we have (th. 261)

$$\int_0^1 f(x,y)\,dy = F(x,1)-F(x,0) = (x^2+1)^{-1}.$$

Hence
$$\int_0^1 dx \int_0^1 f(x,y)\,dy = \int_0^1 (x^2+1)^{-1}\,dx = [\arctan x]_0^1 = \tfrac{1}{4}\pi,$$

and, since $f(y,x) = -f(x,y)$, it follows easily that

$$\int\limits_0^1 dy \int\limits_0^1 f(x,y)\,dx = -\tfrac{1}{4}\pi.$$

Since

$$\int\limits_0^1 dy \int\limits_0^1 f(x,y)\,dx \neq \int\limits_0^1 dx \int\limits_0^1 f(x,y)\,dy,$$

$f(x,y)$ cannot be summable over I, and, since $f(x,y)$ is known to be measurable in I, it must be that

$$\int\limits_I |f(x,y)|\,d(x,y) = \infty, \quad \text{i.e. (th. 279)} \quad \int\limits_0^1 dx \int\limits_0^1 |f(x,y)|\,dy = \infty.$$

This is easily verified; for, if $0 < x < 1$, it follows as before that

$$\int\limits_0^x f(x,y)\,dy = F(x,x) - F(x,0) = \frac{1}{2x},$$

and so

$$\int\limits_0^1 |f(x,y)|\,dy \geqslant \frac{1}{2x},$$

which means that

$$\int\limits_0^1 dx \int\limits_0^1 |f(x,y)|\,dy \geqslant \frac{1}{2} \int\limits_0^1 \frac{dx}{x} = \infty.$$

Example (ii) Let $f(x,y)$ be defined in R_2 so that

$$f(x,y) = \frac{xy}{(x^2+y^2)^2} \quad \text{when} \quad x^2+y^2 > 0;$$

we shall show that $f(x,y)$ is not summable over R_2, although

$$(1) \qquad \int\limits_{-\infty}^{\infty} dx \int\limits_{-\infty}^{\infty} f(x,y)\,dy = \int\limits_{-\infty}^{\infty} dy \int\limits_{-\infty}^{\infty} f(x,y)\,dx = 0.$$

It is easy to see that, if $x \neq 0$, then

$$\int\limits_0^{\infty} f(x,y)\,dy = \frac{1}{2x} \quad \& \quad \int\limits_{-\infty}^0 f(x,y)\,dy = -\frac{1}{2x},$$

and that

$$\int\limits_{-\infty}^{\infty} f(x,y)\,dy = 0, \quad \text{while} \quad \int\limits_{-\infty}^{\infty} |f(x,y)|\,dy = \frac{1}{|x|},$$

all the integrals in question existing in the Cauchy-Riemann sense. A similar argument shows that $\int\limits_{-\infty}^{\infty} f(x,y)\,dx = 0$ if $y \neq 0$, and so it follows that (1) is true. At the same time

$$\int\limits_{-\infty}^{\infty} dx \int\limits_{-\infty}^{\infty} |f(x,y)|\, dy = \int\limits_{-\infty}^{\infty} \frac{dx}{|x|} = \infty,$$

and this means (th. 282) that $f(x,y)$ is not summable over R_2.

Although th. 282 was proved only for real functions $f(x,y)$, it is obvious that the same proof, with slight modifications, will establish the theorem when $f(x,y)$ is complex; the following example is an application of th. 282 to complex functions.

Example. Let z and ζ be complex numbers each of which has a positive real part; then (see example, p. 159)

$$\Gamma(z)\Gamma(\zeta) = \Gamma(z+\zeta) \int\limits_{0}^{1} u^{\zeta-1}(1-u)^{z-1}\, du.$$

Proof. We have

$$\Gamma(z) = \int\limits_{0}^{\infty} e^{-x}x^{z-1}\, dx, \quad \text{and so} \quad e^{-y}\Gamma(z) = \int\limits_{0}^{\infty} e^{-y-x}x^{z-1}\, dx$$

for every real number y; moreover (th. 241)

$$\int\limits_{0}^{\infty} e^{-y-x}x^{z-1}\, dx = \int\limits_{y}^{\infty} e^{-x}(x-y)^{z-1}\, dx = \int\limits_{0}^{\infty} f(x,y)\, dx,$$

where
$$f(x,y) = \begin{cases} e^{-x}(x-y)^{z-1} & \text{if } 0 < y < x \\ 0 & \text{otherwise;} \end{cases}$$

hence

(1) $$e^{-y}\Gamma(z) = \int\limits_{0}^{\infty} f(x,y)\, dx.$$

Also it is clear that $\int\limits_{0}^{\infty} |f(x,y)|\, dx = e^{-y}\int\limits_{0}^{\infty} |e^{-x}x^{z-1}|\, dx$, and so, since $\Gamma(z)$ and $\Gamma(\zeta)$ are finite, we have (th. 197 (i))

(2) $$\int\limits_{0}^{\infty} dy \int\limits_{0}^{\infty} |y^{\zeta-1}f(x,y)|\, dx = \int\limits_{0}^{\infty} |e^{-y}y^{\zeta-1}|\, dy \int\limits_{0}^{\infty} |e^{-x}x^{z-1}|\, dx < \infty.$$

From (2) and th. 282 it follows that, if

(3) $$y^{\zeta-1}f(x,y) \text{ is measurable in } S,$$

where $$S = \mathscr{S}((x,y);\ x > 0\ \&\ y > 0),$$

then, by (1),

(4) $$\Gamma(z)\int\limits_{0}^{\infty} e^{-y}y^{\zeta-1}\, dy = \int\limits_{0}^{\infty} dx \int\limits_{0}^{\infty} f(x,y)y^{\zeta-1}\, dy.$$

Now, if $x > 0$, it follows, on substituting $u = y/x$, that

$$\int\limits_0^\infty f(x,y)y^{\zeta-1}\,dy = e^{-x}\int\limits_0^x y^{\zeta-1}(x-y)^{z-1}\,dy$$

$$= e^{-x}x^{z+\zeta-1}\int\limits_0^1 u^{\zeta-1}(1-u)^{z-1}\,du,$$

and hence, by (4),

$$\Gamma(z)\Gamma(\zeta) = \int\limits_0^\infty e^{-x}x^{z+\zeta-1}\,dx\int\limits_0^1 u^{\zeta-1}(1-u)^{z-1}\,du,$$

which is the required result. It remains only to prove (3); now $y^{\zeta-1}$ is continuous in S, and $f(x,y)$ is continuous at all points (x,y) of S except possibly at those for which $y = x$, and since these exceptional points form a plane null set (th. 169), it follows that $y^{\zeta-1}f(x,y)$ is continuous almost everywhere in S and is therefore measurable in S (th. 163, cor. (ii)).

Corollary. $\Gamma(\tfrac{1}{2}) = \sqrt{\pi}$; for, from the above example, since $\Gamma(1) = 1$,

$$\{\Gamma(\tfrac{1}{2})\}^2 = \Gamma(1)\int\limits_0^1 \frac{du}{\sqrt{\{(1-u)u\}}}$$

$$= (CR)\int\limits_0^1 \frac{2\,du}{\sqrt{\{1-(2u-1)^2\}}} = [\arcsin(2u-1)]_0^1 = \pi.$$

IX

EXTENSIONS OF THE LEBESGUE INTEGRAL

§ 1. Hölder-Lebesgue Integral

SUPPOSE $f(x)$ is defined in an interval (a, b) so that $f(x)$ is summable over $(a+\epsilon, b)$ for all sufficiently small ϵ; if we put

$$F(\epsilon) = \int\limits_{a+\epsilon}^{b} f(x)\, dx,$$

then either

(1) $f(x)$ is summable over (a, b), in which case (th. 211.1)

$$\int\limits_{a}^{b} f(x)\, dx = \lim_{\epsilon \to 0} F(\epsilon),$$

or else

(2) $f(x)$ is not summable over (a, b), in which case $\lim\limits_{\epsilon \to 0} F(\epsilon)$ may or may not exist.

For example, if $f(x) = \dfrac{d}{dx}\left(\dfrac{1}{x}\sin\dfrac{\pi}{x}\right)$ in $(0, 1)$,

then (th. 261) $\int\limits_{\epsilon}^{1} f(x)\, dx = -\dfrac{1}{\epsilon}\sin\dfrac{\pi}{\epsilon}$,

and hence $\lim\limits_{\epsilon \to 0} \int\limits_{\epsilon}^{1} f(x)\, dx$ does not exist.

On the other hand, if

$$f(x) = \frac{d}{dx}\left(x^2 \sin\frac{\pi}{x^2}\right),$$

then

$$\int\limits_{\epsilon}^{1} f(x)\, dx = -\epsilon^2 \sin\frac{\pi}{\epsilon^2}, \quad \text{and hence} \quad \lim_{\epsilon \to 0} \int\limits_{\epsilon}^{1} f(x)\, dx = 0;$$

but, as we have seen (example following th. 211.2), $f(x)$ is not summable over $(0, 1)$. In view of (1) it would be natural and consistent, in those cases where $\lim\limits_{\epsilon \to 0} F(\epsilon)$ exists and is finite, to extend the definition of the Lebesgue integral, and to say that $f(x)$ has a *Cauchy-Lebesgue* integral over (a, b) whose value is $\lim\limits_{\epsilon \to 0} \int\limits_{a+\epsilon}^{b} f(x)\, dx$. This definition could be further extended to include the case where there is a net over (a, b) defined by $a = x_0 < x_1 < ... < x_n = b$ such that each of the limits

$$\lim \int_{x_{r-1}+\epsilon}^{x_r-\epsilon'} f(x)\, dx \quad (r = 1, 2, ..., n)$$

exists and is finite as ϵ and ϵ' tend independently to zero. When such a decomposition of (a, b) into a finite number of intervals is impossible, the problem of extending the Lebesgue integral becomes much more difficult. Before discussing these difficulties, it is convenient to consider some general theorems on aggregates of linear intervals.

Definition 63. Let J denote a closed interval $[a, b]$, and let α be any given aggregate of sub-intervals of J; a point x of J will be said to be *regular* for α if x belongs to a member of α, or, in the special cases $x = a$ and $x = b$, if x is an end-point of a member of α; a point of J which is not regular for α will be said to be *singular* for α, and the aggregate of the points singular for α will be denoted by S_α.

From def. 63 it follows at once that

Theorem 283. S_α *is closed.*

Theorem 284. *Let J be a closed interval $[a, b]$, and let α be any aggregate of sub-intervals of J satisfying the following conditions:*

(1)   *every sub-interval of a member of α also belongs to α, and*

(2)   *if (a_0, b_0) and (b_0, c_0) belong to α, then so does (a_0, c_0);*

then every sub-interval of J whose closed envelope includes no point of S_α belongs to α.

Proof. Let I be any sub-interval of J such that (def. 20)

(3) $I^c S_\alpha = 0,$

and suppose that

(4) $I \bar{\in} \alpha.$

To show that (4) implies a contradiction we construct a sequence of intervals as follows: let $I_1 = I$, and, when $I_1, I_2, ..., I_{n-1}$ have been defined and are intervals not belonging to α, define I_n to be a sub-interval of I_{n-1} such that

$$|I_n| = \tfrac{1}{2}|I_{n-1}| \quad \& \quad I_n \bar{\in} \alpha,$$

the existence of such an interval being an immediate consequence of (2). If $I_n = (a_n, b_n)$, then clearly

(5) $a \leqslant a_1 \leqslant a_2 \leqslant ..., \quad b \geqslant b_1 \geqslant b_2 \geqslant ..., \quad \text{and} \quad \lim_{n \to \infty} (b_n - a_n) = 0,$

from which it follows easily that $\{a_n\}$ and $\{b_n\}$ both converge to the same point of I^c, say to ξ. By (3) ξ is regular for α, and so, by def. 63 and (5), there is a member of α which contains I_n for all sufficiently large n, and this contradicts (1). Hence (4) is false and the theorem is proved.

Definition 64. Let $f(x)$ be defined in a closed interval J and let α be the aggregate of all the sub-intervals of J over which $f(x)$ is summable; then, with the notation of def. 63, S_α is said to be the set of the *points of non-summability* of $f(x)$ in J.

Theorem 285. *Let $f(x)$ be defined in a closed interval J, and let N be the set of the points of non-summability of $f(x)$ in J; then N is closed, and $f(x)$ is summable over every closed interval contained in $J-N$.*

Proof. That N is closed follows at once from def. 64 and th. 283. Moreover, it is clear that α, the aggregate of the sub-intervals of J over which $f(x)$ is summable, satisfies (1) and (2) of th. 284 (ths. 206 and 209); hence th. 284 completes the proof.

We can now define an extension of the Lebesgue integral along the lines suggested at the beginning of this chapter.

Definition 65. Let $f(x)$ be defined in a closed interval $[a, b]$, and suppose

(1) the set of the points of non-summability of $f(x)$ in $[a, b]$ is finite or enumerable,

and

(2) there exists a function $F(x)$ continuous throughout $[a, b]$ and such that, if $a \leqslant \lambda < \mu \leqslant b$ and $f(x)$ is summable over (λ, μ), then $F(\mu) - F(\lambda) = \int_\lambda^\mu f(x)\, dx$ (the integral on the right being a Lebesgue integral);

then $f(x)$ is said to be integrable in the *Hölder-Lebesgue* sense (*integrable-H*) over $[a, b]$, and

$$(H) \int_a^b f(x)\, dx = F(b) - F(a).$$

Clearly $(H) \int_a^b f(x)\, dx$ is the Lebesgue integral of $f(x)$ over (a, b) whenever $f(x)$ is summable over (a, b); but, when $f(x)$ is not summable over (a, b), the definition, as it stands, requires a uniqueness theorem, namely, that, if $F_1(x)$ and $F_2(x)$ both satisfy (2), then

$$F_1(b)-F_1(a) = F_2(b)-F_2(a);$$

this is supplied by the following theorem.

Theorem 286. *Suppose $f(x)$ is integrable-H over $[a,b]$, and let $F_1(x)$ and $F_2(x)$ both satisfy the conditions laid down for $F(x)$ in (2) of def. 65; then* $\quad F_1(b)-F_1(a) = F_2(b)-F_2(a).$

Proof. Let $G(x) = F_2(x)-F_1(x)$, and $J = [a,b]$; we have to show that $G(x)$ is constant in J, or, with the notation of def. 45, that $G(J)$ consists of a single point. Since $G(x)$ is continuous throughout J (def. 65 (2)), $G(J)$ consists of a single point or else $G(J)$ is a closed interval (Hardy, § 100), and since every closed interval is non-enumerable (ths. 21 and 37.1), our theorem is proved if we show that $G(J)$ is finite or enumerable. N being defined as in th. 285, $G(N)$ is finite or enumerable (def. 65 (1) and th. 2), and so, by th. 6, it is sufficient to show that $G(J-N)$ is finite or enumerable. Since N is closed (th. 283), it follows at once, by def. 22, that we need only show that $G(x)$ is constant in each of the intervals of J° contiguous to N. So suppose (λ, μ) is such an interval and let ξ and η be freely chosen so that $\lambda < \xi < \eta < \mu$; then $[\xi, \eta] \subset J-N$, and so, by th. 285, $f(x)$ is summable over $[\xi, \eta]$, and hence, by def. 65 (2), $G(\eta) = G(\xi)$. This means that $G(x)$ is constant in (λ, μ), and so completes the proof.

It might be thought that the Hölder-Lebesgue definition could be extended by omitting the restriction on the set of the points of non-summability of $f(x)$ in $[a, b]$; but it can be shown that the effect of omitting (1) from def. 65 is to deprive that definition of all meaning whenever the set of the points of non-summability of $f(x)$ in $[a, b]$ is non-enumerable. More precisely, if $f(x)$ does not satisfy (1), then to every function $F_1(x)$ satisfying (2) of def. 65 there is another, $F_2(x)$, satisfying the same condition and such that

$$F_1(b)-F_1(a) \neq F_2(b)-F_2(a).$$

For suppose the points of non-summability of $f(x)$ in $[a, b]$ form a non-enumerable set N; by ths. 285 and 40.2, N contains a perfect subset, say K, and it is then possible, following the lines of th. 259, to construct a function $\theta(x)$ such that $\theta(x)$ is continuous throughout $[a, b]$, $\theta(b)-\theta(a) = 1$, and $\theta(x)$ is constant in each of the intervals of (a, b) contiguous to K; it is easily seen that, if $F(x) = F_1(x)$

satisfies (2) of def. 65, so does $F_2(x) = F_1(x) + k\theta(x)$ for every finite real number k, and hence (2) fails to define a *unique* number

$$F(b) - F(a).$$

§ 2. General Denjoy Integral

Now it is possible for a function $F(x)$ to be such that $F'(x)$ is finite throughout a closed interval $[a, b]$ while the set of the points of non-summability of $F'(x)$ in (a, b) is non-enumerable, so that $F'(x)$ is not integrable-H over (a, b); an example of such a function $F(x)$ is given on p. 226. Clearly, if we wish to extend the Hölder-Lebesgue definition to obtain an integral applicable to such a function $F'(x)$, we must omit condition (1) of def. 65, but, at the same time, we must replace (2) by something more stringent. One such set of conditions is enunciated in def. 67 and gives rise to an integral known as the general Denjoy integral; the validity of this definition rests on an extension of th. 284 which we consider at once.

Theorem 287 (ROMANOVSKI). *Let J denote a closed interval $[a, b]$, and let α be any aggregate of sub-intervals of J which satisfies the following conditions:*

(1) *every sub-interval of a member of α also belongs to α;*

(2) *if (a_0, b_0) and (b_0, c_0) belong to α, then so does (a_0, c_0);*

(3) *if $\{(a_n, b_n)\}$ is a sequence of members of α contained in (a_0, b_0) and if $\lim\limits_{n \to \infty} a_n = a_0$ & $\lim\limits_{n \to \infty} b_n = b_0$, then $(a_0, b_0) \in \alpha$;*

(4) *if K is a perfect subset of J such that every interval of J° contiguous to K belongs to α (including the case $K = J$), then at least one point of K belongs to a member of α;*

then $\qquad\qquad\qquad$ *(a, b) belongs to α.*

Proof. Let (a_0, b_0) be any sub-interval of J which includes no point of S_α (def. 63); by (1), (2), and th. 284, $(a_0 + 1/n, b_0 - 1/n) \in \alpha$ for all sufficiently large n, and so, by (3), $(a_0, b_0) \in \alpha$. Hence we have that (5) every sub-interval of J which includes no point of S_α belongs to α; in particular, every interval of J° contiguous to the closed set S_α (th. 283) belongs to α, and this, by (4) and the definition of S_α, implies that S_α is not perfect. Since S_α is closed, this means that either $S_\alpha = 0$, in which case the theorem is proved by (5), or else we may choose x so that

(6) $\qquad\qquad\qquad x \in S_\alpha$ & $x \bar{\in} S_\alpha'$;

hence it will be sufficient to prove that (6) implies a contradiction. Suppose x satisfies (6) and $a < x < b$; then y and z exist in J such that
$$(y, x)S_\alpha = 0 \quad \& \quad (x, z)S_\alpha = 0,$$
and hence, by (5) and (2), (y, x), (x, z), and consequently (y, z) belong to α, which contradicts the assumption $x \in S_\alpha$. A similar argument draws a contradiction from (6) when x is at a or at b, and this completes the proof.

Definition 66. Let $F(x)$ be a finite function defined in a closed interval of which I is the interior; let S be any closed set (so that $I\bar{S}$ is open, ths. 25 and 17); if

(i) $\qquad I\bar{S} = \sum\limits_{r=1}^{\infty} (a_r, b_r) \quad \& \quad \sum\limits_{r=1}^{\infty} |F(b_r) - F(a_r)| < \infty,$

or if

(ii) $\qquad I\bar{S} = \sum\limits_{r=1}^{k} (a_r, b_r)$, where k is a positive integer,

we write $\qquad V(F; I\bar{S}) = \sum\limits_{r} \{F(b_r) - F(a_r)\},$

where r runs through all positive integers in case (i), and from 1 to k in case (ii); if $I\bar{S} = 0$, we put $V(F; I\bar{S}) = 0$; if in case (i)
$$\sum_{r=1}^{\infty} |F(b_r) - F(a_r)| = \infty,$$
$V(F; I\bar{S})$ is not defined. It follows (Hardy, §185) that, when $V(F; I\bar{S})$ is defined, its value is independent of the way in which the intervals of $I\bar{S}$ are enumerated.

We can now state the definition of the general Denjoy integral due to P. Romanovski (*Fundamenta Math.*, 1932).

Definition 67. Let $f(x)$ be defined in J, a closed interval $[a, b]$, and suppose there exists a function $F(x)$ such that

(1) $F(x)$ is continuous throughout J,

and

(2) if K is any perfect subset of J, then K includes points λ and μ such that $(\lambda, \mu)K \neq 0$ and
$$\xi \in [\lambda, \mu]K \text{ implies } F(\xi) - F(\lambda) = \int_{(\lambda,\xi)K} f(x)\, dx + V(F; (\lambda, \xi)\bar{K}),$$
the integral on the right being a Lebesgue integral.

Under these conditions $f(x)$ is said to be integrable in the *general*

Denjoy sense (*integrable-D*) over J, and we write

$$(D) \int_a^b f(x)\, dx = F(b) - F(a);$$

$F(x)$ is said to be an *indefinite D-integral* of $f(x)$ in J. (It follows easily from ths. 206 and 209 that, if λ and μ satisfy (2) above, then $\lambda \leqslant \xi < \eta \leqslant \mu$ implies

(i) $f(x)$ is summable over $(\xi, \eta)K$,

(ii) $V(F; (\xi, \eta)\bar{K})$ is defined,

and

(iii) $F(\eta) - F(\xi) = \int_{(\xi,\eta)K} f(x)\, dx + V(F; (\xi, \eta)\bar{K}))$.

Just as with the Hölder-Lebesgue definition, a uniqueness theorem is now necessary, namely

Theorem 288. *Suppose $f(x)$ is integrable-D over $[a, b]$; then*

$$(D) \int_a^b f(x)\, dx \text{ is unique.}$$

Proof. We first prove a lemma.

Lemma. Let $F_r(x)$ be an indefinite D-integral of a function $f_r(x)$ in $[a, b]$ ($r = 1, 2$), and let K be any perfect subset of $[a, b]$; then K includes points λ and μ such that $(\lambda, \mu)K \neq 0$, $f_r(x)$ is summable over $(\lambda, \mu)K$, and $\xi \in [\lambda, \mu]$ implies

$$F_r(\xi) - F_r(\lambda) = \int_{(\lambda,\xi)K} f_r(x)\, dx + V(F_r; (\lambda, \xi)\bar{K}) \quad (r = 1, 2).$$

Proof of Lemma. By def. 67 λ' and μ' exist in K so that $(\lambda', \mu')K \neq 0$, and

(1) $\lambda' \leqslant \xi < \eta \leqslant \mu'$ implies

$$F_1(\eta) - F_1(\xi) = \int_{(\xi,\eta)K} f_1(x)\, dx + V(F_1; (\xi, \eta)\bar{K}).$$

Since $(\lambda', \mu')K \neq 0$, it follows easily that λ'' and μ'' exist in K so that $\lambda' \leqslant \lambda'' < \mu'' \leqslant \mu'$ & $[\lambda'', \mu'']K$ is perfect, and hence (def. 67) λ and μ exist in $[\lambda'', \mu'']K$ so that $(\lambda, \mu)K \neq 0$, and $\lambda \leqslant \xi \leqslant \mu$ implies

$$F_2(\xi) - F_2(\lambda) = \int_{(\lambda,\xi)K_1} f_2(x)\, dx + V(F_2; (\lambda, \xi)\bar{K}_1),$$

where $K_1 = [\lambda'', \mu'']K$. Since $\lambda'' \leqslant \lambda < \mu \leqslant \mu''$, it follows that

$$K_1(\lambda, \xi) = K(\lambda, \xi) \quad \text{if} \quad \lambda \leqslant \xi \leqslant \mu,$$

and hence we have $\lambda' \leqslant \lambda < \mu \leqslant \mu'$, and

$$\xi \in [\lambda, \mu] \quad \text{implies} \quad F_2(\xi) - F_2(\lambda) = \int\limits_{(\lambda, \xi)K} f_2(x) \, dx + V(F_2; (\lambda, \xi)\overline{K}),$$

which, together with (1), proves the lemma.

Proof of th. 288.

Suppose $F_1(x)$ and $F_2(x)$ satisfy the conditions of def. 67 for $F(x)$, and put $G(x) = F_2(x) - F_1(x)$; if $J = [a, b]$, we have to show that $G(x)$ is constant in J. Let α be the aggregate of all the sub-intervals of J in which $G(x)$ is constant; obviously α satisfies (1) and (3) of th. 287, and it satisfies (2) of that theorem because $G(x)$, like $F_1(x)$ and $F_2(x)$, is continuous throughout J (def. 67 (1)). Now let K be any perfect subset of J such that

(2)   every interval of J^o contiguous to K belongs to α.

By the lemma, it follows that λ and μ exist in K so that $(\lambda, \mu)K \neq 0$, and $\xi \in [\lambda, \mu]$ implies

$$F_r(\xi) - F_r(\lambda) = \int\limits_{(\lambda, \xi)K} f(x) \, dx + V(F_r; (\lambda, \xi)\overline{K}) \quad (r = 1, 2);$$

and since, by (2),

$$\xi \in K \quad \& \quad \lambda < \xi \quad \text{implies} \quad V(F_1; (\lambda, \xi)\overline{K}) = V(F_2; (\lambda, \xi)\overline{K}),$$

it follows that

(3) $\xi \in [\lambda, \mu]K$ implies $G(\xi) = G(\lambda)$.

Now, by (2), $G(x)$ is constant in every sub-interval of $(\lambda, \mu)\overline{K}$, and, since $G(x)$ is continuous throughout J, it now follows from (3) that $G(x)$ is constant in (λ, μ). Since $(\lambda, \mu)K \neq 0$, this means that α also satisfies (4) of th. 287, and hence $J^o \in \alpha$, which implies that the continuous function $G(x)$ is constant in J.

To show that the general Denjoy integral is a generalization of the Hölder-Lebesgue integral, we prove the following theorem:

Theorem 289. *Let $f(x)$ be integrable-H over J, a closed interval $[a, b]$; then $f(x)$ is integrable-D over J, and*

$$(D) \int\limits_a^b f(x) \, dx = (H) \int\limits_a^b f(x) \, dx.$$

Proof. Let $F(x)$ satisfy condition (2) of def. 65; we have then to show that $f(x)$ and $F(x)$ satisfy (2) of def. 67. To this end let K be any perfect subset of J. Since the set of the points of non-summability of $f(x)$ in J is finite or enumerable (def. 65), it follows (th. 37.1) that the perfect set K includes at least one point belonging to an interval over which $f(x)$ is summable, and consequently, since K is perfect, there must exist points λ and μ such that

(1) $$\lambda \in K \quad \& \quad \mu \in K \quad \& \quad (\lambda, \mu)K \neq 0,$$

and

(2) $$f(x) \text{ is summable over } (\lambda, \mu).$$

By (2) and th. 206 it now follows that, if ξ is any point of $[\lambda, \mu]K$, then $f(x)$ is summable over $(\lambda, \xi)K$ and over $(\lambda, \xi)\overline{K}$; since $f(x)$ is integrable-H over J, this implies (th. 209 and def. 65)

(3) $$F(\xi) - F(\lambda) = \int_{\lambda}^{\xi} f(x)\,dx = \int_{(\lambda,\xi)K} f(x)\,dx + \int_{(\lambda,\xi)\overline{K}} f(x)\,dx,$$

and, by ths. 210 and 211,

(4) $$V(F;(\lambda,\xi)\overline{K}) = \int_{(\lambda,\xi)\overline{K}} f(x)\,dx.$$

From (1), (3), and (4) it follows that $F(x)$ and $f(x)$ satisfy (2) of def. 67, and this completes the proof.

Theorem 290. *Let $f(x)$ be integrable-D over a closed interval J; then $f(x)$ is measurable in J and finite almost everywhere in J.*

Proof. Let α be the aggregate of all the sub-intervals of J in which $f(x)$ is measurable and almost everywhere finite. It follows from ths. 148, 149, and 86 that α satisfies conditions (1), (2), and (3) of th. 287. Let K be any perfect subset of J such that every interval of J° contiguous to K belongs to α; by (2) of def. 67 there are points λ and μ in K such that $(\lambda, \mu)K \neq 0$ and $f(x)$ is summable over $(\lambda, \mu)K$. Hence (th. 199)

(1) $f(x)$ is measurable and finite almost everywhere in $(\lambda, \mu)K$.

Since K is closed, there is a sequence or else a finite number of intervals whose sum is $(\lambda, \mu)\overline{K}$, and each of these intervals belongs to α; hence it follows from ths. 149 and 86 that $f(x)$ is measurable and finite almost everywhere in $(\lambda, \mu)\overline{K}$, and so, by (1), it follows that $(\lambda, \mu) \in \alpha$. Since $(\lambda, \mu)K \neq 0$, we have shown that α also satisfies (4) of th. 287, and hence $J^\circ \in \alpha$, which gives the result required.

Theorem 291. *If $f(x)$ is integrable-D over J, a closed interval $[a, b]$, and $g(x)$ is defined in J so that*

$$f(x) \sim g(x) \text{ in } J, \text{ then } (D)\int_{a}^{b} f(x)\,dx = (D)\int_{a}^{b} g(x)\,dx.$$

Proof. By def. 67 and th. 217.

Theorem 292. *Let $f(x)$ and $g(x)$ be finite functions integrable-D over J, a closed interval $[a, b]$, and let α and β be any finite real numbers; then*

$$(D) \int_a^b \{\alpha f(x) + \beta g(x)\}\, dx = \alpha\, (D) \int_a^b f(x)\, dx + \beta\, (D) \int_a^b g(x)\, dx.$$

Proof. It follows easily from def. 67 that

$$(D) \int_a^b \alpha f(x)\, dx = \alpha\, (D) \int_a^b f(x)\, dx,$$

and so we need only show that

$$(1) \qquad (D) \int_a^b \{f(x) + g(x)\}\, dx = (D) \int_a^b f(x)\, dx + (D) \int_a^b g(x)\, dx.$$

Let $F(x)$ and $G(x)$ be indefinite D-integrals of $f(x)$ and $g(x)$ respectively in J; it will be sufficient to show that $F(x) + G(x)$ is an indefinite D-integral of $f(x) + g(x)$ in J. Let K be any perfect subset of J. By the lemma to th. 288 there are points λ and μ in K such that $(\lambda, \mu)K \neq 0$, $f(x)$ and $g(x)$ are both summable over $(\lambda, \mu)K$, and $\xi \in [\lambda, \mu]K$ implies

$$F(\xi) - F(\lambda) = \int_{(\lambda, \xi)K} f(x)\, dx + V(F; (\lambda, \xi)\bar{K})$$

and

$$G(\xi) - G(\lambda) = \int_{(\lambda, \xi)K} g(x)\, dx + V(G; (\lambda, \xi)\bar{K}),$$

whence, by th. 227, $f(x) + g(x)$ is summable over $(\lambda, \mu)K$, and, if $H(x) = F(x) + G(x)$, then $\xi \in [\lambda, \mu]K$ implies

$$H(\xi) - H(\lambda) = \int_{(\lambda, \xi)K} \{f(x) + g(x)\}\, dx + V(H; (\lambda, \xi)\bar{K}).$$

Since $H(x)$ is, like $F(x)$ and $G(x)$, continuous throughout J, and since $(\lambda, \mu)K \neq 0$, this completes the proof that $H(x)$ is an indefinite D-integral of $f(x) + g(x)$ in J.

Theorem 293. *Let $f(x)$ and $g(x)$ be integrable-D over J, a closed interval $[a, b]$, and such that*

$$f(x) \geqslant g(x) \text{ for all } x \text{ in } J; \text{ then } (D) \int_a^b f(x)\, dx \geqslant (D) \int_a^b g(x)\, dx.$$

Proof. By ths. 290 and 291 there is no loss of generality in assuming that $f(x)$ and $g(x)$ are both finite throughout J, and it then

follows from th. 292 that we need only show that, if $h(x)$ is a non-negative function which is integrable-D over J, then $\int_a^b h(x)\,dx \geq 0$.
Let $H(x)$ be an indefinite D-integral of $h(x)$ in J, and let α be the aggregate of all the sub-intervals of J in which $H(x)$ is a non-decreasing function of x. Clearly α satisfies (1), (2), and (3) of th. 287; to show that α also satisfies (4) of th. 287, which will complete the proof of th. 293, let K be a perfect subset of J such that every interval of J° contiguous to K belongs to α. Then, by def. 67, λ and μ exist such that $\lambda \in K$, $\mu \in K$, $(\lambda,\mu)K \neq 0$, and

$$\xi \in [\lambda,\mu]K \quad \text{implies} \quad H(\xi)-H(\lambda) = \int_{(\lambda,\xi)K} h(x)\,dx + V(H;(\lambda,\xi)\bar{K});$$

since $h(x) \geq 0$ throughout J, and since $H(x)$ is non-decreasing in the intervals of J° contiguous to K, this implies that $H(x)$ is non-decreasing in (λ,μ). Hence, since $(\lambda,\mu)K \neq 0$, (4) of th. 287 is verified.

Theorem 294. *Let $f(x)$ be a* non-negative *function which is integrable-D over J, a closed interval $[a,b]$; then $f(x)$ is summable over J.*

Proof. By th. 290 $f(x)$ is measurable in J, and so, by th. 170, there is a sequence of functions $\{f_n(x)\}$ such that

(1) $x \in J$ implies $0 \leq f_1(x) \leq f_2(x) \leq \ldots$ & $\lim_{n\to\infty} f_n(x) = f(x)$,

and

(2)   each of the functions $f_n(x)$ is bounded and measurable in J.

By (2) and th. 183, $f_n(x)$ is summable over J for every positive integer n, which, by th. 289, implies

(3) $$\int_a^b f_n(x)\,dx = (D)\int_a^b f_n(x)\,dx \quad (n - 1, 2, \ldots).$$

By (1), (3), and ths. 186 and 293,

$$\int_a^b f(x)\,dx = \lim_{n\to\infty} \int_a^b f_n(x)\,dx = \lim_{n\to\infty} (D)\int_a^b f_n(x)\,dx \leq (D)\int_a^b f(x)\,dx,$$

and since $(D)\int_a^b f(x)\,dx$ is finite by hypothesis, this means that $f(x)$ is summable over J.

One of the most striking properties of the general Denjoy integral is contained in the following theorem.

Theorem 295. *Let $F(x)$ be a function having a* finite *derivative throughout J, a closed interval $[a,b]$; then*

$$(D) \int_a^b F'(x)\, dx = F(b) - F(a).$$

Proof. It is convenient to prove the following two lemmas:

Lemma 1. Let S be a perfect subset of J for which there is an integer n such that

(1) $x \in S$ & $y \in S$ implies $|F(y) - F(x)| \leqslant n|y - x|$;

then $F'(x)$ is summable over S, and

$$F(\beta) - F(\alpha) = \int_S F'(x)\, dx + V(F; (\alpha, \beta)\bar{S}),$$

where α and β are respectively the lower and the upper bounds of the aggregate of the numbers x which belong to S.

Lemma 2. To every perfect set K contained in J there are points λ and μ such that $\lambda \in K$, $\mu \in K$, $(\lambda, \mu)K \neq 0$, and there is an integer n such that, if x and y are any points of $K[\lambda, \mu]$, then

$$|F(x) - F(y)| \leqslant n|y - x|.$$

Proof of Lemma 1. Let $G(x)$ be defined in $[\alpha, \beta]$ so that

(2) $G(x) = F(x)$ if $x \in S$,

and

(3)   if x belongs to (a_0, b_0), an interval of (α, β) contiguous to S, then

$$G(x) = F(a_0) + (x - a_0)\frac{F(b_0) - F(a_0)}{b_0 - a_0}.$$

It follows easily from (1), (2), and (3) that

(4) $\alpha \leqslant x < y \leqslant \beta$ implies $|G(y) - G(x)| \leqslant n(y - x)$,

and hence, by th. 260,

(5) $\int_\alpha^\beta G'(x)\, dx = G(\beta) - G(\alpha).$

Now, by (4), $V(G; (\alpha, \beta)\bar{S})$ is defined, and, by (3) and th. 210,

$$V(F; (\alpha, \beta)\bar{S}) = V(G; (\alpha, \beta)\bar{S}) = \int_{(\alpha, \beta)\bar{S}} G'(x)\, dx,$$

and since α and β clearly belong to the closed set S, it now follows by (2), (5), and th. 209 that

(6) $F(\beta) - F(\alpha) = \int_S G'(x)\, dx + V(F; (\alpha, \beta)\bar{S}).$

Now, if ξ is a point of S for which $G'(x)$ exists, then, since $\xi \in S'$ (S is perfect), it follows from (2) that $G'(\xi) = F'(\xi)$. Hence the required result is implied by (6).

Proof of Lemma 2. To every positive integer r let E_r be the set of all the points x of J for which

(7) $$y \in J \quad \text{implies} \quad |F(x) - F(y)| \leqslant r|y - x|.$$

The sets E_r are closed: for, if r is any chosen positive integer and E_r is not closed, then there must be a sequence of points $\{x_n\}$ of E_r, converging to some point ξ of J, and a point y of J such that

$$|F(\xi) - F(y)| > r|y - \xi|;$$

but, since $F(x)$ is continuous throughout J, this is inconsistent with the sequence of inequalities derived from (7), namely

$$|F(x_n) - F(y)| \leqslant r|x_n - y| \quad (n = 1, 2, \ldots).$$

Moreover, $J = \sum_{r=1}^{\infty}{}^{*} E_r$; for suppose $\xi \in J$, and let r be a positive integer such that $|F'(\xi)| < r$; then δ exists such that

$$y \in J \quad \& \quad |\xi - y| < \delta \quad \text{implies} \quad |F(\xi) - F(y)| \leqslant r|\xi - y|,$$

and since

$$y \in J \quad \& \quad |\xi - y| \geqslant \delta \quad \text{implies} \quad |F(\xi) - F(y)| \leqslant \frac{2M}{\delta}|\xi - y|,$$

where M is the upper bound of $|F(x)|$ in J, it follows that ξ belongs to E_N, where N exceeds both r and $2M/\delta$. Now let K be any perfect subset of J; then

$$K = \sum_{r=1}^{\infty}{}^{*} KE_r,$$

and the sets KE_r are closed (th. 27); so, by th. 37, there is an integer n and a point ξ of K which is the centre of a closed interval Δ such that $K\Delta \subset E_n$. If we now take λ and μ to be respectively the lower and the upper bounds of the aggregate of the numbers x which belong to the closed infinite (th. 20) set $K\Delta$, it follows from (7) that λ and μ satisfy the conditions of lemma 2.

Proof of th. 295. Since $F'(x)$ is finite, it follows that $F(x)$ is continuous throughout J; hence we have only to show that $f(x) = F'(x)$ satisfies (2) of def. 67. Let K be any perfect subset of J, let λ and μ be chosen to satisfy lemma 2, and let ξ be any point of $[\lambda, \mu]K$. If

$[\lambda, \xi]K$ is perfect, then, by lemma 1,

$$F'(x) \text{ is summable over } (\lambda, \xi)K,$$

and

(8) $$F(\xi) - F(\lambda) = \int_{(\lambda, \xi)K} F'(x)\, dx + V(F; (\lambda, \xi)\overline{K});$$

otherwise, let α and β be the bounds of $(\lambda, \xi)K$, $\alpha < \beta$; it follows easily that $[\alpha, \beta]K$ is perfect, that the integrals of $F'(x)$ over $(\alpha, \beta)K$ and over $(\lambda, \xi)K$ are equal if either exists, and that

(9) $$V(F; (\lambda, \xi)\overline{K}) = V(F; (\alpha, \beta)\overline{K}) + F(\alpha) - F(\lambda) + F(\xi) - F(\beta).$$

Now, by lemma 1, $F'(x)$ is summable over $(\alpha, \beta)K$, and

$$F(\beta) - F(\alpha)$$
$$= \int_{(\alpha, \beta)K} F'(x)\, dx + V(F; (\alpha, \beta)\overline{K}) = \int_{(\lambda, \xi)K} F'(x)\, dx + V(F; (\alpha, \beta)\overline{K}),$$

and so, by (9), (8) is again verified; this completes the proof.

(Note: The following generalization of th. 295 is also true: Let $F(x)$ be continuous throughout J, a closed interval $[a, b]$, and let $f(x)$ be a finite function defined in J and such that the set of the points x of J for which the equation $f(x) = F'(x)$ is false is finite or enumerable; then

$$(D) \int_a^b f(x)\, dx = F(b) - F(a).$$

The proof of this generalization is substantially the same as that of th. 295; the necessary modifications of detail are left to the reader.)

We can now show that a function may be integrable-D without being integrable-H over a closed interval J. In virtue of the last theorem and def. 65, it is sufficient to show that there exists a function $F(x)$ such that $F'(x)$ is finite throughout J, while the set of the points of non-summability of $F'(x)$ in J is non-enumerable.

Let $J = [0, 1]$, and let K be a perfect subset of J obtained as in th. 123, θ having been arbitrarily chosen. We first define $F(x)$ to be zero in $K + \overline{J}$, and then define $F(x)$ in each of the intervals of J° contiguous to K as follows: let c be freely chosen so that

(1) $$0 < c < \tfrac{1}{2} \quad \& \quad \frac{d}{dx}\left(x^2 \sin \frac{1}{x^2}\right) = 0 \text{ when } x = c,$$

and let $f(x)$ be defined in $(0, 1)$ so that

(2)
$$f(x) = \begin{cases} x^2 \sin 1/x^2 & \text{if } 0 < x \leqslant c \\ f(c) & \text{if } c < x \leqslant \frac{1}{2} \\ f(1-x) & \text{if } \frac{1}{2} < x < 1. \end{cases}$$

If (a, b) is one of the intervals of $(0, 1)$ contiguous to K, we define $F(x)$ for $a < x < b$ by the equation

(3)
$$F(x) = f\left(\frac{x-a}{b-a}\right)(b-a)^2.$$

By (1), (2), and (3), $F'(x)$ is defined and finite in $J - K$. Now let ξ be any chosen point of K, and let x be a variable point; if $x \in K + \bar{J}$, then $F(\xi) - F(x) = 0$; if $x \in J - K$, let (a, b) denote the interval of $(0, 1)$ contiguous to K which includes x, and it then follows from (3) and (2) that

$$|F(\xi) - F(x)| = |F(x)| \leqslant \min((x-a)^2, (b-x)^2) \leqslant (x-\xi)^2,$$

and consequently that $F'(\xi) = 0$. It remains only to prove that N, the set of the points of non-summability of $F'(x)$ in J, is non-enumerable, and for this it is sufficient (th. 37.1) to show that $K \subset N$. Now it follows easily from the example following th. 211.2 that the end-points of every interval of $(0, 1)$ contiguous to K belong to N, and since every point of K is a limit point of such end-points, it follows from th. 285 that $K \subset N$.

X

FOURIER SERIES

§ 1. Introduction

LET a_0, a_1, a_2,... and b_1, b_2,... be any given sequences of finite real numbers; then the series

$$(1) \qquad \tfrac{1}{2}a_0 + \sum_{n=1}^{\infty} (a_n \cos nx + b_n \sin nx)$$

is called a trigonometric series. Each term of the series being of period 2π in x, the same must be true of the sum function in the set of points in which it is defined. Suppose this sum function to be defined for all x and denoted by $f(x)$; now we know from Taylor's theorem that, if a finite function $g(x)$ is defined as the sum of a power series, say $\sum_{n=0}^{\infty} c_n x^n$, then there is a simple formula which relates the numbers c_n to the function $g(x)$, namely $n! \, c_n = g^{(n)}(0)$ ($n = 0, 1, 2,...$), and it is natural to inquire whether there is a formula which relates the coefficients in (1) to $f(x)$, the sum of that series.

Theorem 296. *If n is any positive integer, then*

$$(i) \qquad \int_0^{2\pi} \cos nx \, dx = \int_0^{2\pi} \sin nx \, dx = \int_0^{2\pi} \cos nx \sin nx \, dx = 0,$$

$$(ii) \qquad \frac{1}{\pi} \int_0^{2\pi} \cos^2 nx \, dx = \frac{1}{\pi} \int_0^{2\pi} \sin^2 nx \, dx = 1,$$

$$(iii) \int_0^{2\pi} \cos nx \cos mx \, dx$$

$$= \int_0^{2\pi} \sin nx \sin mx \, dx = \int_0^{2\pi} \sin nx \cos mx \, dx = 0$$

for every positive integer m different from n.

The proof is left to the reader.

Theorem 297. *If the series $\tfrac{1}{2}a_0 + \sum_{n=1}^{\infty} (a_n \cos nx + b_n \sin nx)$ converges boundedly in $(0, 2\pi)$ to $f(x)$, then*

$$a_n = \frac{1}{\pi} \int_0^{2\pi} f(x)\cos nx \, dx \quad \& \quad b_n = \frac{1}{\pi} \int_0^{2\pi} f(x)\sin nx \, dx \quad (n = 0, 1, 2,...).$$

Proof. Since each of the terms of the series is continuous and therefore measurable in $(0, 2\pi)$, the result follows from ths. 231 and 296.

Since the partial sums of a trigonometric series are continuous functions, it follows that, when such a series converges for all x, its sum function is measurable in $(0, 2\pi)$; but it does not follow that this function is summable over $(0, 2\pi)$. It may therefore happen that the coefficients of a trigonometric series are not obtainable from its sum function by means of the formulae given in th. 297. On the other hand, it follows from th. 230 that if $f(x)$ is any finite function summable over $(0, 2\pi)$, then $f(x)\cos nx$ and $f(x)\sin nx$ are summable over $(0, 2\pi)$ for every integer n; this enables us to associate a definite trigonometric series with $f(x)$ as follows:

Definition 68. Let $f(x)$ be finite and such that

(i) $f(x)$ is summable over $(0, 2\pi)$,

and

(ii) $f(x) = f(x+2\pi)$;

then the numbers $a_0, a_1, a_2,..., b_1, b_2,...$, given by the formulae

$$a_n = \frac{1}{\pi} \int_0^{2\pi} f(x)\cos nx \, dx, \qquad b_n = \frac{1}{\pi} \int_0^{2\pi} f(x)\sin nx \, dx,$$

are called the *Fourier coefficients* of f; we write

$$s_0(f; x) \quad \text{for} \quad \tfrac{1}{2}a_0,$$

and for every positive integer n we put

$$s_n(f; x) = \tfrac{1}{2}a_0 + \sum_{r=1}^{n} (a_r \cos rx + b_r \sin rx);$$

the trigonometric series

$$\tfrac{1}{2}a_0 + \sum_{n=1}^{\infty} (a_n \cos nx + b_n \sin nx), \text{ denoted by } \mathfrak{S}(f; x),$$

is called the *Fourier series of f*.

As the following theorem shows, the Fourier coefficients of f may equally well be evaluated by integrating

$$f(x)\cos nx \quad \text{and} \quad f(x)\sin nx$$

over any linear interval of length 2π.

Theorem 298. *Let $g(t)$ be summable over $(0, 2\pi)$ and of period 2π; let x be any real number; then*

$$\int_x^{2\pi+x} g(t)\, dt = \int_0^{2\pi} g(x+t)\, dt = \int_0^{2\pi} g(x-t)\, dt = \int_0^{2\pi} g(t)\, dt.$$

Proof. From the periodicity of g it follows easily that $g(t)$ is summable over every linear interval, and further, by th. 241,

$$\int_0^x g(t)\, dt = \int_{2\pi}^{2\pi+x} g(t)\, dt,$$

and so (th. 209.1)

$$\int_0^{2\pi} g(t)\, dt = \int_0^x g(t)\, dt + \int_x^{2\pi} g(t)\, dt = \int_{2\pi}^{2\pi+x} g(t)\, dt + \int_x^{2\pi} g(t)\, dt = \int_x^{2\pi+x} g(t)\, dt;$$

hence (th. 241)

$$(1) \qquad \int_0^{2\pi} g(t)\, dt = \int_x^{2\pi+x} g(t)\, dt = \int_0^{2\pi} g(x+t)\, dt.$$

By th. 241 and the periodicity of g, we have

$$\int_0^{2\pi} g(x+t)\, dt = \int_{-2\pi}^0 g(x-t)\, dt = \int_0^{2\pi} g(x-t)\, dt,$$

and this, by (1), completes the proof.

Theorem 298.1. *Let f be a function whose Fourier series is defined; then, for $n = 0, 1, 2,...$,*

$$\int_0^{2\pi} f(x)\sin nx\, dx = \int_0^{\pi} \{f(x)-f(-x)\}\sin nx\, dx$$

and
$$\int_0^{2\pi} f(x)\cos nx\, dx = \int_0^{\pi} \{f(x)+f(-x)\}\cos nx\, dx.$$

Proof. To verify the first equation, put $g(x) = f(x)\sin nx$; by ths. 298 and 209.1, we have

$$\int_0^{2\pi} g(x)\, dx = \int_{-\pi}^{\pi} g(x)\, dx = \int_{-\pi}^0 g(x)\, dx + \int_0^{\pi} g(x)\, dx,$$

and since (th. 241)

$$\int_{-\pi}^0 g(x)\, dx = \int_0^{\pi} g(-x)\, dx = - \int_0^{\pi} f(-x)\sin nx\, dx,$$

the result follows at once.

Examples.

(i) Let $f(x) = x$ if $-\pi \leqslant x < \pi$; then

$$\mathfrak{S}(f;x) = 2(\sin x - \tfrac{1}{2}\sin 2x + \tfrac{1}{3}\sin 3x - ...).$$

Proof. Since $f(x)$ is odd in $(-\pi, \pi)$, it follows from th. 298.1 that

$$\int_0^{2\pi} f(x)\cos nx\, dx = 0 \quad (n = 0, 1, 2, ...),$$

and

$$\int_0^{2\pi} f(x)\sin nx\, dx = 2\int_0^{\pi} x\sin nx\, dx = \frac{2\pi}{n}(-1)^{n-1} \quad (n = 1, 2, ...).$$

(ii) Let $f(x) = x$ if $0 \leqslant x < 2\pi$; then

$$\mathfrak{S}(f;x) = \pi - 2(\sin x + \tfrac{1}{2}\sin 2x + \tfrac{1}{3}\sin 3x + ...).$$

Proof.

$$\frac{1}{2\pi}\int_0^{2\pi} f(x)\, dx = \frac{1}{2\pi}\int_0^{2\pi} x\, dx = \pi, \quad \text{and,} \quad \text{if } n = 1, 2, ...,$$

we have

$$\int_0^{2\pi} f(x)\cos nx\, dx = \int_0^{2\pi} x\cos nx\, dx = 0$$

and

$$\int_0^{2\pi} f(x)\sin nx\, dx = \int_0^{2\pi} x\sin nx\, dx = -2\pi/n.$$

(iii) Let $f(x) = |x|$ if $-\pi \leqslant x < \pi$; then

$$\mathfrak{S}(f;x) = \tfrac{1}{2}\pi - \frac{4}{\pi}\left\{\cos x + \frac{\cos 3x}{3^2} + \frac{\cos 5x}{5^2} + ...\right\}.$$

Proof. Since $f(x)$ is even in $(-\pi, \pi)$, we have from th. 298.1 that

$$\int_0^{2\pi} f(x)\sin nx\, dx = 0 \quad (n = 1, 2, ...),$$

and

$$\int_0^{2\pi} f(x)\cos nx\, dx = 2\int_0^{\pi} x\cos nx\, dx = \begin{cases} -\dfrac{2}{n^2}(1-(-1)^n) & (n = 1, 2, ...) \\ \pi^2 & \text{if } n = 0. \end{cases}$$

(iv) Let $\qquad f(x) = \begin{cases} 1 & \text{if } 0 < x \leqslant \pi \\ -1 & \text{if } -\pi < x < 0, \end{cases}$

and let $f(0)$ be freely assigned; then

$$\mathfrak{S}(f;x) = \frac{4}{\pi}\{\sin x + \tfrac{1}{3}\sin 3x + \tfrac{1}{5}\sin 5x + ...\}.$$

Proof. Since $f(x)$ is odd in $(-\pi, \pi)$ (there will be a single exception if $f(0) \neq 0$, but this will not affect the integrals in question), we have from th. 298.1

$$\int_0^{2\pi} f(x)\cos nx \, dx = 0 \quad (n = 0, 1, 2,...),$$

and $$\int_0^{2\pi} f(x)\sin nx \, dx = 2 \int_0^{\pi} \sin nx \, dx = \frac{2}{n}(1-(-1)^n).$$

It is clear that the notion of Fourier coefficients may be incorporated with definitions of integration other than that of Lebesgue. Strictly speaking, what we have defined as Fourier series should be called Fourier-Lebesgue series, to distinguish them, for example, from Fourier-Riemann series which are obtained from def. 68 when the notion of summability is replaced by integrability in the Riemann sense. With this wider prospect in view, it is obvious that whether a given trigonometric series is a Fourier series or not depends on the definition of integration which is to be the admitted source of Fourier coefficients. However, the term *Fourier series* in this chapter will be used to denote Fourier-Lebesgue series only. A number of questions at once suggest themselves:

(i) If the Fourier series of $f(x)$ is defined, for what values of x does $\mathfrak{S}(f;x)$ converge, and how is its sum related to $f(x)$ for such values of x?

(ii) Are there trigonometric series which converge for all x without being Fourier series?

(iii) What conditions must be satisfied by the coefficients of a trigonometric series if it is to be a Fourier series?

(iv) If a given trigonometric series is a Fourier series, is there more than one function of which it is the Fourier series, and what is the relation between all the possible functions of which it is the Fourier series?

In this chapter it will be possible to answer (ii) and (iv) completely, but the other questions receive only partial answers, for their general solution is not yet known, and a detailed study of them is beyond the scope of this book; the interested reader may refer to *Trigonometrical Series* by A. Zygmund.

§ 2. Convergence Tests

The following theorem is of fundamental importance in the study of Fourier series:

Theorem 299 (RIEMANN-LEBESGUE). *Let $g(x)$ be summable over (a, b), and let $\phi(x)$ denote either of the functions $\cos x$ and $\sin x$; then*

$$\lim_{k \to \infty} \int_a^b g(x)\phi(kx)\, dx = 0.$$

Proof. By th. 249, on putting $f(x) = g(x)$ in (a, b) and $f(x) = 0$ elsewhere.

Working directly from def. 68, we can easily obtain a formula for the partial sums of a Fourier series.

Definition 69. If n is a positive integer and x any real number, $D_n(x)$ (*Dirichlet's kernel*) is defined by the equation

$$D_n(x) = \tfrac{1}{2} + \sum_{r=1}^{n} \cos rx.$$

It follows at once that, if cosec $\tfrac{1}{2}x$ exists, then

$$D_n(x) = \frac{1}{2} \frac{\sin(n+\tfrac{1}{2})x}{\sin \tfrac{1}{2}x}.$$

Theorem 300. *Let f be a function whose Fourier series is defined; let n be any positive integer and x any real number; then (def. 68)*

$$(1) \qquad\qquad s_n(f; x) = \frac{1}{\pi} \int_0^{2\pi} f(t) D_n(t-x)\, dt.$$

Proof. By def. 68

$$\pi s_n(f; x)$$

$$= \tfrac{1}{2} \int_0^{2\pi} f(t)\, dt + \sum_{r=1}^{n} \left\{ \cos rx \int_0^{2\pi} f(t)\cos rt\, dt + \sin rx \int_0^{2\pi} f(t)\sin rt\, dt \right\},$$

and so, by th. 228,

$$\pi s_n(f; x) = \int_0^{2\pi} f(t) \left\{ \tfrac{1}{2} + \sum_{r=1}^{n} (\cos rx \cos rt + \sin rx \sin rt) \right\} dt,$$

which, by def. 69, gives (1).

Before examining the formula for $s_n(f; x)$ just obtained, we consider some of the properties of Dirichlet's kernel.

Theorem 301. *Let n be any positive integer; then*

$$(i) \qquad\qquad \int_0^{\pi} D_n(t)\, dt = \tfrac{1}{2}\pi,$$

$$(ii) \quad \left| \int_0^{x} D_n(t)\, dt \right| < 2\sqrt{\pi} + \tfrac{1}{2}|x| \quad \& \quad \left| \int_x^{y} D_n(t)\, dt \right| \leqslant 4\sqrt{\pi} + \tfrac{1}{2}|x-y|$$

for all real numbers x and y.

Proof. It follows at once from def. 69 that

$$\int\limits_0^x D_n(t)\,dt = \tfrac12 \int\limits_0^x dt + \sum_{r=1}^n \int\limits_0^x \cos rt\,dt = \tfrac12 x + \sum_{r=1}^n \frac1r \sin rx;$$

(i) is now an immediate conclusion, and (ii) follows from ths. 230.1 and 209.1.

Theorem 302.

(i) *If* $0 < x \leqslant \pi$ *and* $g(t)$ *is summable over* (x, π), *then*

$$\lim_{n\to\infty} \int\limits_x^\pi g(t) D_n(t)\,dt = 0;$$

(ii) *if* $$D(x) = \lim_{n\to\infty} \int\limits_0^x D_n(t)\,dt,$$

then $D(x)$ *is an odd function of* x, $D(0) = 0$, *and*

$$D(x) = \tfrac12 \pi \quad \text{if} \quad 0 < x < 2\pi.$$

Proof. Suppose $0 < x \leqslant \pi$; then $\operatorname{cosec}\tfrac12 t$ is bounded and continuous in (x, π); hence (th. 230), if $g(t)$ is summable over (x, π), so is $g(t)\operatorname{cosec}\tfrac12 t$, and so, by th. 299,

$$\lim_{n\to\infty} \int\limits_x^\pi g(t) D_n(t)\,dt = \lim_{n\to\infty} \int\limits_x^\pi \tfrac12 g(t)\operatorname{cosec}\tfrac12 t \sin(n+\tfrac12)t\,dt = 0,$$

proving (i). Further, from 301 (i), we have

$$\tfrac12\pi = \int\limits_0^\pi D_n(t)\,dt = \int\limits_0^x D_n(t)\,dt + \int\limits_x^\pi D_n(t)\,dt \quad (n = 1, 2, ...);$$

hence, if we put $g(t) = 1$ in (i) of this theorem, we have

$$D(x) = \tfrac12\pi \quad \text{if} \quad 0 < x \leqslant \pi.$$

Suppose now that $\pi < x < 2\pi$, and put $y = 2\pi - x$; since $D_n(t)$ is an even function of t with period 2π, it follows from th. 241 that

$$\int\limits_\pi^x D_n(t)\,dt = \int\limits_y^\pi D_n(t)\,dt \quad (n = 1, 2, ...),$$

and hence, by (i), that

$$\lim_{n\to\infty} \int\limits_\pi^x D_n(t)\,dt = 0;$$

since (th. 301 (i))

$$\int\limits_0^\pi D_n(t)\,dt = \tfrac12\pi \quad (n = 1, 2, ...),$$

it now follows from th. 209.1 that $D(x) = \frac{1}{2}\pi$. It is obvious that $D(0) = 0$, and that $D(x)$ is an odd function of x is easily deduced from th. 241 in virtue of the fact that $D_n(t)$ is an even function of t for every positive integer n.

Theorem 303. *Let $g(t)$ be a bounded non-negative and non-decreasing function of t in an interval $(0, \delta)$, where $0 < \delta < \pi$, and such that $\lim\limits_{t \to +0} g(t) = 0$; then*

$$\lim_{n \to \infty} \int_0^\delta g(t) D_n(t)\, dt = 0.$$

Proof. If η satisfies $0 < \eta < \delta$, then, by ths. 244 and 301 (ii), we have

$$\left| \int_0^\eta g(t) D_n(t)\, dt \right| \leqslant g(\eta)\{4\sqrt{\pi} + \tfrac{1}{2}\pi\} \quad (n = 1, 2, \ldots);$$

hence, if ϵ is freely chosen, it follows, since $g(+0) = 0$, that η exists such that

(1) $\qquad 0 < \eta < \delta \quad \& \quad \left| \int_0^\eta g(t) D_n(t)\, dt \right| < \tfrac{1}{2}\epsilon \quad (n = 1, 2, \ldots).$

Since $g(t)$ is summable over (η, δ), it follows from th. 302 (i) that N exists such that

$$n > N \quad \text{implies} \quad \left| \int_\eta^\delta g(t) D_n(t)\, dt \right| < \tfrac{1}{2}\epsilon,$$

and hence, by (1), we have

$$n > N \quad \text{implies} \quad \left| \int_0^\delta g(t) D_n(t)\, dt \right| < \epsilon,$$

which is the required result.

We now proceed to examine conditions under which a Fourier series converges; it is convenient for this purpose to transform the formula for $o_n(f; x)$ obtained in th. 300.

Definition 70. If f is a function whose Fourier series is defined, then for every pair of finite real numbers x and t we write

$$\psi_x(f; t) = f(x+t) + f(x-t).$$

Theorem 304. *Let f be a function whose Fourier series is defined; then for every real number x*

(i) *$\psi_x(f; t)$ is a function of t with period 2π summable over every linear interval,*

(ii) *if $0 < \delta < \pi$, then $\lim\limits_{n \to \infty} \int_\delta^\pi \psi_x(f; t) D_n(t)\, dt = 0$.*

Proof. Since $f(t)$ is summable over $(0, 2\pi)$, and since $f(t)$ is of period 2π, it follows easily that $f(t)$ is summable over every linear interval. Hence (i) follows from def. 70 and ths. 227 and 241, and consequently (ii) follows from th. 302 (i).

Theorem 305. *Let f be a function whose Fourier series is defined, and let x be any real number; then*

(i) $$s_n(f;x) = \frac{1}{\pi} \int\limits_0^\pi \psi_x(f;t) D_n(t)\, dt \quad (n = 1, 2, \dots),$$

(ii) $0 < \delta < \pi$ implies $$\lim_{n \to \infty} \left\{ s_n(f;x) - \frac{1}{\pi} \int\limits_0^\delta \psi_x(f;t) D_n(t)\, dt \right\} = 0.$$

Proof. By th. 300, if n is any positive integer,

$$\pi s_n(f;x) = \int\limits_0^{2\pi} f(t) D_n(t-x)\, dt,$$

and since $f(t) D_n(t-x)$ satisfies the conditions of th. 298 for $g(t)$, we have

(1) $$\pi s_n(f;x) = \int\limits_0^{2\pi} f(x+t) D_n(t)\, dt.$$

On making the substitution $u = 2\pi - t$, we find (th. 241) that

$$\int\limits_\pi^{2\pi} f(x+t) D_n(t)\, dt = \int\limits_0^\pi f(x-u) D_n(u)\, du,$$

and so it follows from (1) and ths. 209.1 and 227 that

$$\pi s_n(f;x) = \int\limits_0^\pi \{f(x+t) + f(x-t)\} D_n(t)\, dt,$$

which means (i). Now, if $0 < \delta < \pi$, then (th. 209.1)

$$\int\limits_0^\pi \psi_x(f;t) D_n(t)\, dt = \int\limits_0^\delta \psi_x(f;t) D_n(t)\, dt + \int\limits_\delta^\pi \psi_x(f;t) D_n(t)\, dt,$$

and so (ii) follows from (i) and th. 304 (ii).

Theorem 306. *Let f be a function whose Fourier series is defined and let x be a point for which there is a finite number s and a number δ, $0 < \delta \leqslant \pi$, such that*

(1) $$\lim_{n \to \infty} \int\limits_0^\delta \{\psi_x(f;t) - 2s\} D_n(t)\, dt = 0;$$

then $$\mathfrak{S}(f;x) = s.$$

Proof. By th. 302 (ii) $\lim\limits_{n\to\infty}\int_0^\delta D_n(t)\,dt = \tfrac12\pi$, and so, by (1) and th. 227,

$$\lim_{n\to\infty}\frac{1}{\pi}\int_0^\delta \psi_x(f;t)D_n(t)\,dt = s;$$

this, by th. 305 (ii), implies $\mathfrak{S}(f;x) = \lim\limits_{n\to\infty} s_n(f;x) = s$.

Theorem 307 (DINI's test). *Let f be a function whose Fourier series is defined, and let x be a point for which there is a finite number s such that*

(1) $\dfrac{1}{t}\{\psi_x(f;t)-2s\}$ *is summable over* $(0,\pi)$;

then $\mathfrak{S}(f;x) = s.$

Proof. If $0 < t < \pi$, then

$$\left|\frac{\psi_x(f;t)-2s}{2\sin\frac12 t}\right| = \left|\frac{\psi_x(f;t)-2s}{t}\right|\left|\frac{\frac12 t}{\sin\frac12 t}\right| \leqslant \left|\frac{\psi_x(f;t)-2s}{t}\right|\tfrac12\pi,$$

and hence, by (1) and th. 201,

$$\frac{\psi_x(f;t)-2s}{2\sin\frac12 t} \text{ is summable over } (0,\pi);$$

the result now follows immediately from ths. 306 and 299.

Corollary. Since $\{\psi_x(f;t)-2s\}/t$ is summable over (δ,π) for every δ satisfying $0 < \delta < \pi$, it follows that (1) of th. 307 may be replaced by the condition

$\dfrac{1}{t}\{\psi_x(f;t)-2s\}$ is summable over $(0,\delta)$ for some δ such that $0 < \delta < \pi$.

Example. $1+\dfrac{1}{3^2}+\dfrac{1}{5^2}+\ldots = \tfrac18\pi^2.$

Proof. Let $f(x) = |x|$ if $-\pi \leqslant x < \pi$; clearly

$$\frac{1}{t}\psi_0(f;t) = 2 \quad\text{if}\quad 0 < t < \pi,$$

and so, by th. 307, $\mathfrak{S}(f;0) = 0$. The result now follows from example (iii) following th. 298.1.

Theorem 308. *Let f be a function whose Fourier series is defined, and let x be a point such that $f'(x)$ is finite; then*

$$\mathfrak{S}(f;x) = f(x).$$

Proof. Put $s = f(x)$; then

$$\frac{\psi_x(f;t)-2s}{t} = \frac{f(x+t)-f(x)}{t} - \frac{f(x-t)-f(x)}{-t},$$

and so, by hypothesis, the function $\{\psi_x(f;t)-2s\}/t$ is bounded in some interval $(0,\delta)$ in which it is also measurable (ths. 304 and 164); hence (th. 203) $\{\psi_x(f;t)-2s\}/t$ is summable over $(0,\delta)$ and the proof is now completed by the corollary to th. 307.

Examples.

(i) If $-\pi < x < \pi$, then $\sin x - \frac{1}{2}\sin 2x + \frac{1}{3}\sin 3x - \ldots = \frac{1}{2}x$.

Proof. Let $f(x) = x$ if $-\pi \leqslant x < \pi$; then $f'(x) = 1$ in $(-\pi,\pi)$, and the result follows from th. 308 and example (1) following th. 298.1. It should be observed that $f'(x)$ does not exist when $x = \pi$, for the periodic nature of $f(x)$ requires

$$f(\pi+0) = f(-\pi+0) = -\pi,$$

whereas
$$f(\pi-0) = \pi.$$

(ii) $\sin x + \frac{1}{3}\sin 3x + \frac{1}{5}\sin 5x + \ldots = \begin{cases} \frac{1}{4}\pi & \text{if } 0 < x < \pi \\ -\frac{1}{4}\pi & \text{if } \pi < x < 2\pi. \end{cases}$

Proof. Let $f(x) = \begin{cases} 1 & \text{if } 0 \leqslant x \leqslant \pi \\ -1 & \text{if } -\pi < x < 0; \end{cases}$

then $f'(x) = 0$ in $(0,2\pi)$ except where $x = \pi$, at which $f'(x)$ does not exist; hence the result follows from th. 308 and example (iv) following th. 298.1.

Theorem 309 (JORDAN's test). *Let f be a function whose Fourier series is defined, and let x be a point which is the centre of a closed interval $[x-\delta, x+\delta]$, $0 < \delta < \pi$, in which f has bounded variation; then*

(1) $\mathfrak{S}(f;x) = \frac{1}{2}\{f(x+0)+f(x-0)\}.$

Proof. It follows easily from def. 61 that $\psi_x(f;t)$ is of bounded variation in $[0,\delta]$, and so, by th. 267, there are functions $g_1(t)$ and $g_2(t)$ which are non-decreasing and bounded in $[0,\delta]$ and such that

$$0 \leqslant t \leqslant \delta \quad \text{implies} \quad \psi_x(f;t) = g_1(t)-g_2(t),$$

and so (th. 227) for every positive integer n

(2) $\int\limits_0^\delta \{\psi_x(f;t)-\{f(x+0)+f(x-0)\}\}D_n(t)\,dt$

$$= \int\limits_0^\delta \{g_1(t)-g_1(+0)\}D_n(t)\,dt - \int\limits_0^\delta \{g_2(t)-g_2(+0)\}D_n(t)\,dt.$$

Since $\{g_r(t)-g_r(+0)\}$ $(r = 1, 2)$ satisfies the conditions of th. 303 for $g(t)$, (1) now follows from (2) in virtue of ths. 303 and 306.

Corollary. The Fourier series of a continuous function converges to the value of the function at every point of an interval in which the function has bounded variation.

Example. Let $r_1, r_2, \ldots$ be a sequence consisting of all the rational numbers of $(0, 1)$, and let

$$f(x) = \sum_n \frac{r_n}{n^2} \quad \text{if} \quad 0 < x \leqslant 2\pi,$$

the condition of summation being $0 < r_n < x$; then

$$0 < x < 1 \quad \text{implies} \quad \mathfrak{S}(f; x) = \begin{cases} f(x) & \text{if} \quad x \text{ is irrational} \\ f(r_n)+\dfrac{\frac{1}{2}r_n}{n^2} & \text{if} \quad x = r_n. \end{cases}$$

Proof. Since $\sum\limits_{n=1}^{\infty} n^{-2} < \infty$, it follows that $f(x)$ is bounded in $(0, 1)$, and it is clear that $f(x)$ is an increasing function in $(0, 1)$; hence (example (i) following def. 61) every point of $(0, 1)$ is the centre of an interval in which $f(x)$ has bounded variation. It therefore follows from th. 309 that we need only show that

(1) $f(x)$ is continuous at every irrational point of $(0, 1)$

and

(2) $f(r_n+0)+f(r_n-0) = 2f(r_n)+\dfrac{r_n}{n^2}$ $(n = 1, 2, \ldots)$.

Now from the definition of $f(x)$ it follows that

(3) $0 < x < 1 \quad \text{implies} \quad f(x-0) = f(x);$

moreover, if $0 < x < x+h < 1$, then

$$f(x+h)-f(x) = \sum_n \frac{r_n}{n^2},$$

the condition of summation being $x \leqslant r_n < x+h$.

Now, if x is fixed, then to every integer N there is an ϵ such that $x < r_n < x+\epsilon$ implies $n > N$, and since

$$\lim_{N\to\infty} \sum_{n=N}^{\infty} \frac{r_n}{n^2} = 0,$$

it now follows that

$$\lim_{h\to 0}\{f(x+h)-f(x)\} = \begin{cases} \dfrac{r_n}{n^2} & \text{if} \quad x = r_n \\ 0 & \text{if} \quad x \text{ is irrational}; \end{cases}$$

hence (1) and (2) follow from (3).

§3. Summability $(C, 1)$ of a Fourier Series

Much of the modern theory of Fourier series is devoted to the study of processes which are analogous to summation and which, when applied to non-convergent Fourier series, give results similar to that of th. 309.

Definition 71. Suppose $\{t_n\}$ is a sequence of numbers such that $\{s_1+s_2+...+s_n\}/n$ tends to a finite limit s as n tends to infinity, s_n denoting the partial sum $t_1+t_2+t_3+...+t_n$; then the series $\sum\limits_{n=1}^{\infty} t_n$ is said to be *summable* $(C, 1)$ to the value s. It is easy to prove (see Hardy, p. 160, Ex. 27) that, if $\sum\limits_{n=1}^{\infty} t_n$ converges to s, then $\sum\limits_{n=1}^{\infty} t_n$ is summable $(C, 1)$ to s.

Theorem 310 (Fejér). *Let f be a function whose Fourier series is defined, and let x be a point such that $\{f(x+0)+f(x-0)\}$ exists and is finite; then*

$$\lim_{n\to\infty} \frac{1}{n} \sum_{r=0}^{n-1} s_r(f;x) = \tfrac{1}{2}\{f(x+0)+f(x-0)\},$$

i.e. the Fourier series of $f(x)$ is summable $(C, 1)$ to

$$\tfrac{1}{2}\{f(x+0)+f(x-0)\}.$$

Proof. Choose n, a positive integer, $n \geqslant 2$; by ths. 305 and 228

$$(1) \qquad \sum_{r=0}^{n-1} s_r(f;x) = \frac{1}{\pi} \int_0^{\pi} \psi_x(f;t)\sigma_n(t)\,dt,$$

where

$$\sigma_n(t) = \tfrac{1}{2} + \sum_{\nu=1}^{n-1} D_\nu(t).$$

It is easy to see that, for $0 < t < \pi$,

$$\tfrac{1}{2}n + \sum_{\nu=1}^{n-1} \sum_{\mu=1}^{\nu} \cos\mu t = \sigma_n(t) = \frac{1}{2}\left(\frac{\sin\tfrac{1}{2}nt}{\sin\tfrac{1}{2}t}\right)^2,$$

from which it follows at once that

$$(2) \qquad \frac{1}{n} \int_0^{\pi} \sigma_n(t)\,dt = \tfrac{1}{2}\pi,$$

and consequently, since $\sigma_n(t) \geqslant 0$, that

$$(3) \qquad 0 < \delta < \pi \quad \text{implies} \quad \int_0^{\delta} |\sigma_n(t)|\,dt \leqslant \tfrac{1}{2}\pi n.$$

If we now put $2s = f(x+0)+f(x-0)$, it follows from (1) and (2) that

$$(4) \qquad s - \frac{1}{n}\sum_{r=0}^{n-1} s_r(f;x) = \frac{1}{n\pi}\int_0^\pi \{2s - \psi_x(f;t)\}\sigma_n(t)\,dt.$$

Choose ϵ freely; by hypothesis δ may be chosen so that $0 < \delta < \pi$ and $0 < t < \delta$ implies $|2s - \psi_x(f;t)| < \epsilon$; then, by (3) and th. 230,

$$(5) \qquad \left| \int_0^\delta \{2s - \psi_x(f;t)\}\sigma_n(t)\,dt \right| \leqslant \epsilon \int_0^\delta |\sigma_n(t)|\,dt \leqslant \tfrac{1}{2}\epsilon n\pi.$$

Now $|\sigma_n(t)| \leqslant \operatorname{cosec}^2\tfrac{1}{2}t$, and so (ths. 197 and 179)

$$\left| \int_\delta^\pi \{2s - \psi_x(f;t)\}\sigma_n(t)\,dt \right| \leqslant \int_\delta^\pi |2s - \psi_x(f;t)|\operatorname{cosec}^2\tfrac{1}{2}t\,dt;$$

since $\operatorname{cosec}^2\tfrac{1}{2}t$ is bounded and measurable in (δ,π), it follows from ths. 304 (i) and 230 that $|2s - \psi_x(f;t)|\operatorname{cosec}^2\tfrac{1}{2}t$ is summable over (δ,π), and we now have that

$$\left| \int_\delta^\pi \{2s - \psi_x(f;t)\}\sigma_n(t)\,dt \right| \leqslant K,$$

where K is a finite real number independent of n; this, together with (5) and (4), gives

$$\left| s - \frac{1}{n}\sum_{r=0}^{n-1} s_r(f;x) \right| \leqslant \tfrac{1}{2}\epsilon + \frac{K}{n\pi} \qquad (n = 1,2,\ldots),$$

and since ϵ is arbitrary, this proves the theorem.

§4. Integration of Fourier Series

Th. 310 and the various convergence tests which we have considered show that, if the function $f(x)$ satisfies certain conditions, then its Fourier series is summable $(C,1)$, or else perhaps converges, to $\tfrac{1}{2}\{f(x+0)+f(x-0)\}$. The following theorem proves a remarkable relation between $\int_0^x f(t)\,dt$ and $\mathfrak{S}(f;x)$ which is valid for *every* function f whose Fourier series is defined.

Theorem 311. *Suppose* $\mathfrak{S}(f;x) = \tfrac{1}{2}a_0 + \sum_{n=1}^\infty (a_n \cos nx + b_n \sin nx)$, *and let u be freely chosen so that $0 < u \leqslant 2\pi$; then*

$$\int_0^u f(x)\,dx = \int_0^u \tfrac{1}{2}a_0\,dx + \sum_{n=1}^\infty \int_0^u (a_n \cos nx + b_n \sin nx)\,dx.$$

Proof. Put

$$g(t) = \begin{cases} 1 & \text{if } 0 < t < u \\ 0 & \text{if } u \leqslant t \leqslant 2\pi, \end{cases} \quad \text{and } g(t+2\pi) = g(t).$$

Let
$$\mathfrak{S}(g;t) = \tfrac{1}{2}\alpha_0 + \sum_{n=1}^{\infty}(\alpha_n \cos nt + \beta_n \sin nt);$$

by th. 308, if $0 < t < u$ or if $u < t < 2\pi$, then

$$g(t) = \tfrac{1}{2}\alpha_0 + \sum_{n=1}^{\infty}(\alpha_n \cos nt + \beta_n \sin nt);$$

it follows easily from th. 231 that, *if*

(1) $\mathfrak{S}(g;x)$ converges boundedly for $0 < x < u$ and for $u < x < 2\pi$, then

$$\int_0^{2\pi} f(x)g(x)\,dx = \tfrac{1}{2}\alpha_0 \int_0^{2\pi} f(x)\,dx + \sum_{n=1}^{\infty} \int_0^{2\pi} f(x)\{\alpha_n \cos nx + \beta_n \sin nx\}\,dx,$$

i.e.

$$\int_0^u f(x)\,dx = \tfrac{1}{2}\pi a_0 \alpha_0 + \pi \sum_{n=1}^{\infty}(a_n \alpha_n + b_n \beta_n)$$

$$= \tfrac{1}{2}a_0 \int_0^{2\pi} g(x)\,dx + \sum_{n=1}^{\infty}\left\{a_n \int_0^{2\pi} g(x)\cos nx\,dx + b_n \int_0^{2\pi} g(x)\sin nx\,dx\right\}$$

$$= \tfrac{1}{2}a_0 \int_0^u dx + \sum_{n=1}^{\infty}\left\{a_n \int_0^u \cos nx\,dx + b_n \int_0^u \sin nx\,dx\right\},$$

which proves the theorem. It remains only to verify (1). Let n be any positive integer; by ths. 300 and 241, if $0 < x < 2\pi$, then

$$\pi s_n(g;x) = \int_0^{2\pi} g(t)D_n(t-x)\,dt = \int_0^u D_n(t-x)\,dt = \int_{-x}^{u-x} D_n(t)\,dt,$$

and this, by th. 301 (ii), implies that

$$|\pi s_n(g;x)| \leqslant 4\sqrt{\pi} + \tfrac{1}{2}u \quad \text{for} \quad 0 < x < 2\pi;$$

the convergence of $\mathfrak{S}(g;x)$ having already been dealt with, this completes the proof of (1).

An important deduction from th. 311 is

Theorem 312. *Let f and g be functions whose Fourier series are defined; then a necessary and sufficient condition for $\mathfrak{S}(f;x)$ and $\mathfrak{S}(g;x)$ to be identical is that $f(x) \sim g(x)$ in $(0, 2\pi)$.*

Proof. If $f(x) \sim g(x)$ in $(0, 2\pi)$, it follows from th. 219 that the Fourier coefficients of f are the same as those of g.

To prove that the condition is necessary, suppose

$$\mathfrak{S}(f;x) \text{ and } \mathfrak{S}(g;x) \text{ are identical.}$$

It is clear from def. 68 and th. 227 that, if $h(x) = f(x) - g(x)$, then the Fourier coefficients of h are all zero, and hence, by th. 311,

$$0 < u \leqslant 2\pi \quad \text{implies} \quad \int\limits_0^u h(x)\,dx = 0,$$

which, by ths. 238 and 209.1, implies $h(x) \sim 0$ in $(0, 2\pi)$, i.e.

$$f(x) \sim g(x) \text{ in } (0, 2\pi).$$

§5. Trigonometric and Fourier Series

We now consider briefly some simple conditions which are necessary and some which are sufficient for a given trigonometric series to be a Fourier series.

Theorem 313. *Suppose* $\frac{1}{2}a_0 + \sum\limits_{n=1}^{\infty} (a_n \cos nx + b_n \sin nx)$ *is a Fourier series; then*

(i) $$\lim_{n \to \infty} a_n = \lim_{n \to \infty} b_n = 0,$$

(ii) $$\sum_{n=1}^{\infty} \frac{b_n}{n} \text{ converges.}$$

Proof. By hypothesis there is a function $f(x)$ summable over $(0, 2\pi)$ and such that for $n = 0, 1, 2, \ldots$

$$a_n = \frac{1}{\pi} \int\limits_0^{2\pi} f(x)\cos nx\,dx \quad \text{and} \quad b_n = \frac{1}{\pi} \int\limits_0^{2\pi} f(x)\sin nx\,dx;$$

hence (i) follows from th. 299. Also

(1) $$\sum_{n=1}^{\infty} \frac{b_n}{n} = \sum_{n=1}^{\infty} \frac{1}{\pi} \int\limits_0^{2\pi} f(x)\frac{1}{n}\sin nx\,dx,$$

and since the series $\sum\limits_{n=1}^{\infty} (1/n)\sin nx$ converges boundedly in $(0, 2\pi)$ (example (iii) following def. 58), (ii) now follows from (1) and th. 231.

It follows from th. 313 (ii) that the series $\sum\limits_{n=2}^{\infty} \dfrac{\sin nx}{\log n}$, which converges for all x (Hardy, § 189), is not a Fourier series, since

$$\sum_{n=2}^{\infty} (n \log n)^{-1} = \infty \quad \text{(Hardy, § 211).}$$

The following theorem is one of the outstanding applications of Lebesgue integration to the theory of Fourier series.

Theorem 314 (RIESZ-FISCHER). *Let a_0, $a_1,\ldots$ and b_1, $b_2,\ldots$ be sequences of real numbers such that $s = \frac{1}{2}a_0^2 + \sum_{n=1}^{\infty} (a_n^2 + b_n^2) < \infty$; then there is a function $f(x)$ for which*

(1) $$\mathfrak{S}(f; x) = \frac{1}{2}a_0 + \sum_{n=1}^{\infty} (a_n \cos nx + b_n \sin nx)$$

and
$$\frac{1}{\pi} \int_0^{2\pi} f^2(x)\, dx = s.$$

Proof. Let n_1, $n_2,\ldots$ be an increasing sequence of positive integers such that

(2) $$\sum_{n=n_r}^{\infty} (a_n^2 + b_n^2) \leqslant 4^{-r}s \quad (r = 1, 2,\ldots).$$

Put
$$f_0(x) = \frac{1}{2}a_0 + \sum_{n=1}^{n_1} (a_n \cos nx + b_n \sin nx),$$
and

(3) $$f_r(x) = \sum_{n=n_r+1}^{n_{r+1}} (a_n \cos nx + b_n \sin nx) \quad (r = 1, 2,\ldots).$$

From (2) and ths. 296 and 228 we have

(4)
$$\int_0^{2\pi} f_0^2(x)\, dx = \frac{1}{2}\pi a_0^2 + \pi \sum_{n=1}^{n_1} (a_n^2 + b_n^2) \leqslant \pi s,$$
$$\int_0^{2\pi} f_r^2(x)\, dx = \pi \sum_{n=n_r+1}^{n_{r+1}} (a_n^2 + b_n^2) \leqslant 4^{-r}s\pi \quad (r = 1, 2,\ldots).$$

By (4) and the corollary to th. 234,
$$\int_0^{2\pi} |f_r(x)|\, dx \leqslant \sqrt{(2s)}2^{-r}\pi \quad (r = 0, 1, 2,\ldots),$$
and so

(5) $$\sum_{r=0}^{\infty} \int_0^{2\pi} |f_r(x)|\, dx < \infty;$$

this, by th. 229, implies that $\sum_{r=0}^{\infty} f_r(x)$ is equivalent in $(0, 2\pi)$ to some finite function $f(x)$ summable over $(0, 2\pi)$ (th. 221). Now let r be any chosen positive integer; by (4) and th. 234

(6) $$\int_0^{2\pi} |f_m(x)f_r(x)|\, dx \leqslant (4^{-m}\pi s\, 4^{-r}\pi s)^{\frac{1}{2}} = 2^{-m-r}\pi s \quad (m = 0, 1, 2,\ldots).$$

Since $f(x)f_r(x)$ is measurable in $(0, 2\pi)$ (th. 165), and

$$|f(x)f_r(x)| \leqslant \sum_{m=0}^{\infty} |f_m(x)f_r(x)| \text{ in } (0, 2\pi),$$

it follows by ths. 179 and 191 and (6) that

$$\int_0^{2\pi} |f(x)f_r(x)|\, dx \leqslant \int_0^{2\pi} \sum_{m=0}^{\infty} |f_m(x)f_r(x)|\, dx = \sum_{m=0}^{\infty} \int_0^{2\pi} |f_m(x)f_r(x)|\, dx \leqslant 2^{1-r}\pi s,$$

and so, by th. 229,

$$(7) \qquad \int_0^{2\pi} f^2(x)\, dx = \int_0^{2\pi} \sum_{r=0}^{\infty} f(x)f_r(x)\, dx = \sum_{r=0}^{\infty} \int_0^{2\pi} f(x)f_r(x)\, dx.$$

To prove (1) let r and n be freely chosen non-negative integers; clearly $f_r(x)\cos nx$ is measurable in $(0, 2\pi)$ and

$$\int_0^{2\pi} |f_r(x)\cos nx|\, dx \leqslant \int_0^{2\pi} |f_r(x)|\, dx;$$

hence, by (5), ths. 229 and 296, and (3),

$$\int_0^{2\pi} f(x)\cos nx\, dx = \int_0^{2\pi} \sum_{r=0}^{\infty} f_r(x)\cos nx\, dx = \sum_{r=0}^{\infty} \int_0^{2\pi} f_r(x)\cos nx\, dx = \pi a_n.$$

A similar argument, applied to $\int_0^{2\pi} f(x)\sin nx\, dx$, completes the proof of (1). It now follows from (3) and def. 68 that

$$\frac{1}{\pi} \int_0^{2\pi} f(x)f_0(x)\, dx = \tfrac{1}{2}a_0^2 + \sum_{n=1}^{n_1} (a_n^2 + b_n^2),$$

and
$$\frac{1}{\pi} \int_0^{2\pi} f(x)f_r(x)\, dx = \sum_{n=n_r+1}^{n_{r+1}} (a_n^2 + b_n^2) \quad (r = 1, 2, ...),$$

and so, by (7), we have

$$\frac{1}{\pi} \int_0^{2\pi} f^2(x)\, dx = s.$$

Theorem 315 (PARSEVAL). *Suppose*

$$\mathfrak{S}(f; x) = \tfrac{1}{2}a_0 + \sum_{n=1}^{\infty} (a_n \cos nx + b_n \sin nx);$$

then

$$(1) \qquad \frac{1}{\pi} \int_0^{2\pi} f^2(x)\, dx = \tfrac{1}{2}a_0^2 + \sum_{n=1}^{\infty} (a_n^2 + b_n^2).$$

Proof. We first prove a lemma.

Lemma (BESSEL's Inequality). $\frac{1}{2}a_0^2 + \sum_{r=1}^{\infty} (a_r^2 + b_r^2) \leqslant \frac{1}{\pi} \int_0^{2\pi} f^2(x)\, dx.$

Proof. Let n be any chosen positive integer; it follows easily from def. 68 and th. 296 that $\int_0^{2\pi} f(x)s_n(f;x)\, dx$ and $\int_0^{2\pi} s_n^2(f;x)\, dx$ are both equal to $\frac{1}{2}\pi a_0^2 + \pi \sum_{r=1}^{n} (a_r^2 + b_r^2)$, and consequently that

(2) $\int_0^{2\pi} \{s_n^2(f;x) - 2f(x)s_n(f;x)\}\, dx = -\pi\left\{\frac{1}{2}a_0^2 + \sum_{r=1}^{n} (a_r^2 + b_r^2)\right\}.$

If $f^2(x)$ is summable over $(0, 2\pi)$ it now follows from (2) and th. 227 that

$$0 \leqslant \int_0^{2\pi} \{f(x) - s_n(f;x)\}^2\, dx = \int_0^{2\pi} f^2(x)\, dx - \pi\left\{\frac{1}{2}a_0^2 + \sum_{r=1}^{n} (a_r^2 + b_r^2)\right\},$$

which implies

$$\frac{1}{2}a_0^2 + \sum_{r=1}^{n} (a_r^2 + b_r^2) \leqslant \frac{1}{\pi} \int_0^{2\pi} f^2(x)\, dx \quad (n = 1, 2, \ldots),$$

thus verifying the lemma. If $f^2(x)$ is not summable over $(0, 2\pi)$, then, since $f^2(x)$ is measurable in $(0, 2\pi)$ (th. 165), it follows that

$$\int_0^{2\pi} f^2(x)\, dx = \infty,$$

and the lemma is obvious.

Proof of th. 315. It is obvious from the lemma that (1) is true whenever the right-hand side diverges. Suppose then that

$$\frac{1}{2}a_0^2 + \sum_{n=1}^{\infty} (a_n^2 + b_n^2) < \infty;$$

by th. 314 there is a function $g(x)$ such that

$$\mathfrak{S}(g;x) = \mathfrak{S}(f;x) \quad \& \quad \frac{1}{\pi} \int_0^{2\pi} g^2(x)\, dx = \frac{1}{2}a_0^2 + \sum_{n=1}^{\infty} (a_n^2 + b_n^2);$$

hence (th. 312) $f(x) \sim g(x)$ in $(0, 2\pi)$, and so, by th. 219, (1) is again verified.

XI

RIEMANN-STIELTJES INTEGRATION

§ 1. Introduction

INTEGRATION, considered as an operation on the integrand, is linear, i.e. the integral of $f+g$ is the sum of the integrals of f and g, and the integral of cf is c times that of f if c is a constant. This property can be used, in various ways, to *define* integration. One method is to define the integral for a chosen class of 'elementary' functions whose linear combinations approximate to a wider class. Thus we may *define* the integral of a function whose value is 1 in an (open or closed) interval (α, β) and zero elsewhere as $\beta-\alpha$; the linearity property then determines the integral of any step function, viz. if $a = x_0 < x_1 < \dots < x_n = b$ and $f(x)$ is equal to a constant c_r in (x_{r-1}, x_r), then

$$(1) \qquad \int_a^b f(x)\,dx = \sum_{r=1}^n c_r(x_r - x_{r-1}).$$

Functions integrable in the Riemann sense are, as we know from Chap. II, well approximable by step functions: if ξ_r is *any* number in $[x_{r-1}, x_r]$ then the step function with $c_r = f(\xi_r)$ has the property that its integral over $[a, b]$, viz.

$$(2) \qquad \sum_{r=1}^n f(\xi_r)(x_r - x_{r-1})$$

tends to a limit as the subdivision is 'refined to zero' in any manner (th. 57).

Every Lebesgue measurable function is approximable, in a weaker sense, by step functions: it is in fact the limit almost everywhere of a sequence of step functions (cf. th. 173). On this basis it is possible to define the Lebesgue integral of a function of one variable as an extension of (1). Alternatively, (1) may be used to define the integral of a function equal to 1 in a set E and zero elsewhere. In the class of sets for which this is satisfactory the integral may be used to *define* mE, the measure of the set E; we may then start from the class of functions which are constant in "measurable" sets and define the integral of $f(x)$ over a set B as

$$\int_B f(x)\,dx = \sum_{r=1}^k y_r\, mB_r$$

if B is the sum of k disjoint measurable sets B_r and f is constant and equal to y_r in B_r. This, in turn, relying on th. 170, can be made the basis of a definition of the Lebesgue integral which is equivalent to that of def. 52 (see §4.1 below).

In this chapter we consider an integral which is linear on the integrand but in which (1) is abandoned. Instead of assigning the value $b-a$ as the integral of 1 over $[a, b]$, we choose a function ϕ and define the integral to be $\phi(b)-\phi(a)$ (when $\phi(x) = x$ this reduces, of course, to (1)). We shall consider sums analogous to (2), viz.

$$(3) \qquad \sum_{r=1}^{n} f(\xi_r)\{\phi(x_r)-\phi(x_{r-1})\}$$

and examine classes of functions f and ϕ for which (3) tends to a limit as the subdivision of $[a, b]$ is refined to zero. Sums such as (3) occur naturally in physical science; thus if there is a mass distribution on $[a, b]$ and $\phi(X)$ is the mass in the interval $a \leqslant x < X$, then (3) with $f(x) = x^2$ is an approximation to the 'second moment' about $x = 0$ of the distribution. ϕ could be discontinuous (at isolated particles), and, where continuous, ϕ could be non-differentiable. However, we shall see that whenever f is continuous and ϕ monotonic in $[a, b]$ the sum (3) tends to a limit as the subdivision is refined to zero. The class of f and ϕ for which this happens is in fact much wider.

The definitions given below allow $f(x)$ and $\phi(x)$ to be complex (though x is real). The case in which f is continuous and ϕ has bounded variation is basic to the theory of contour integration (see § 4.4).

§ 2. The Riemann-Stieltjes Integral

We shall consistently use the notation of Chap. II, modified as necessary for complex-valued functions. Thus, ϕ being bounded on $[a, b]$, $\omega(\phi; S)$ is the upper bound of numbers $|\phi(\beta)-\phi(\alpha)|$ with α and β in S. $\omega(\phi; \xi)$, the oscillation of ϕ at a point ξ, is the limit as $n \to \infty$ of $\omega(\phi; [\xi-1/n, \xi+1/n])$. The total variation of ϕ in $[a, b]$, denoted by $T(\phi; [a, b])$, is the upper bound of numbers

$$\sum_{r=1}^{n} |\phi(x_r)-\phi(x_{r-1})| \quad \text{where} \quad a = x_0 < x_1 < ... < x_n = b;$$

when this is finite we say ϕ has bounded variation in $[a, b]$.

The definitions of a net N over $[a, b]$, and of $g(N)$, are as given on page 32. For any given N we denote by δ_r the r-th cell of N and by

ξ_r an arbitrarily chosen point of δ_r; the succession $a = x_0 \leqslant \xi_1$ $\leqslant x_1 \leqslant \xi_2 \leqslant ... \leqslant x_{n-1} \leqslant \xi_n \leqslant x_n = b$ is denoted by N^*. If to each N^* over $[a, b]$ is assigned a number $\mu(N^*)$, real or complex, we say that $\mu(N^*)$ converges to λ as N is refined to zero, written

$$\lim_{g(N) \to 0} \mu(N^*) = \lambda,$$

if to every positive number ϵ there is a positive number η such that (cf. def. 35) $|\mu(N^*) - \lambda| < \epsilon$ for all N^* with $g(N) < \eta$. Clearly for a given μ there cannot be more than one such number λ.

For a given N there may be infinitely many values $\mu(N^*)$ arising from the arbitrary choice of the ξ_r; the upper bound of the modulus of the difference between any pair of such values will be called the oscillation of $\mu(N)$. If $\mu(N^*)$ converges as $g(N) \to 0$ then the oscillation of $\mu(N)$ tends to zero with $g(N)$.

As an analogue of the general principle of convergence we prove

Theorem 316. *Suppose μ has the property that for every positive number ϵ there is a positive number $\eta(\epsilon)$ such that $|\mu(N_1^*) - \mu(N_2^*)| < \epsilon$ whenever $g(N_1)$ and $g(N_2)$ are less than η. Then $\mu(N^*)$ converges as N is refined to zero.*

Proof. By hypothesis there is a sequence $N_1^*, N_2^*, ...$ with $g(N_r) < 2^{-r}$ and $|\mu(N_r^*) - \mu(N_{r+1}^*)| < 2^{-r}$. Hence

$$\sum_{r=1}^{\infty} \{\mu(N_{r+1}^*) - \mu(N_r^*)\}$$

converges absolutely and $\mu(N_r^*)$ tends to a finite limit λ as $r \to \infty$. This implies, for all N,

$$|\mu(N^*) - \lambda| \leqslant |\mu(N^*) - \mu(N_r^*)| + 2^{1-r}.$$

Now let ϵ be any positive number. If r is chosen so that 2^{-r} is less than ϵ and less than $\eta(\epsilon)$ then, provided $g(N) < \eta(\epsilon)$,

$$|\mu(N^*) - \lambda| < \epsilon + 2^{1-r} < 3\epsilon.$$

This means that $\mu(N^*) \to \lambda$ as $g(N) \to 0$.

Definition 72. Let f and ϕ be (complex-valued) functions bounded on $[a, b]$. For every N^* over $[a, b]$,

$$(4) \qquad \sigma_{N^*}(f; \phi) = \sum_{r=1}^{n} f(\xi_r)\{\phi(x_r) - \phi(x_{r-1})\}$$

is called a *Stieltjes sum* of f with respect to ϕ over $[a, b]$. It will be convenient to denote by $\sigma_N(f; \phi)$ the value of $\sigma_{N^*}(f; \phi)$ when $\xi_r = x_r$. f is said to be integrable $d\phi$ over $[a, b]$ if $\sigma_{N^*}(f; \phi)$ converges as

$g(N) \to 0$; the limit is then denoted by

$$\int_a^b f(x)\, d\phi(x), \quad \text{or by} \quad \int_a^b f\, d\phi \quad \text{for short,}$$

and is called the integral of $f d\phi$ over $[a, b]$. The sense to be attributed to the integral symbol when $b \leqslant a$ is as described on p. 33.

It is clear from th. 57 that when $\phi(x) = x$ the Stieltjes integral coincides with the Riemann integral (the modifications needed in th. 57 when f is complex are trivial).

In view of the working definition used in Chap. II (due to Darboux) it may be pointed out that a Stieltjes type of integral can be defined in terms of upper and lower sums when f is real and ϕ is monotonic increasing, viz. (cf. def. 32)

(5)
$$L(f; \phi; N) = \sum_{r=1}^{n} m(f; \delta_r)\{\phi(x_r) - \phi(x_{r-1})\},$$

$$U(f; \phi; N) = \sum_{r=1}^{n} M(f; \delta_r)\{\phi(x_r) - \phi(x_{r-1})\}.$$

Upper and lower integrals of $f d\phi$ may then be defined and the analogues of ths. 45 and 49 established without difficulty, since every upper sum exceeds (or is equal to) every lower sum. A Darboux-Stieltjes integral would exist when the upper and lower integrals are equal. An integral so defined is more general than the Riemann-Stieltjes integral of def.72. To see this, suppose first that $\sigma_{N*}(f; \phi) \to \lambda$ as $g(N) \to 0$; then $L(f; \phi; N)$ and $U(f; \phi; N)$ both tend to λ as $g(N) \to 0$ and, by the analogue of th. 45, the Darboux-Stieltjes integral exists and has the value λ. But there are functions integrable in the Darboux-Stieltjes sense which are not integrable in the Riemann-Stieltjes sense: let $f(x) = \phi(x) = 0$ for $-1 \leqslant x < 0$ and $f(x) = \phi(x) = 1$ for $x > 0$, while $f(0) = 0$ and $\phi(0) = 1$; then the Darboux-Stieltjes integral of $f d\phi$ exists, since with $-1, 0, 1$ constituting N, $U(f; \phi; N) = L(f; \phi; N) = 0$. But $\sigma_N{}^*(f; \phi)$ does not tend to zero with $g(N)$ since $f(1/n)\{\phi(1/n) - \phi(-1/n)\} = 1$ for $n = 1, 2, \dots$. This could have been anticipated from

Theorem 317. *If f is integrable $d\phi$ (in the Riemann-Stieltjes sense) then f and ϕ are nowhere simultaneously discontinuous.*

Proof. Suppose $\omega(f; X) = 2p > 0$ and $a < X < b$; then $\omega(f; [X, X+h]) \geqslant p$ or $\omega(f; [X-h, X]) \geqslant p$ for all $h > 0$: suppose the former. If $f d\phi$ is integrable over $[a, b]$, then $\phi(X) = \phi(X+0) = \phi(X-0)$ since $\omega(f; [X, X+h])\{\phi(X+h) - \phi(X)\}$ and $\omega(f; [X-h, X+h])$ $\{\phi(X+h) - \phi(X-h)\}$ tend to zero as $h \to +0$. A slight change of proof is needed if X is a or b.

It can be proved (cf. th. 56), that if ϕ is monotonic and f is continuous wherever ϕ is discontinuous, then $fd\phi$ is integrable in the Riemann-Stieltjes sense if and only if it is so in the Darboux-Stieltjes sense.

§ 3. Properties of the Riemann-Stieltjes Integral

The following theorem lists some immediate consequences of def. 72; all f and ϕ are assumed to be bounded and, unless otherwise stated, complex-valued.

Theorem 318.

(i) $\int_a^b k \, d\phi = k\{\phi(b)-\phi(a)\}$ *if k is a constant;*

(ii) $\int_a^b f \, d\phi = 0$ *if ϕ is constant in $[a, b]$;*

(iii) $\int_a^b \{\lambda_1 f_1+\lambda_2 f_2\}d\phi = \lambda_1 \int_a^b f_1 \, d\phi+\lambda_2\int_a^b f_2 \, d\phi$ *if λ_1 and λ_2 are constants and f_1, f_2 are integrable $d\phi$ over $[a, b]$;*

(iv) $\int_a^b f \, d(\lambda_1\phi_1+\lambda_2\phi_2) = \lambda_1 \int_a^b f \, d\phi_1+\lambda_2\int_a^b f \, d\phi_2$ *if λ_1, λ_2 are constants and f is integrable $d\phi_1$ and $d\phi_2$ over $[a, b]$;*

(v) *if ϕ is a constant k in (a, b) and f is continuous at a and b, then*

$$\int_a^b f \, d\phi = f(a)\{k-\phi(a)\}+f(b)\{\phi(b)-k\}.$$

The following inequalities also follow from def. 72.

Theorem 319. *J denotes the interval $[a, b]$;*

(i) $|\sigma_{N*}(f; \phi)| \leqslant M(|f|; J)T(\phi; J)$,

(ii) $|\int_a^b f \, d\phi| \leqslant M(|f|; J)T(\phi; J)$ *if the integral exists;*

(iii) *if f is real and ϕ monotonic then*

$$\int_a^b f \, d\phi = \{\phi(b)-\phi(a)\}K$$

for some K between the bounds of f in J, assuming the integral exists;

(iv) *the oscillation of* $\sigma_N(f; \phi)$ *when* f *and* ϕ *are real is*

$$\sum_{r=1}^{n} \omega(f; \delta_r)|\phi(x_r)-\phi(x_{r-1})|.$$

One of the commonest cases of integrability is covered by

Theorem 320. *Suppose* f *is continuous and* ϕ *has bounded variation in* $[a, b]$; *then* $f\,d\phi$ *is integrable over* $[a, b]$.

Proof. Suppose N_1 and N_2 are nets over $[a, b]$ and $N_1 \subset N_2$; let ω_r be the greatest value of $\omega(f; \delta)$ for cells δ of N_r: then (see def. 72)

$$(6) \qquad |\sigma_{N_2}(f; \phi)-\sigma_{N_1}(f; \phi)| \leqslant \omega_1 T(\phi; [a, b]);$$

this follows from the fact that if $[\alpha_1, \alpha_k]$ is a cell of N_1 and $\alpha_1 < \alpha_2 < \dots < \alpha_k$, then

$$|f(\alpha_k)\{\phi(\alpha_k)-\phi(\alpha_1)\} - \sum_{r=2}^{k} f(\alpha_r)\{\phi(\alpha_r)-\phi(\alpha_{r-1})\}|$$

$$= \left| \sum_{r=2}^{k} \{f(\alpha_k)-f(\alpha_r)\}\{\phi(\alpha_r)-\phi(\alpha_{r-1})\} \right| \leqslant \omega_1 \sum_{r=2}^{k} |\phi(\alpha_r)-\phi(\alpha_{r-1})|.$$

Let N_n be the net obtained by dividing $[a, b]$ into 2^n equal parts. Assume, as we may without loss of generality, that $T(\phi; [a, b]) = 1$. Then by (6)

$$|\sigma_{N_{n+p}}-\sigma_{N_n}| \leqslant \omega_n \quad \text{for} \quad p = 1, 2, \dots .$$

Since f is uniformly continuous in $[a, b]$, $\omega_n \to 0$, and it follows from the general principle of convergence that σ_{N_n} converges as $n \to \infty$, say to σ.

Now let ϵ be any positive number. Choose n so large and N so fine that the oscillation of f in any cell of N or N_n is less than ϵ. By (6), if S_n is the union of N and N_n, then

$$|\sigma_N(f; \phi)-\sigma_{N_n}(f; \phi)| \leqslant |\sigma_N(f; \phi)-\sigma_{S_n}(f; \phi)|+|\sigma_{S_n}(f; \phi)$$
$$-\sigma_{N_n}(f; \phi)| < 2\epsilon.$$

This being so for all large n, $|\sigma_N(f; \phi)-\sigma| \leqslant 2\epsilon$ provided $g(N)$ is small enough, i.e. $\sigma_N(f; \phi) \to \sigma$ as $g(N) \to 0$. Since

$$|\sigma_{N^*}(f; \phi)-\sigma_N(f; \phi)| \to 0 \quad \text{as } g(N) \to 0$$

(th. 319 (iv)), this completes the proof that $\sigma_{N^*}(f; \phi) \to \sigma$ as $g(N) \to 0$.

The integrals whose existence is proved in th. 320 can often be evaluated as Riemann or as Lebesgue integrals or as sums of infinite series.

Theorem 321. *Suppose f is continuous and real and ϕ is strictly increasing in $[a, b]$; then*

$$\int\limits_a^b f(x)\, d\phi(x) = (R) \int\limits_{\phi(a)}^{\phi(b)} f\{\phi^{-1}(y)\}\, dy,$$

where $\phi^{-1}(y)$ is the upper bound of x in $[a, b]$ with $\phi(x) < y$.

Proof. For $\phi(a) \leqslant y \leqslant \phi(b)$, $\phi^{-1}(y)$ is non-decreasing and lies in $[a, b]$. Since $\phi^{-1}\{\phi(x)\} = x$ for all x in $[a, b]$, it follows that every number in $[a, b]$ is a value of ϕ^{-1} and hence ϕ^{-1} has no discontinuities. Thus if $a \leqslant \alpha < \beta \leqslant b$, $f\{\phi^{-1}(y)\}$ is a continuous function of y for $\phi(\alpha) \leqslant y \leqslant \phi(\beta)$ and

$$(R) \int\limits_{\phi(\alpha)}^{\phi(\beta)} f\{\phi^{-1}(y)\}\, dy = \{\phi(\beta) - \phi(\alpha)\} f(\xi)$$

for some ξ in $\phi^{-1}\{[\phi(\alpha), \phi(\beta)]\}$, i.e. for some ξ in $[\alpha, \beta]$. If $a = x_0 < x_1 < \ldots < x_n = b$ defines a net N, there must be a ξ_r in each $[x_{r-1}, x_r]$ such that

$$(R) \int\limits_{\phi(a)}^{\phi(b)} f\{\phi^{-1}(y)\}\, dy = \sum_{r=1}^n (R) \int\limits_{\phi(x_{r-1})}^{\phi(x_r)} f\{\phi^{-1}(y)\}\, dy = \sum_{r=1}^n f(\xi_r)\{\phi(x_r)$$
$$-\phi(x_{r-1})\}.$$

This holds for all N, and since the last written sum tends to the integral of $f d\phi$ over $[a, b]$ (th. 320), this completes the proof.

Theorem 322. *Suppose f is continuous and ϕ' is integrable-R over $[a, b]$; then*

$$(7) \qquad\qquad \int\limits_a^b f\, d\phi = (R) \int\limits_a^b f(x)\phi'(x)\, dx.$$

Proof. Let $a = x_0 < x_1 < \ldots < x_n = b$ define N. For each r there is a ξ_r in (x_{r-1}, x_r) satisfying $\phi(x_r) - \phi(x_{r-1}) = (x_r - x_{r-1})\phi'(\xi_r)$. If we use these ξ_r to define N^* we get

$$(8) \qquad\qquad \sigma_{N^*}(f; \phi) = \sum_{r=1}^n (x_r - x_{r-1}) f(\xi_r)\phi'(\xi_r).$$

ϕ' being bounded, $T(\phi; [a, b]) < \infty$, and so by th. 320 the left-hand side of (8) tends to that of (7) as $g(N) \to 0$ while the right-hand side of (8) tends to the Riemann integral of $f\phi'$ over $[a, b]$.

The class of functions f which are integrable $d\phi$ is widened by the following generalisation of th. 322.

Theorem 322.1. *Suppose f is integrable-R over $[a, b]$ and ϕ is absolutely continuous, i.e. (th. 274)*

$$(9) \qquad \phi(x) - \phi(a) = \int_a^x \phi'(t)\, dt \quad \text{for} \quad a \leqslant x \leqslant b.$$

Then f is integrable $d\phi$ over $[a, b]$ and

$$(10) \qquad \int_a^b f(x)\, d\phi(x) = \int_a^b f(x)\phi'(x)\, dx$$

(the integrals on the right-hand side of (9) and (10) are Lebesgue integrals).

Proof. Choose any N^* over $[a, b]$; by th. 274,

$$\sum_{r=1}^n f(\xi_r)\{\phi(x_r) - \phi(x_{r-1})\} = \int_a^b f_N^*(x)\phi'(x)\, dx$$

where

$$f_N^*(x) = f(\xi_r) \quad \text{for} \quad x_{r-1} \leqslant x < x_r \quad (r = 1, 2, ..., n).$$

Using th. 230, it remains now to prove that

$$(11) \qquad \lim_{g(N) \to 0} \int_a^b \{f(x) - f_N^*(x)\}\phi'(x)\, dx = 0.$$

Choose any $\epsilon > 0$ and let $S_N(\epsilon)$ be the set of x with $|f(x) - f_N^*(x)| > \epsilon$; by th. 230

$$(12) \qquad \left| \int_a^b \{f(x) - f_N^*(x)\}\phi'(x)\, dx \right| \leqslant \epsilon \int_a^b |\phi'(x)|\, dx + K \int_{S_N(\epsilon)} |\phi'(x)|\, dx$$

where K is the oscillation of f in $[a, b]$. Now, for real f,

$$\epsilon |S_N(\epsilon)| \leqslant \int_a^b |f(x) - f_N^*(x)|\, dx \leqslant U(f; N) - L(f; N),$$

from which we see, by th. 56, that $|S_N(\epsilon)| \to 0$ as $g(N) \to 0$. Thus

$$\lim_{g(N) \to 0} \int_{S_N(\epsilon)} |\phi'(x)|\, dx = 0 \quad \text{(th. 236)};$$

this and (12) justify (11). If f is complex, the above argument applies to its real and imaginary parts and th. 318 (iii) finishes the proof.

The theorem on integration by parts for Stieltjes integrals is remarkably simple and it serves to establish the integrability of a wide class of functions.

Theorem 323. *Suppose f is integrable $d\phi$ over $[a, b]$; then ϕ is integrable df over $[a, b]$ and*

$$\int\limits_a^b \phi \, df + \int\limits_a^b f \, d\phi = f(b)\phi(b) - f(a)\phi(a).$$

Proof. Let

$$\xi_0 = a = x_0 \leqslant \xi_1 \leqslant x_1 \leqslant \ldots \leqslant \xi_n \leqslant x_n = b = \xi_{n+1}$$

define N^*. Then

$$\sum_{r=1}^n \phi(\xi_r)\{f(x_r) - f(x_{r-1})\}$$

$$= \sum_{r=1}^n \phi(\xi_r)f(x_r) - \sum_{r=0}^{n-1} \phi(\xi_{r+1})f(x_r)$$

$$= f(b)\phi(b) - f(a)\phi(a) - \sum_{r=0}^n \{\phi(\xi_{r+1}) - \phi(\xi_r)\}f(x_r).$$

The last written summation is a Stieltjes sum of f with respect to ϕ for a net whose gauge is at most $2g(N)$; hence its limit, as $g(N) \to 0$, is the integral of $fd\phi$ over $[a, b]$. This completes the proof.

In contrast with integrals defined earlier, the integrability of $f \, d\phi$ over $[a, b]$ and over $[b, c]$ does not in general imply integrability over $[a, c]$. The f and ϕ defined in the example preceding th. 317 illustrate this. By th. 318 $f \, d\phi$ is integrable over $[-1, 0]$ and over $[0, 1]$ but not, by th. 317, over $[-1, 1]$. However,

Theorem 324. *Suppose f is integrable $d\phi$ over $[a, b]$ and over $[b, c]$, and f and ϕ are not both discontinuous at b, i.e. $\omega(f; b)\omega(\phi; b) = 0$. Then*

(13) $$\int\limits_a^c f \, d\phi = \int\limits_a^b f \, d\phi + \int\limits_b^c f \, d\phi.$$

Proof. Let N be a net over $[a, c]$. If $b \in N$ then $\sigma_{N^*}(f; \phi)$ will be arbitrarily close to the right-hand side of (13) if N is fine enough. If, however, b is interior to a cell $[x_{\rho-1}, x_\rho]$, the change made in

$\sigma_{N^*}(f; \phi)$ by substituting b for ξ_ρ is not greater than $\omega(f; [x_{\rho-1}, x_\rho])$ $|\phi(x_{\rho-1}) - \phi(x_\rho)|$ in magnitude, and this change is arbitrarily small if $g(N)$ is small enough since $\omega(f; b)\omega(\phi; b) = 0$. The changed value of $\sigma_{N^*}(f; \phi)$ is however a Stieltjes sum of f with respect to ϕ for a net including b, and this case has been dealt with. It follows that in all cases $\sigma_{N^*}(f; \phi)$ tends to the right-hand side of (13) as $g(N) \to 0$.

Conversely

Theorem 325. *Suppose f is integrable $d\phi$ over $[a, c]$; then for every b in (a, c)*

$$\int\limits_a^b f\, d\phi + \int\limits_b^c f\, d\phi = \int\limits_a^c f\, d\phi.$$

Proof. If N_1 and N_2 are nets over $[a, b]$ and $[b, c]$ respectively, then their union is a net over $[a, c]$ and so, if $\epsilon > 0$ is chosen,

$$(14) \qquad \left| \sigma_{N_1^*}(f; \phi) + \sigma_{N_2^*}(f; \phi) - \int\limits_a^c f\, d\phi \right| < \epsilon$$

for all N_1 and N_2 sufficiently fine. Keeping N_2 fixed and varying N_1 it follows that, for all N_{11} and N_{12} over $[a, b]$ with fine enough gauge,

$$\left| \sigma_{N_{11}^*}(f; \phi) - \sigma_{N_{12}^*}(f; \phi) \right| < 2\epsilon.$$

This, by th. 316, implies the integrability of $f\, d\phi$ over $[a, b]$. A similar argument applies to $[b, c]$, and the result follows from (14).

Theorem 326. *Let ϕ be a step function whose discontinuities in $[a, b]$ are at $t_1 < t_2 < \ldots < t_k$; suppose f is bounded in $[a, b]$ and continuous at $t_1, t_2, \ldots, t_k$. Then*

$$\int\limits_a^b f\, d\phi = \sum_{r=1}^k j(t_r)f(t_r)$$

where

$$j(t) = \lim_{\epsilon \to +0} \{\phi(t+\epsilon) - \phi(t-\epsilon)\} \quad if \quad a < t < b,$$

$$j(a) = \lim_{\epsilon \to +0} \{\phi(a+\epsilon) - \phi(a)\}, \qquad j(b) = \lim_{\epsilon \to +0} \{\phi(b) - \phi(b-\epsilon)\}.$$

Proof. For $2 \leqslant r \leqslant k$, th. 318 (v) gives

$$\int\limits_{t_{r-1}}^{t_r} f\, d\phi = f(t_{r-1})\{c_r - \phi(t_{r-1})\} + f(t_r)\{\phi(t_r) - c_r\}$$

where c_r is the value of ϕ in (t_{r-1}, t_r). Hence by th. 324

$$\int_{t_1}^{t_k} f \, d\phi = f(t_k)\phi(t_k) - f(t_1)\phi(t_1) + \sum_{r=1}^{k-1} f(t_r)c_{r+1} - \sum_{r=2}^{k} f(t_r)c_r$$

$$= f(t_k)\{\phi(t_k) - c_k\} + f(t_1)\{c_2 - \phi(t_1)\} + \sum_{r=2}^{k-1} j(t_r)f(t_r).$$

Further application of th. 318 (v), depending on whether $t_1 = a$ or $t_k = b$, completes the proof.

This theorem is generalised below.

Theorem 327. *Let $w_1, w_2, \ldots$ be complex numbers with $\sum\limits_{r=1}^{\infty} |w_r| < \infty$, and let $\{t_n\}$ be a sequence in $[a, b]$. Suppose*

$$\phi = \sum_{r=1}^{\infty} w_r \chi_r \quad where \quad \chi_r(x) = \begin{cases} 0 \ if \ x \leqslant t_r \\ 1 \ if \ x > t_r. \end{cases}$$

Then for every f continuous on $[a, b]$

$$\int_a^b f \, d\phi = \sum_{r=1}^{\infty} w_r f(t_r).$$

Proof. If $a \leqslant \alpha < \beta \leqslant b$, then

$$\chi_r(\beta) - \chi_r(\alpha) = \begin{cases} 1 \ if \ \alpha \leqslant t_r < \beta. \\ 0 \ \text{otherwise} \end{cases}$$

Hence $\phi(\beta) - \phi(\alpha)$, which is

$$\sum_{r=1}^{\infty} w_r \{\chi_r(\beta) - \chi_r(\alpha)\},$$

cannot, in magnitude, exceed the sum of those $|w_r|$ for which $\alpha \leqslant t_r < \beta$. This implies $T(\phi; [a, b]) < \infty$, and a similar argument shows that

(15) $$T\left(\sum_{r=n}^{\infty} w_r \chi_r; [a, b]\right) \to 0 \quad \text{as} \quad n \to \infty.$$

By th. 320, f is integrable $d\phi$ over $[a, b]$, and so by th. 318 (iv)

$$\int_a^b f \, d\phi = \sum_{r=1}^{n} w_r \int_a^b f \, d\chi_r + \int_a^b f \, d\left(\sum_{r>n} w_r \chi_r\right).$$

By th. 319 (ii) and (15) this implies

$$\int\limits_a^b f \, d\phi = \sum_{r=1}^\infty w_r \int\limits_a^b f \, dX_r;$$

since

$$\int\limits_a^b f \, dX_r = \int\limits_{t_r}^b f \, dX_r = f(t_r)$$

by th. 318 (v), this completes the proof.

The argument of th. 327 can be further generalised to prove

Theorem 328. *Suppose f is integrable $d\phi_r$ over $[a, b]$ for $r = 1, 2,...,$ and $\sum\limits_r T(\phi_r; [a, b]) < \infty$. Then*

$$\int\limits_a^b f \, d\Big(\sum_{r=1}^\infty \phi_r \Big) = \sum_{r=1}^\infty \int\limits_a^b f \, d\phi_r \quad if \quad \sum_{r=1}^\infty \phi_r(a) \ converges.$$

Other useful theorems on Stieltjes integration of limit functions are the following.

Theorem 329. *Suppose $f_1, f_2, \ldots$ are all integrable $d\phi$ over $[a, b]$ in which ϕ has bounded variation. Suppose also that $f_n(x)$ converges uniformly to $f(x)$ in $[a, b]$; then*

$$\int\limits_a^b \lim_{n \to \infty} f_n(x) \, d\phi(x) = \lim_{n \to \infty} \int\limits_a^b f_n(x) \, d\phi(x).$$

Proof. Let $I_n = \int\limits_a^b f_n \, d\phi$. By th. 318 (iii) and th. 319 (ii)

$$|I_n - I_{n+p}| \leqslant M(|f_n - f_{n+p}|; J) T(\phi; J), \quad J = [a, b],$$

and this, by the general principle of convergence, implies that I_n tends to a finite limit, say I, as $n \to \infty$. Now let ϵ be any chosen positive number; choose $q(\epsilon)$ so that

(16) $|I_q - I| < \epsilon \quad \text{and} \quad M(|f - f_q|; J) < \epsilon.$

For every N^* over J

$$|\sigma_{N*}(f; \phi) - I| \leqslant |\sigma_{N*}(f; \phi) - I_q| + |I_q - I|$$

and

$$|\sigma_{N*}(f_q; \phi) - I_q| < \epsilon \quad \text{if } N \text{ is fine enough};$$

hence by (16)

$$|\sigma_{N*}(f; \phi) - I| < 2\epsilon + |\sigma_{N*}(f; \phi) - \sigma_{N*}(f_q; \phi)| < 2\epsilon + \epsilon T(\phi; J)$$

if N is fine enough. This completes the proof.

Theorem 330. *Suppose $f_1, f_2, \ldots$ are real and continuous and they converge boundedly to f which is continuous on $[a, b]$; then, if ϕ has bounded variation in $[a, b]$,*

$$\int_a^b f(x)\, d\phi(x) = \lim_{n\to\infty} \int_a^b f_n(x)\, d\phi(x).$$

Proof. If ϕ increases strictly in $[a, b]$ then by ths. 321 and 223

$$\int_a^b f\, d\phi = \int_{\phi(a)}^{\phi(b)} f\{\phi^{-1}(y)\}\, dy = \lim_{n\to\infty} \int_{\phi(a)}^{\phi(b)} f_n\{\phi^{-1}(y)\}\, dy = \lim_{n\to\infty} \int_a^b f_n\, d\phi.$$

If ϕ is real and of bounded variation, it is the difference of two increasing functions (th. 267) which will be strictly increasing if x is added to each; if ϕ is complex, the above will apply to its real and imaginary parts, and finally th. 318 (iv) completes the proof.

In contrast with the Lebesgue integral, the Stieltjes integral is not always a continuous function of its limits. Thus if $\phi(x) = 0$ for $0 \leqslant x < 1$ and $\phi(1) = 1$ then by th. 318 (i)

$$\int_0^t 1\, d\phi = \begin{cases} 0 & \text{if } t < 1 \\ 1 & \text{if } t = 1. \end{cases}$$

Theorem 331. *Suppose f is integrable $d\phi$ over $[a, b]$ and (th. 325)*

$$F(t) = \int_a^t f(x)\, d\phi(x) \quad \text{for} \quad a \leqslant t \leqslant b.$$

Then, if ϕ is continuous at T, so is F.

Proof. Consider $a < T < b$. Choose $\epsilon > 0$ and then $\delta > 0$ so that

(17) $$\left| \sigma_{N*}(f; \phi) - \int_T^b f\, d\phi \right| < \epsilon$$

for every N^* over $[T, b]$ with $g(N) < \delta$. Now take any h with

(18) $$0 < h < \delta \quad \text{and} \quad |f(T)\{\phi(T+h) - \phi(T)\}| < \epsilon.$$

If S is a net over $[T+h, b]$ with $g(S) < \delta$, then by (17)

$$|f(T)\{\phi(T+h)-\phi(T)\}+\sigma_S(f;\phi)-\int\limits_T^b f\,d\phi| < 2\epsilon.$$

Letting $g(S) \to 0$, we see from this and (18) that

$$\left|\int\limits_{T+h}^b f\,d\phi - \int\limits_T^b f\,d\phi\right| < 2\epsilon \quad \text{whenever} \quad 0 < h < \delta.$$

The proof is then completed by a similar argument when $h < 0$. A slight but obvious modification is needed if T is a or b.

Theorem 332. *Suppose f is integrable $d\phi$ over $[a, b]$ and*

$$F(t) = \int\limits_a^t f(x)\,d\phi(x) \quad a \leqslant t \leqslant b.$$

Suppose f is continuous and ϕ differentiable at T and that ϕ is monotonic in some interval centred at T. Then $F'(T) = f(T)\phi'(T)$.

Proof. Since

$$F(T+h)-F(T) = \int\limits_T^{T+h} \{f(x)-f(T)\}\,d\phi + f(T)\{\phi(T+h)-\phi(T)\},$$

it follows from th. 319 (ii) that for $h > 0$

$$(19) \quad \left|\frac{F(T+h)-F(T)}{h}-f(T)\frac{\phi(T+h)-\phi(T)}{h}\right|$$
$$< \omega(f;[T, T+h])\frac{|\phi(T+h)-\phi(T)|}{h}.$$

A similar inequality holds for negative h. Since $\omega(f;[T, T+h]) \to 0$ as $h \to 0$, and ϕ is differentiable at T, the result follows at once from (19).

The assumption in th. 332 that f is continuous and ϕ differentiable at T will not by itself make $F'(T) = f(T)\phi'(T)$ as the following example shows.

Example. We define f and ϕ on $[0, 1]$ as follows.

$$(20) \qquad \text{For } n = 1, 2,\dots \quad f(x) = \begin{cases} x^{\frac{1}{2}} & \text{if } x = (2n)^{-\frac{1}{2}} \\ 0 & \text{if } x = (2n-1)^{-\frac{1}{2}}, \end{cases}$$

$f(0) = 0$, and f is linear in $[(n+1)^{-\frac{1}{2}}, n^{-\frac{1}{2}}]$.

(21)   For $n = 1, 2,...,$ $\phi(x) = x^2$ if $x = (2n)^{-\frac{1}{2}}$, ϕ is constant in $[(2n)^{-\frac{1}{2}}, (2n-1)^{-\frac{1}{2}}]$, and $\phi(x) = 0$ for all x which do not belong to any such closed interval.

f and ϕ are clearly of unbounded variation in $[0, 1]$ and so the integrability of $f\,d\phi$ is not apparent. If q is any chosen positive integer and $X_q = (2q+\frac{1}{2})^{-\frac{1}{2}}$, then ϕ is a step function and f is continuous in $[X_q, 1]$; hence, by th. 326, and using (20 and (21),

$$(22) \qquad \int\limits_{X_q}^{1} f\,d\phi = \sum_{n=1}^{q} \left(\frac{1}{\sqrt{2n}}\right)^{\frac{1}{2}}\left(\frac{1}{\sqrt{2n}}\right)^{2} = \sum_{n=1}^{q} (2n)^{-\frac{5}{4}}.$$

Now choose any positive number ϵ and then q so that $\sum\limits_{n=q}^{\infty} (2n)^{-\frac{5}{4}} < \epsilon$. Let N be any net over $[0, 1]$ which includes X_q and satisfies

$$(23) \qquad \left| \int\limits_{X_q}^{1} f\,d\phi - \sum_{r} f(\xi_r)\{\phi(x_r) - \phi(x_{r-1})\} \right| < \epsilon,$$

the summation being over all cells of N in $[X_q, 1]$. To estimate $\sigma_{N*}(f; \phi)$, we have next to consider the cells of N in $[0, X_q]$. We can ignore every cell which has no point $n^{-\frac{1}{2}}$ in it, for in such a cell ϕ is constant and there is no contribution to σ. For every other cell δ let $\{n(\delta)\}^{-\frac{1}{2}}$ be the greatest number $n^{-\frac{1}{2}}$ in δ. Then in δ

$$0 \leqslant \phi(x) < \{n(\delta)-1\}^{-1} \quad \text{and} \quad 0 \leqslant f(x) \leqslant \{n(\delta)-1\}^{-\frac{1}{2}},$$

and so the contribution to σ from δ will be less than $\{n(\delta)-1\}^{-\frac{5}{4}}$ while $n(\delta) \geqslant 2q+1$ (since $X_q = (2q+\frac{1}{2})^{-\frac{1}{2}}$). Since no point $n^{-\frac{1}{2}}$ can belong to more than two cells, it follows that the contribution to σ from all the cells of N in $[0, X_q]$ will be less than $2 \sum\limits_{r \geqslant 2q} r^{-\frac{5}{4}}$ which is less than $4 \sum\limits_{n \geqslant q} (2n)^{-\frac{5}{4}}$ which is less than 4ϵ.

Thus, by (23)

$$\left| \sigma_{N*}(f; \phi) - \sum_{n=1}^{\infty} (2n)^{-\frac{5}{4}} \right| < 6\epsilon$$

for all fine enough nets N which include X_q. Since ϕ is continuous at X_q, the latter restriction on N is of no importance and it follows that the integral of $f\,d\phi$ over $[0, 1]$ exists and is equal to $\sum\limits_{n} (2n)^{-\frac{5}{4}}$.

Hence, by (22)

$$\int\limits_{0}^{X_q} f\,d\phi = \sum_{n=q+1}^{\infty} (2n)^{-\frac{5}{4}} > \int\limits_{q+1}^{\infty} (2x)^{-\frac{5}{4}}\,dx$$

from which we see that

$$\lim_{q \to \infty} \frac{1}{X_q} \int_0^{X_q} f \, d\phi = \infty,$$

in spite of the fact that f is continuous and $\phi'(0) = 0$.

§ 4. Applications of Stieltjes Integration

1. The Lebesgue integral of a function which is bounded and measurable in a set of finite measure can be expressed as a Stieltjes integral and, incidentally, as a Riemann integral as follows. Suppose f is measurable in B and $mB < \infty$ and $\lambda < f(P) < \Lambda$ for all P in B. If $e(y)$ is the measure of those P in B with $f(P) < y$, then $e(\lambda) = 0$, $e(\Lambda) = mB$ and $e(y)$ is monotonic in $[\lambda, \Lambda]$. Hence $e(y)$ has a Riemann integral over $[\lambda, \Lambda]$ and by th. 323

$$\int_\lambda^\Lambda y \, de(y) = \Lambda mB - (R) \int_\lambda^\Lambda e(y) \, dy.$$

If $\lambda = y_0 < y_1 < \ldots < y_n = \Lambda$, then $e(y_r) - e(y_{r-1}) = mB_r$ where B_r is the set of P in B with $y_{r-1} \leqslant f(P) < y_r$. Since

$$(mB_r)y_{r-1} \leqslant \int_{B_r} f(P) \, dP \leqslant (mB_r)y_r,$$

we have

$$\sum_{r=1}^n y_{r-1}\{e(y_r) - e(y_{r-1})\} \leqslant \int_B f(P) \, dP \leqslant \sum_{r=1}^n y_r\{e(y_r) - e(y_{r-1})\}.$$

Both the Stieltjes sums in the last inequality tend to the integral of $y \, de(y)$ over $[\lambda, \Lambda]$, and so

$$\int_B f(P) \, dP = \int_\lambda^\Lambda y \, de(y).$$

2. The second mean-value theorem for Lebesgue integrals (th. 244) can be proved, using th. 322.1, by writing

$$\int_a^b f(x)g(x) \, dx = -\int_a^b g(x) \, dF(x) \quad \text{where} \quad F(x) = \int_x^b f(t) \, dt.$$

By th. 323,

$$\int_a^b f(x)g(x) \, dx = g(a)F(a) + \int_a^b F(x) \, dg(x) = g(a)F(a) + \{g(b) - g(a)\}F(\xi)$$

for some ξ in $[a, b]$ (th. 319 (iii)). Hence

$$\int\limits_a^b f(x)g(x)\,dx = g(a)\int\limits_a^\xi f(t)\,dt + g(b)\int\limits_\xi^b f(t)\,dt.$$

3. The theorem on integration by parts for Lebesgue integrals can be proved similarly since (with the notation of th. 242),

$$\int\limits_a^b f(x)G(x)\,dx = \int\limits_a^b G(x)\,dF(x) = [FG]_a^b - \int\limits_a^b F(x)\,dG(x)$$

(ths. 322.1 and 323). A further application of th. 322.1 gives the desired formula.

4. Contour integrals

Let ϕ be complex-valued, continuous, and of bounded variation in $[0, 1]$. As t increases from 0 to 1, $\phi(t)$ describes a path Γ in the complex plane whose total length is $T(\phi; [0, 1])$. If $f(z)$ is defined for all z on Γ, then the integral of $f(z)\,dz$ along Γ is by definition

$$\int\limits_0^1 f\{\phi(t)\}\,d\phi(t)$$

if this exists. It is also denoted by $\int_\Gamma f(z)\,dz$. By th. 320 the integral must exist if $f\{\phi(t)\}$ is continuous on $[0, 1]$, and by th. 319 (ii)

$$\left|\int\limits_\Gamma f(z)\,dz\right| \leqslant ML$$

where L is the length of Γ and M is the greatest value of $|f(z)|$ for z on Γ.

Example. If Γ is the circular path $\phi(t) = e^{2\pi it}$ $(0 \leqslant t \leqslant 1)$ and f is continuous on Γ then by th. 322

$$\int\limits_\Gamma \frac{f(z)}{z}\,dz = 2\pi i \int\limits_0^1 f(e^{2\pi it})\,dt$$

The following basic theorem relates contour integration to inverse differentiation.

Theorem 333. *Let Γ be given by $\phi(t)$ $(0 \leqslant t \leqslant 1)$ and suppose $\phi(t)$ is differentiable for all but an enumerable set of values of t. Suppose*

$f\{\phi(t)\}$ *is integrable-R over* $[0, 1]$ *and there exists a function* F *such that for every* ζ *on* Γ

(24) $$\lim_{z \to \zeta} \frac{F(z) - F(\zeta)}{z - \zeta} = f(\zeta), z \text{ being restricted to } \Gamma.$$

Then

$$\int_\Gamma f(z) \, dz = F\{\phi(1)\} \quad F\{\phi(0)\}.$$

Proof. By ths. 269 and 264,

$$\phi(T) - \phi(0) = \int_0^T \phi'(t) \, dt \quad \text{for} \quad 0 \leqslant T \leqslant 1.$$

Hence by th. 322 (or th. 322.1)

(25) $$\int_0^1 f\{\phi(t)\} \, d\phi(t) = \int_0^1 f\{\phi(t)\}\phi'(t) \, dt.$$

By hypothesis

$$\frac{d}{dt} F\{\phi(t)\} = f\{\phi(t)\}\phi'(t)$$

for all but an enumerable set of t. Since $F \{\phi(t)\}$ is continuous for $0 \leqslant t \leqslant 1$ by (24), it follows from th. 264 and (25) that

$$F\{\phi(1)\} - F\{\phi(0)\} = \int_0^1 f\{\phi(t)\}\phi'(t) \, dt = \int_\Gamma f(z) \, dz.$$

If $f\{\phi(t)\}$ is continuous on $[0, 1]$ and the limit in (24) is approached uniformly (i.e. for every positive number ϵ there is a positive number η such that

$$\left| \frac{F(z) - F(\zeta)}{z - \zeta} - f(\zeta) \right| < \epsilon$$

for all z and ζ on Γ with $0 < |z - \zeta| < \eta$), then the conclusion of th. 333 is valid without making any assumptions about the differentiability of ϕ. To see this we note that if $[t_{r-1}, t_r]$ is a cell of any sufficiently fine net N over $[0, 1]$ then $|\phi(t_r) - \phi(t_{r-1})| < \eta$ and hence

$$|F\{\phi(t_r)\} - F\{\phi(t_{r-1})\} - \{\phi(t_r) - \phi(t_{r-1})\}f\{\phi(t_{r-1})\}| \leqslant \epsilon|\phi(t_r) - \phi(t_{r-1})|,$$

which implies that

$$\left| F\{\phi(1)\} - F\{\phi(0)\} - \sum_{r=1}^n \{\phi(t_r) - \phi(t_{r-1})\}f\{\phi(t_{r-1})\} \right| \leqslant \epsilon T(\phi; [0, 1]).$$

The proof is then completed by th. 320.

§5. Riesz's Theorem

In § 1 we emphasised the linear character of integration. The Stieltjes integral of $fd\phi$ is linear on f (th. 318 (iii)) and, for a given ϕ with bounded variation in $[a, b]$, it is defined for all f continuous on $[a, b]$ (th. 320). It is a remarkable fact that any linear operation which assigns a real number to every real function continuous on $[a, b]$ is, if continuous (see below), expressible as a Stieltjes integral.

We denote by $\mathscr{C}$ the class of all real functions f which are continuous on $[0, 1]$; for each f in $\mathscr{C}$, $\|f\|$ denotes the maximum of $|f(x)|$ for $0 \leqslant x \leqslant 1$. Suppose that to every f in $\mathscr{C}$ is assigned a real number, denoted by $\Omega(f)$, so that the following conditions are satisfied:

(i) if f_1 and f_2 are in $\mathscr{C}$ then $\Omega(\lambda f_1 + \mu f_2) = \lambda\Omega(f_1) + \mu\Omega(f_2)$ for all real constants λ and μ,

(ii) Ω is continuous, i.e. $\Omega(f) \to 0$ as $\|f\| \to 0$.

Ω is then said to be a real continuous linear functional on $\mathscr{C}$.

Two immediate consequences of this definition will be useful in what follows; they are

(α) if $F_1, F_2, ..., F_q$ belong to $\mathscr{C}$ then

$$\sum_{r=1}^{q-1} |\Omega(F_r) - \Omega(F_{r+1})| = \Omega\left(\sum_{r=1}^{q-1} \epsilon_r(F_r - F_{r+1})\right)$$

where $\epsilon_1, \epsilon_2, ..., \epsilon_{q-1}$ are all ± 1;

(β) there is a real number B (depending on Ω) such that

$$|\Omega(f)| \leqslant B\|f\| \quad \text{for all } f \text{ in } \mathscr{C}.$$

To justify (α) we observe that if θ is a *real* number then $|\theta|$ is θ or $-\theta$; hence, by (i)

$$|\Omega(F_r) - \Omega(F_{r+1})| = |\Omega(F_r - F_{r+1})| = \epsilon_r\Omega(F_r - F_{r+1}) = \Omega\{\epsilon_r(F_r - F_{r+1})\},$$

and by summing a series of such terms we obtain (α).

To justify (β) we use (ii) which implies the existence of a real number B such that $|\Omega(f)| \leqslant 1$ whenever $\|f\| = 1/B$. Now from the definition of $\|F\|$,

$$\left\|\frac{f}{B\|f\|}\right\| = 1/B \quad \text{if} \quad \|f\| \neq 0,$$

and so, by (i), for all f with $\|f\| \neq 0$,

$$|\Omega(f)| = B\|f\| \left|\Omega\left(\frac{f}{B\|f\|}\right)\right| \leqslant B\|f\|.$$

The inequality (β) is trivially true when $\|f\| = 0$ by (ii) or by (i).

Theorem 334 (F. Riesz). *Let Ω be a real continuous linear functional on $\mathscr{C}$; then there exists a function ϕ such that*

$$(26) \qquad \Omega(f) = \int\limits_0^1 f(x)\,d\phi(x) \quad \text{for all } f \text{ in } \mathscr{C}.$$

Proof. Assuming that ϕ exists to satisfy (26), we can identify $\phi(X) - \phi(0)$ at any X in $(0, 1)$ for which ϕ is continuous; for if we denote by $f_X^{(\epsilon)}$ the function which is 1 in $[0, X]$, zero in $[X + \epsilon, 1]$ and linear in $[X, X + \epsilon]$, we can show that

$$(27) \qquad \lim_{\epsilon \to 0} \Omega(f_X^{(\epsilon)}) = \phi(X) - \phi(0)$$

as follows.

$$\Omega(f_X^{(\epsilon)}) = \int\limits_0^X 1\,d\phi + \int\limits_X^{X+\epsilon} f_X^{(\epsilon)}\,d\phi + \int\limits_{X+\epsilon}^1 0\,d\phi = \phi(X) - \phi(0) + \int\limits_X^{X+\epsilon} f_X^{(\epsilon)}\,d\phi;$$

Since $f_X^{(\epsilon)}(X + \epsilon) = 0$ and $f_X^{(\epsilon)\prime}(x) = -1/\epsilon$ for $X < x < X + \epsilon$, we have from ths. 323 and 322,

$$\int\limits_X^{X+\epsilon} f_X^{(\epsilon)}\,d\phi = -\phi(X) - \int\limits_X^{X+\epsilon} \phi(x) f_X^{(\epsilon)\prime}(x)\,dx = \frac{1}{\epsilon}\int\limits_X^{X+\epsilon} \{\phi(x) - \phi(X)\}\,dx;$$

because ϕ is continuous at X the last written expression tends to zero as $\epsilon \to 0$ (th. 62 (2)). This proves (27).

We return now to the main proof. For each X in $(0, 1)$ we define a sequence $\chi_X^{(n)}$ in $\mathscr{C}$:

$$(28) \quad \chi_X^{(n)}(x) = 1 \quad \text{in} \quad [0, X], \qquad \chi_X^{(n)}(x) = 0 \quad \text{in} \quad \left[X + \frac{1-X}{n}, 1\right],$$

$$\chi_X^{(n)}(x) \text{ is linear in } \left[X, X + \frac{1-X}{n}\right].$$

It is convenient to define also

$$(28.1) \qquad \chi_0^{(n)} = 0 \quad \text{and} \quad \chi_1^{(n)} = 1 \quad \text{for all } n.$$

A function $\phi(X)$ is now defined for $0 \leqslant X \leqslant 1$ by

$$(29) \qquad \phi(X) = \lim_{n \to \infty} \Omega(\chi_X^{(n)});$$

to prove this limit exists, it is enough to prove that

$$(30) \qquad \sum_{n=1}^\infty \{\Omega(\chi_X^{(n+1)}) - \Omega(\chi_X^{(n)})\} \quad \text{converges.}$$

Choose any X in $[0, 1]$; by (α) we may write

$$(31) \qquad \sum_{n=1}^{\nu} |\Omega(X_X^{(n+1)}) - \Omega(X_X^{(n)})| = \Omega(S_X^{(\nu)})$$

where

$$S_X^{(\nu)}(x) = \sum_{n=1}^{\nu} \epsilon_n \{X_X^{(n+1)}(x) - X_X^{(n)}(x)\}.$$

Since $0 \leqslant X_X^{(n+1)}(x) \leqslant X_X^{(n)}(x) \leqslant 1$, it follows that $\|S_X^{(\nu)}\| \leqslant 1$ and so, applying (β) to (31), we justify (30).

We have now to verify (26). Choose any f in $\mathscr{C}$; if N is an arbitrary net over $[0, 1]$ (with k cells say), we have to prove

$$(32) \qquad \Omega(f) - \sum_{r=1}^{k} f(\xi_r)\{\phi(x_r) - \phi(x_{r-1})\} \to 0 \quad \text{as} \quad g(N) \to 0.$$

Take any positive number ϵ and then any N^* such that

$$(33) \qquad \omega(f; \delta) < \epsilon \quad \text{for every cell } \delta \text{ of } N.$$

We show next that if $\gamma(N)$ is the length of the shortest cell in N, and

$$f^{(\rho)} = \sum_{r=1}^{k} f(\xi_r)\{X_{x_r}^{(\rho)} - X_{x_{r-1}}^{(\rho)}\},$$

then

$$(34) \qquad \|f - f^{(\rho)}\| \leqslant 3\epsilon \quad \text{whenever} \quad \rho^{-1} < \gamma(N).$$

Once this is proved, it will follow that

$$|\Omega(f) - \Omega(f^{(\rho)})| \leqslant 3B\epsilon,$$

i.e.

$$|\Omega(f) - \sum_{r=1}^{k} f(\xi_r)\{\Omega(X_{x_r}^{(\rho)}) - \Omega(X_{x_{r-1}}^{(\rho)})\}| \leqslant 3B\epsilon$$

for all large ρ, and hence by (29) that

$$(35) \qquad |\Omega(f) - \sum_{r=1}^{k} f(\xi_r)\{\phi(x_r) - \phi(x_{r-1})\}| \leqslant 3B\epsilon$$

for all N satisfying (33), i.e. for all N with $g(N)$ small enough; hence (32) will follow from (35). It remains to justify (34). Now by (28.1)

$$(36) \qquad |f(x) - f^{(\rho)}(x)| = |\sum_{r=1}^{k} \{f(x) - f(\xi_r)\}\{X_{x_r}^{(\rho)}(x) - X_{x_{r-1}}^{(\rho)}(x)\}|,$$

and by (28), if $\rho^{-1} < \gamma(N)$,

$$(37) \qquad |X_{x_r}^{(\rho)}(x) - X_{x_{r-1}}^{(\rho)}(x)| \leqslant \begin{cases} 1 \text{ in } (x_{r-1}, x_{r+1}). \\ 0 \text{ elsewhere} \end{cases}$$

Hence, if $x \in [x_{\mu-1}, x_\mu]$, the only non-zero terms of the summation in (36) come from those r such that $[x_{\mu-1}, x_\mu]$ intersects (x_{r-1}, x_{r+1}), i.e. from $r = \mu$ and $r = \mu+1$, so that by (36)

$$
\begin{aligned}
|f(x) - f^{(\rho)}(x)| &\leqslant |f(x) - f(\xi_\mu)| + |f(x) - f(\xi_{\mu+1})| \\
&\leqslant |f(x) - f(\xi_\mu)| + |f(x) - f(x_\mu)| + |f(x_\mu) - f(\xi_{\mu+1})|.
\end{aligned}
$$

Since x and ξ_μ are in $[x_{\mu-1}, x_\mu]$ and $\xi_{\mu+1}$ is in $[x_\mu, x_{\mu+1}]$, it follows from (33) that $|f(x) - f^{(\rho)}(x)| \leqslant 3\epsilon$, and this justifies (34).

1. Nature and non-uniqueness of the function ϕ.

The function ϕ defined in the proof of Riesz's theorem satisfies (26) and also $\phi(0) = 0$. It is of interest to show that there are infinitely many functions ϕ with these properties and to characterise the family of all such ϕ.

In the first place, suppose $\phi = \phi_1$ satisfies (26) and $\phi_1(0) = 0$. Let ψ be any function which has bounded variation in $[0, 1]$, and which vanishes at 0, at 1, and at every point where ψ is continuous. Then if $\phi_2 = \phi_1 + \psi$, it is obvious that $\phi_2(0) = 0$ and also that $\phi = \phi_2$ satisfies (26) if

$$
(38) \qquad \int_0^1 f \, d\psi = 0 \quad \text{for every } f \text{ in } \mathscr{C}.
$$

Now the integral in (38) exists (th. 320) because $f \in \mathscr{C}$ and ψ has bounded variation in $[0, 1]$; hence the value of the integral is the limit of $\sigma_N(f; \psi)$ as $g(N) \to 0$, N being any net over $[0, 1]$. Since the discontinuities of ψ are finite or enumerable (ths. 243 and 267) N can be taken arbitrarily fine but with all its points to be points of continuity of ψ; for such nets $\sigma_N(f; \psi) = 0$ from the definition of ψ: hence (38) holds.

Conversely, if ϕ is any function satisfying (26) and $\phi(0) = 0$, we show that every other function ϕ_1 with the same properties must be such that $\phi - \phi_1$ has bounded variation in $[0, 1]$, vanishes wherever it is continuous and vanishes also at 0 and at 1. If we write ψ for $\phi - \phi_1$ then our hypothesis is that (38) holds and that $\psi(0) = 0$. By taking $f = 1$ it follows from (38) that $\psi(1) = 0$. Furthermore, at any X in $(0, 1)$ for which ψ is continuous, we may consider the function $f_X^{(\epsilon)}$ defined in the proof of th. 334 and deduce from (38) that

$$
0 = \psi(X) + \int_X^{X+\epsilon} f_X^{(\epsilon)} \, d\psi,
$$

and as in the proof of (27) it follows that

$$
-\psi(X) = \lim_{\epsilon \to 0} \int_X^{X+\epsilon} f_X^{(\epsilon)} \, d\psi = 0.
$$

It remains only to prove that ψ has bounded variation in $[0, 1]$, and this is a consequence, as the next theorem shows, of the fact that every f in $\mathscr{C}$ is integrable $d\psi$ over $[0, 1]$.

Theorem 335. *Suppose ϕ is real and bounded but has unbounded variation in $[0, 1]$. Then there exist functions f which are continuous on $[0, 1]$ and are not integrable $d\phi$ over $[0, 1]$.*

Proof. Consider first the case where $T(\phi; [0, h]) = \infty$ whenever $0 < h < 1$. Then there must be a sequence $1 = x_1 > x_2 > \cdots > x_n > x_{n+1} \to 0$ such that for some sequence $1 = n_1 < n_2 < \cdots$

$$(39) \qquad \sum_{n_s \leqslant r < n_{s+1}} \{\phi(x_r) - \phi(x_{r+1})\}\epsilon_r > 1 \quad (s = 1, 2, \ldots)$$

where each ϵ_r is ± 1 (cf. (α) §5). Define f on $[0, 1]$ as follows: $f(0) = 0$, $f(x_r) = \epsilon_r/s$ for $n_s \leqslant r < n_{s+1}$, and f is linear in $[x_{r+1}, x_r]$. Then f is continuous on $[0, 1]$ and by (39)

$$(40) \qquad \sum_{n_s \leqslant r < n_{s+1}} f(x_r)\{\phi(x_r) - \phi(x_{r+1})\} > 1/s \quad (s = 1, 2, \ldots).$$

Now suppose, if possible, that $f\,d\phi$ is integrable over $[0, 1]$. Then there is a positive number η such that the Stieltjes sums of f with respect to ϕ for any two nets over $[0, 1]$ with gauge less than η differ by less than 1 in magnitude. If now n_q is chosen so that $0 < x_{n_q} < \eta$, it follows that for $t > q$

$$\left| f(0)\{\phi(x_{n_q}) - \phi(0)\} - \left(f(0)\{\phi(x_{n_t}) - \phi(0)\} + \right. \right.$$
$$\left. \left. + \sum_{n_q \leqslant r < n_t} f(x_r)\{\phi(x_r) - \phi(x_{r+1})\} \right) \right| < 1.$$

Since $f(0) = 0$, this implies by (40) that

$$\sum_{q \leqslant s < t} 1/s < 1 \quad \text{for all } t > q$$

which is false. Thus $f\,d\phi$ is not integrable over $[0, 1]$.

Consider next the case in which $T(\phi; [0, h]) < \infty$ for some h in $(0, 1)$, and let ξ be the upper bound of all such h. Then either $T(\phi; [\xi_1, \xi]) = \infty$ whenever $0 < \xi_1 < \xi$, or else $T(\phi; [\xi, \xi_2]) = \infty$ whenever $\xi < \xi_2 < 1$. If the latter, we may use the argument given above, replacing the interval $[0, 1]$ by the interval $[\xi, 1]$, and if the former then an obvious variant of this argument would show that there is a continuous function f which is not integrable $d\phi$ over $[0, 1]$.

EXERCISES

1. Prove that every non-enumerable set of real numbers includes a sequence x_1, x_2,... of distinct numbers such that $x_1+x_2+...+x_n+... = \pm\infty$.

2. $\{E_n\}$ is a sequence of enumerable sets, and f_n maps E_n one-one on to the set of all natural numbers. F is the set of all possible objects $(x_1, x_2, ..., x_q)$ where q is any positive integer and $x_r \in E_r$ $(r = 1, 2,..., q)$. f is defined on F by the formula

$$f\{(x_1, x_2,..., x_q)\} = 2^{f_1(x_1)} \cdot 3^{f_2(x_2)}...p_q^{f_q(x_q)}$$

where p_q is the qth prime number (ordered by magnitude). Show that f maps F one-one on to all the integers exceeding 1.

Prove that the set of all polynomials with rational coefficients is enumerable, and deduce that the zeros of all such polynomials form an enumerable set.

3. $f(x)$ is defined for all real x and the limits $f(x+0)$, $f(x-0)$ (the limits of $f(x+h)$ and $f(x-h)$ as $h \to 0$ through positive values) exist and are finite everywhere. If $\theta > 0$, prove that the set of x for which $|f(x+0)-f(x)| > \theta$ has no limit points. Show that the set of discontinuities of f is finite or enumerable.

4. Using the fact that every infinite set contains an enumerable subset, show that if S is infinite and T is enumerable then the union of S and T can be mapped one-one on to S.

5. Find functions which map the interval $(-1, 1)$ one-one on to (i) an arbitrary interval (a, b) of R_1, (ii) on to R_1, (iii) on to $[-1, 1]$.

6. Prove that the rational numbers in $(0, 1)$ can be arranged in a sequence $\{r_n\}$ such that $r_n-r_{n+1} \to 0$ as $n \to \infty$. Hence define a function on $(0, 1)$ which (i) maps $(0, 1)$ one-one on to $[0, 1]$, and (ii) is continuous except at the points of an enumerable set. Prove that a function which satisfies (i) cannot be everywhere continuous.

If $f(x) = \sum_n (nx)n^{-2}$ where $(t) = t-[t]$, where are the discontinuities of f in $(0, 1)$?

7. Prove that the correspondence which assigns the number $2^{-n_1}+2^{-n_2}+...$ to the increasing sequence of integers $n_1 < n_2...$ is one-one. Find a function which maps the aggregate of all positive integer sequences (whether monotonic or not) one-one on to the numbers t with $0 < t \leqslant 1$.

8. q is any chosen integer exceeding 1. If $0 < x \leqslant 1$, define for $r = 1, 2, \ldots$ $a_r(x) = [q^r x] - q[q^{r-1} x]$. Prove (i) $a_r(x)$ is an integer less than q and is the remainder on dividing $[q^r x]$ by q, and (ii)

$$x = \sum_{r=1}^{\infty} a_r(x) q^{-r}.$$

If $y = \sum_{r=1}^{\infty} y_r q^{-r}$, where y_r is an integer, $0 \leqslant y_r < q$, and $a_r(x) = y_r$ for all $r \leqslant \mu$ while $a_{\mu+1}(x) > y_{\mu+1}$, show that either $x > y$ or else $x = y$ and $y_r = q-1$ for all $r > \mu+1$ and $a_{\mu+1}(x) = 1 + y_{\mu+1}$.

9. If q is a fixed integer exceeding 1, and $0 < x \leqslant 1$, define r_k as the greatest integer r satisfying $r q^{-k} < x$, and $a_k = r_k - q r_{k-1}$ ($k = 1, 2, \ldots$); prove that

$$x = \sum_{k=1}^{\infty} a_k q^{-k}, \text{ and } a_k > 0 \text{ for infinitely many } k$$

(the 'normal' expansion of x in scale q). If

$$x = \sum_{r=1}^{\infty} x_r 2^{-r} \quad \text{and} \quad y = \sum_{r=1}^{\infty} y_r 2^{-r}$$

are the normal scale 2 expansions of x and y, and

$$f(x, y) = \sum_{r=1}^{\infty} x_r 2^{1-2r} + \sum_{r=1}^{\infty} y_r 2^{-2r},$$

prove that f maps the unit square $0 < x < 1$, $0 < y < 1$ one-one on to a subset of $(0, 1)$. Prove that every subinterval of the square includes points of discontinuity of f.

10. If $S_1, S_2, \ldots$ are disjoint and each can be mapped one-one on to R_1, prove that $S_1 + S_2 + \ldots$ can be mapped one-one on to R_1. If to every real number t is assigned a set S_t which can be mapped one-one on to R_1, and the sets S_t are disjoint, show that their union can be mapped one-one on to R_1 (see Exercise 9).

11. $\{x_n\}$ is a sequence of numbers in $(0, 1)$ and $x_n = \sum_{r=1}^{\infty} x_n^{(r)} 2^{-r}$ is the normal scale 2 expansion of x_n. If

$$f(\{x_n\}) = \sum_{r=1}^{\infty} \sum_{n=1}^{\infty} x_n^{(r)} 2^{-2^r 3^n},$$

prove that f maps one-one.

12. Let $x = \sum\limits_{r=1}^{\infty} x_r 10^{-r}$ be the normal scale 10 expansion of x. If x is such that $x_r(x_r-1) = 0$ for all $r > N$ while $x_N(x_N-1) \neq 0$, define

$$f(x) = \sum_{r=1}^{\infty} x_{N+r} 2^{-r};$$

let $f(x) = 0$ for all other x. Prove that f is discontinuous at every point of $(0, 1)$ and that the values assumed by $f(x)$ when x is restricted to any subinterval of $(0, 1)$ include all numbers in $(0, 1)$.

13. If f is a real function satisfying $f(x+y) = f(x)+f(y)$ for all real x and y, prove that $f(x) = xf(1)$ for all rational x and that if f is continuous for one argument x then f is everywhere continuous. Prove that $f(x)$ must be $xf(1)$ for all real x if f is monotonic in any one interval.

14. A set $\mathscr{B}$ of real numbers is called a basis for the real numbers over the rationals if every real non-zero x can be expressed in exactly one way as $x = r_1\beta_1 + r_2\beta_2 + ... + r_q\beta_q$ where $\beta_1, \beta_2, ..., \beta_q$ are distinct elements of $\mathscr{B}$ and $r_1, ..., r_q$ are non-zero rational numbers. If $f(x)$ is defined to be the sum of these rational multipliers, and $f(0) = 0$, prove that $f(x+y) = f(x)+f(y)$ for all x and y. Prove that f is discontinuous everywhere. If $\phi(x)$ is the sum of the squares of the multipliers r_n, prove that ϕ is everywhere discontinuous and $\phi(a+h)+\phi(a-h) \geqslant 2\phi(a)$ for all real numbers a and h.

15. Find a function ϕ which is bounded in $(-\infty, \infty)$ and satisfies $\phi(x+y) \leqslant \phi(x)+\phi(y)$ for all real x, y. By assuming the existence of a basis for the real numbers, define a function F which is unbounded in every interval of R_1 and satisfies $F(x+y) \leqslant F(x)+F(y)$ for all real x and y, with equality if and only if $xy = 0$ or else x/y is a positive rational number.

16. $f(x)$ is real and defined for all real x so that for all real a and b, $f(a) \neq 0$ and $f(a+b) = f(a)f(b)$. Prove that $f(x) > 0$ for all x and that $f(x) = \{f(1)\}^x$ for all rational x. Assuming the existence of a basis for the real numbers, find such a function f which is discontinuous everywhere.

17. Let α be the aggregate of all real functions $f(x)$ which are continuous for $-\infty < x < \infty$ and vanish outside a finite interval (the interval depending on f). Show that α includes a sequence

$f_1, f_2,..., f_n,...$ such that every element of α is the limit of a uniformly convergent subsequence of $\{f_n\}$.

18. Suppose a correspondence is defined which assigns to every real number x a set of real numbers $S(x)$ so that to different numbers are assigned different sets. if $\mathscr{E}$ is the set of those numbers θ which satisfy $\theta \ \bar{\in} \ S(\theta)$, prove that $\mathscr{E}$ is different from all the sets $S(x)$.

Given any set E, let $\mathscr{P}(E)$ denote the aggregate of all subsets of E. Prove that E can be mapped one-one on to a subset of $\mathscr{P}(E)$ but not conversely.

19. S and T are disjoint sets, and a function f maps $S+T$ one-one on to a subset of S. A function ϕ is defined on S by the rule $\phi(x) = f^{-1}(x)$ if $x \in \{f(T)+f^2(T)+...+f^n(T)+...\}$ and $\phi(x) = x$ for all other x in S. Prove that ϕ maps S one-one on to $S+T$..

If A and B are disjoint sets such that $A \sim B_1$, where B_1 is a subset of B, and $B \sim A_1$ where A_1 is a subset of A, prove by taking $S = A$ and $T = B-B_1$ that $A \sim B$.

20. If A and B are points of R_n and O is the origin, prove that $OA^2+OB^2 = 2OM^2+\frac{1}{2}AB^2$ (Apollonius, theorem).

21. If A and B are distinct points of a closed sphere in R_n having its centre at O and of unit radius, prove that all points of the 'open segment' joining A and B are in the interior of the sphere, i.e. if $A = (a_1, a_2,..., a_n)$, $B = (b_1, b_2,..., b_n)$, $C = (c_1, c_2,..., c_n)$ and $c_r = \theta a_r+(1-\theta)b_r$, where $0 < \theta < 1$, then $c_1^2+...+c_n^2 < 1$.

If $D = (d_1, d_2,..., d_n)$ is in the interior of the triangle OAB, i.e. $d_r = \theta a_r+\phi b_r$ $(r = 1, 2,..., n)$ where $0 < \theta, 0 < \phi, \theta + \phi < 1$, prove that at least one of the distances OA, OB must exceed the distance OD.

22. If x and y are points of R_n, $x = (x_1, x_2,..., x_n), y = (y_1,..., y_n)$, let $(x|y)$ denote the 'scalar product' $x_1y_1+...+x_ny_n$, and let $\|x\| = (x|x)^{\frac{1}{2}}$. If $x \neq 0$ and $y \neq 0$, prove that (i) $|(x|y)| = \|x\|\|y\|$ if and only if there is a number k such that $x_r = ky_r$ $(r = 1, 2,..., n)$, and (ii) $\|x+y\| = \|x\|+\|y\|$ if and only if there is a positive number k such that $x_r = ky_r$ $(r = 1, 2,..., n)$.

23. A non-empty set in R_n is both open and closed. Prove that it must be the whole of R_n.

24. E and F are sets in R_n and each is the intersection of a sequence of open sets. Show that the union of E and F has the same property.

25. α is an infinite aggregate of disjoint subsets of R_n each of which includes at least one rational point; prove that α is enumerable.

26. A function f defined on R_n is said to have a strict maximum at P_0 if there is a positive number δ such that $f(P) < f(P_0)$ for all P with $0 < \mathrm{dist}\,(P, P_0) < \delta$. Prove that the set of strict maxima of f must be finite or enumerable.

27. Prove that every closed set in R_n is the intersection of a sequence of open sets and that every open set is the union of a sequence of closed sets.

Is the set of all irrational numbers the union of a sequence of closed sets or the intersection of a sequence of open sets? Find a set which is not the intersection of a sequence of open sets or the union of a sequence of closed sets.

28. N is the set of all points (x, y) of R_2 which have at least one of x and y irrational. Prove that every two points of N are vertices of a triangle, two of whose sides are in N and also that every two points of N can be joined by an arc of a circle lying wholly in N.

29. U is an open set in R_n. Points A and B in U are said to be connected in U if there is a finite set of spheres $S_1,...,S_q$ in U such that A is the centre of S_1, B is the centre of S_q, and each S_{r+1} has points in common with S_r. Show that for a given point A, the set of points B connected to A in U is open.

Show that U may be decomposed into a finite or enumerable collection of disjoint open sets $\Omega_1, \Omega_2,...$ such that (i) every pair A, B in Ω_n is connected in Ω_n, (ii) if $A \in \Omega_r$ and $B \in \Omega_s$ and $r \neq s$, then A and B are not connected in U.

30. If $f(x)$ is strictly monotonic in an interval I, prove that $f(I)$ can be expressed as $K+E_1-E_2$ where K is perfect and E_1, E_2 are finite or enumerable.

31. S and T are closed disjoint sets in R_n and S is bounded. Prove that there are points s and t in S and T respectively such that for all σ in S and τ in T, $\mathrm{dist}\,(\sigma, \tau) \geqslant \mathrm{dist}\,(s, t)$. Give an example of disjoint closed sets of real numbers X and Y, for which there are sequences $\{x_n\}$ in X and $\{y_n\}$ in Y with $\lim_{n \to \infty} (x_n - y_n) = 0$.

32. S is a set of real numbers such that $x-y$ belongs to S whenever x and y do, and zero is an isolated point of S. Prove that S consists of all the integer multiples of the least positive element of S. Deduce that if θ is irrational then the lower bound of the numbers $|\cos \pi\theta|$, $|\cos 2\pi\theta|$,..., $|\cos n\pi\theta|$,... is zero.

33. S is a set of complex numbers such that (i) if a and b belong to S then so does $a-b$, (ii) zero is an isolated point of S, and (iii) there are numbers a and b in S such that a/b is not real. Prove that there is a number ζ_1 in S such that $0 < |\zeta_1| \leqslant |z|$ for all non-zero z in S. Prove also that there is a number ζ_2 such that $0 < |\zeta_2| \leqslant |z|$ for all z in S which are not integer multiples of ζ_1. Prove that S consists of all numbers $m\zeta_1+n\zeta_2$ where m and n are integers.

34. C is a closed set and Ω a sphere in R_n such that some interior points of Ω are in C, and some boundary points of Ω are not in C. Prove that Ω contains a closed sphere with points of C on its boundary but none in its interior.

If $C_1, C_2,...$ are disjoint closed sets in Ω show (by taking as C a succession of partial sums $C_1+C_2+...+C_q$) that Ω includes points which are not in any of the sets C_r.

35.   A function $f(x, y)$ is defined on R_2 so that $f(a, y)$ is a continuous function of y at all points $(a, 0)$, and $f(x, y)$ is everywhere a continuous function of x. If S_n is the set of all x such that

$$|f(x, y)-f(x, 0)| \leqslant 1 \quad \text{for all } y \text{ with} \quad |y| \leqslant 1/n,$$

prove that S_n is closed. Prove (i) there is a plane interval bisected by the line $y = 0$ in which the oscillation of f is less than 3, and (ii) every linear interval on the line $y = 0$ includes points at which f is continuous as a function of (x, y).

36.   If a and h are positive numbers and $x > a\{1+[a/h]\}$, prove that $na < x < na+nh$ for some positive integer n. If $S \subset R_1$ and R_1-S is unbounded, and n is a positive integer, prove that the intersection of all the sets $(1/r)S$ with $r \geqslant n$ cannot contain an interval (kS denotes the set of all kx with x in S). If S is closed, prove that there are numbers ξ such that $r\xi \in R_1-S$ for infinitely many positive integers r.

37.   If $f_1(x)$, $f_2(x)$,... are continuous and the series $\sum_{n=1}^{\infty} f_n(x)$ converges to $g(x)$ when $0 \leqslant x \leqslant 1$, prove that g is bounded on some subinterval of $[0, 1]$. If $r_1, r_2,...$ are all the rational numbers in $[0, 1]$ and

$$f_n(x) = \sum_{s=1}^{\infty} \frac{(x-r_s)^2}{2^s}\{1-(x-r_s)^2\}^{n-1}$$

show that g is discontinuous wherever x is rational.

38.   A function $f(x)$ is continuous for all real x, and $E_{m,n}$ is the set of all x such that $|f(x+h)-f(x)|/|h| \leqslant n$ whenever $0 < |h| \leqslant 1/m$, m and n being any positive integers. Prove that $E_{m,n}$ is closed, and by using Baire's theorem prove that if $f'(x)$ is finite for all x then there is an interval (a, b) and a real number K such that

$$|f(p)-f(q)| < K|p-q| \quad \text{whenever} \quad a < p < q < b.$$

39. K is the set of all numbers $x = \sum_{r=1}^{\infty} a_r 3^{-r}$ where each a_r is 0 or 2. Prove that every point of K is a limit point of K and of its complement. Show, by considering the complement of K, that K is closed (Cantor's set). Show that the function f on K defined by

$$f\left(\sum_{r=1}^{\infty} a_r 3^{-r}\right) = \sum_{r=1}^{\infty} a_r 2^{-r}$$

is monotonic increasing and maps K on $[0, 2]$. If $f(x)$ is defined for all x in $[0, 1] - K$ as the upper bound of $f(t)$ for all t in $(0, x)K$, prove that f is everywhere continuous.

40.   If S is a non-enumerable subset of R_n, prove that S contains an enumerable set S_1 whose closed envelope is identical with that of S. If S is the set of all numbers $\sum_{r=1}^{\infty} a_r 3^{-r}$ where each a_r is 1 or 0, find a set S_1.

41.   If $t_1, t_2,...$ are positive numbers and $t_n > \sum_{r>n} t_r$ for $n = 1, 2,...,$ show that the set of all numbers $\sum_{r=1}^{\infty} t_r \lambda_r$, where λ_r is 0 or 1, is perfect but contains no interval.

42. p and q are chosen integers such that $0 \leqslant p < q$ and $q > 1$. $\mathscr{E}_N$ is the set of all x in $(0, 1)$ whose normal scale q expansion satisfies the condition $x_r \neq p$ for $r = 1, 2,..., N$. Prove that $\mathscr{E}_N$ can be covered by $(q-1)^N$ closed intervals each of length q^{-N}. Prove that the intersection $\mathscr{E}_1 \cdot \mathscr{E}_2 \cdot ...$ can be covered by a finite number of intervals the sum of whose lengths is arbitrarily small.

43. If $J_1, J_2, \ldots$ is the aggregate of all rational cubes in R_n and U is any open set in R_n, prove that the function f defined by $f(U)$ $= \sum_{r=1}^{\infty} a_r 3^{-r}$, where $a_r = 1$ if $J_r \subset U$ and $a_r = 0$ otherwise, maps different open sets on to different numbers. Is this true if the integer 3 is replaced by 2?

Find a function F which maps the closed sets of R_n one-one on to real numbers so that if K_1 is a proper closed subset of a closed set K_2, then $F(K_1) < F(K_2)$.

44. $\mathscr{P}$ is the set of all periodic continuous functions of a real variable. $\mathscr{P}$ is made metric by defining the distance between ϕ and ψ in $\mathscr{P}$ to be the maximum of $|\phi(t) - \psi(t)|$. $\mathscr{E}$ is the subset of $\mathscr{P}$ consisting of all functions $\cos kt$ where k is an arbitrary constant. By first considering the distance between $\cos t$ and $\cos kt$, prove that no point of $\mathscr{E}$ is a point of condensation of $\mathscr{E}$. Show that although $\sum_{r=1}^{n} r^{-2} \cos (t/r)$ is a member of $\mathscr{E}$ for $n = 1, 2, \ldots$, its limit as $n \to \infty$ is not.

45. If $f(x)$ is continuous for $0 \leqslant x \leqslant 1$ and ϵ is any positive number, prove that there is a positive number δ such that

$$|f(x) - f(y)| < \epsilon + \omega(x-y)^2 \delta^{-2}$$

for all x, y in $[0, 1]$, where ω is the oscillation of f in $[0, 1]$. Deduce that if

$$\phi_n(x) = \sum_{r=0}^{n} f(r/n) x^r (1-x)^{n-r} \binom{n}{r},$$

then $|f(x) - \phi_n(x)| < \epsilon + \omega/n\delta^2$ for all x in $[0, 1]$. Deduce that the polynomials converge to f uniformly in $[0, 1]$.

46. A function $f(x)$ is defined for $0 \leqslant x \leqslant 1$ and D is the set of x at which f is discontinuous. Prove that D is the union of a sequence of closed sets. Prove that D cannot be the set of all irrational numbers in $[0, 1]$. If E is any given enumerable set in $[0, 1]$, show how to define f so that $D = E$.

If f is given and $0, 1, x_1, x_2, \ldots$ is a sequence whose closure is $[0, 1]$, let f_n be defined so that $f_n(x) = f(x)$ for $x = 0, 1, x_1, \ldots, x_n$ and so that f is linear in the contiguous intervals. Prove that $\lim_{n \to \infty} f_n(x)$ $= f(x)$ for all x not in D. Deduce that if f is monotonic, then f is the limit of a sequence of continuous functions. Is it the limit of a sequence of polynomials?

47. A function $f(P)$ is continuous relative to a closed bounded set K at all points of K but is not defined outside K. $\{P_n\}$ is a sequence of points of K and the closure of the set of P_n is K. If P is any point whose distance from K is δ, define

$$f(P)_. = \sum_{n=1}^{\infty} r_n f(P_n) n^{-2} \Big/ \sum_{n=1}^{\infty} r_n n^{-2}$$

where $r_n = 2\delta - PP_n$ if this difference is positive and r_n is zero otherwise. Prove that this extension of the range of definition of f makes f continuous everywhere.

48. Q denotes the set of all rational numbers; f is defined on Q by $f(x) = \sin\{1/\pi(x - \sqrt{2})\}$. Prove that f is continuous relative to Q but that there is no function continuous throughout R_1 which is equal to $f(x)$ whenever x is rational. If a function ϕ is defined on Q and is uniformly continuous relative to Q prove that there is a unique function continuous on R_1 which is equal to $\phi(x)$ whenever x is rational.

49. $\{r_n\}$ is a sequence consisting of all the rational numbers. To every function f defined on R_1, and everywhere continuous, is assigned the sequence $f(r_1), f(r_2), \ldots$; prove that the correspondence is one-one. If α is the aggregate of functions defined on R_1 and having a finite or enumerable set of discontinuities, prove that α can be mapped one-one on to a set of real numbers. Using Exercises 39, 42 and 18 prove that the set of all functions which are integrable-R over $[0, 1]$ cannot be mapped one-one on to a set of real numbers.

50. $r_1, r_2, \ldots$ is a sequence consisting of all the rational numbers in $(0, 1)$ and ϕ is defined by the relation

$$\phi(x) = \sum_{\substack{n \\ r_n < x}} r_n n^{-2}.$$

Prove that

$$\int_0^1 \phi(x)\, dx = \sum_{n=1}^{\infty} r_n n^{-2} - \sum_{n=1}^{\infty} r_n^2 n^{-2}.$$

51. If $f(x)$ and $g(x)$ are integrable-R over $[a, b]$ and $\phi(x)$ is defined as the greater of $f(x)$ and $g(x)$ (or as their common value when $f(x)$ and $g(x)$ are equal), prove that ϕ is integrable-R over $[a, b]$ and

$$2 \int_a^b \phi(x)\,dx = \int_a^b f(x)\,dx + \int_a^b g(x)\,dx + \int_a^b |f(x) - g(x)|\,dx.$$

52. U is an open set in $(0, 1)$ including all the rational numbers in $(0, 1)$ and l is the sum of the lengths of the disjoint intervals composing U. If $f(x) = 0$ for all x in U and $f(x) = 1$ for all other x, prove that the upper and lower Riemann integrals of f over $[0, 1]$ differ by $1 - l$.

53. If $f(x) = \sum\limits_{r=1}^{\infty} 2^{-n_r}$ for all x of the form $x = \sum\limits_{r=1}^{\infty} 4^{-n_r}$, where $\{n_r\}$ is an increasing sequence of positive integers, and $f(x) = 1$ for all other x, prove that for every ϕ which is integrable-R over $[0, 1]$

$$\int_0^1 f(x)\phi(x)\,dx = \int_0^1 \phi(x)\,dx.$$

54. ϕ is a given function such that $\int_a^b f(x)\phi(x)\,dx = 0$ for every f integrable-R over $[a, b]$. Prove that for every positive number ϵ the set of x with $|\phi(x)| > \epsilon$ must have a null closure. Must the set of x with $|\phi(x)| > 0$ have a null closure?

55. Discuss the validity of the following statements: (i) if $f(x)$ is defined on $[0, 1]$ and is monotonic and unbounded in $(0, 1)$, then $\cos\{f(x)\}$ is integrable-R over $[0, 1]$; (ii) if $x(t)$ is continuous and strictly increasing for $0 \leqslant t \leqslant 1$ and f is integrable-R over the range of values of $x(t)$, then $f\{x(t)\}$ is integrable-R over the range $0 \leqslant t \leqslant 1$.

56. If $f(x)$ is continuous on $[a, b]$ and T is the upper bound of sums $\sum\limits_{r=1}^{n} |f(x_r) - f(x_{r-1})|$ where $a = x_0 < x_1 < \ldots < x_n = b$, prove that

$$\sum_{r=1}^{n} |f(x_r) - f(x_{r-1})| \to T$$

as $g(N) \to 0$. Is this true if f is somewhere discontinuous?

57. If $f_1(x), f_2(x), \ldots$ are continuous in $[a, b]$ and $f_1(x) \geqslant f_2(x) \geqslant \ldots$ and $\lim\limits_{n \to \infty} f_n(x) = 0$ throughout $[a, b]$, prove that for every positive number ϵ and for every ξ in $[a, b]$ there exist numbers δ and N such that $|f_n(x)| < \epsilon$ for all x in $(\xi-\delta, \xi+\delta)$ and $n > N$. Show that $f_n(x) \to 0$ uniformly in $[a, b]$. Deduce that if $g_1(x), g_2(x),\dots$ are non-negative and continuous in $[a, b]$ and their sum is continuous in $[a, b]$ then

$$\int_a^b \sum_{n=1}^\infty g_n(x) \, dx = \sum_{n=1}^\infty \int_a^b g_n(x) \, dx.$$

58. $I_1, I_2,\dots$ is a sequence of disjoint intervals of $(0, 1)$ such that for every n, and every r from 1 to 2^n, it is true that $[(r-1)2^{-n}, r2^{-n}]$ intersects at least one I_r with $r \leqslant 2^n$. If $|I_1|+|I_2|+\dots < 1$ and C is the set of x in $[0, 1]$ which are not in any I_r, prove that C is closed but not measurable-J.

59. If $S \subset [0, 1]$ and S is measurable-J prove that $[0, 1]-S$ is measurable-J. If S and T are measurable-J, prove that their intersection is measurable-J.

60. $r_1, r_2,\dots$ is a sequence consisting of all the rational numbers in $(0, 1)$ and I_n is the interval $(1/(n+1), 1/n)$. In each I_n there is defined a closed set C_n which is not measurable-J. $f(x)$ is defined in I_n as the sum of r_n and the least value of $|x-t|$ for t in C_n, and $f(x) = 0$ for all other x. Prove that f is integrable-R over $[0, 1]$ but that, for every n, the set of x in $[0, 1]$ with $f(x) = r_n$ is not measurable-J.

61. If f is integrable-R over $[a, b]$, prove that $|f|$ and f^2 are also integrable-R over $[a, b]$ and that

$$\left| \int_a^b f(x) \, dx \right| \leqslant \int_a^b |f(x)| dx \leqslant (b-a)^{\frac{1}{2}} \left(\int_a^b f^2(x) \, dx \right)^{\frac{1}{2}}.$$

If f and g are both integrable-R over $[a, b]$ prove that

$$\sum_{r=1}^n f(\xi_r) g(\xi_r')(x_r-x_{r-1}) \to (R) \int_a^b f(x)g(x) \, dx$$

as $\max(x_r-x_{r-1}) \to 0$, ξ_r and ξ_r' being any points of $[x_{r-1}, x_r]$ and $a = x_0 < \dots < x_n = b$. Prove that

$$\lim_{n \to \infty} \sum_{r=1}^n \frac{r}{4n^2+(2r+1)^2} = \tfrac{1}{8} \log 2.$$

62. If f is integrable-R over $[a, b]$ and N is any net over $[a, b]$, prove that for every real λ

$$\left| \int_a^b f(x) \cos \lambda x \, dx - \sum_{r=1}^n m(f; \delta_r) \int_{x_{r-1}}^{x_r} \cos \lambda x \, dx \right| \leqslant U(f; N) - L(f; N).$$

Deduce that

$$\lim_{\lambda \to \infty} \int_a^b f(x) \cos \lambda x \, dx = 0.$$

If $0 < x < 2\pi$, prove that

$$\tfrac{1}{2}(x - \pi) + \sum_{r=1}^n \frac{1}{r} \sin rx = \tfrac{1}{2} \int_\pi^x \frac{\sin (n + \tfrac{1}{2})t}{\sin \tfrac{1}{2}t} \, dt$$

and deduce that

$$\sum_{r=1}^\infty \frac{1}{r} \sin rx = \tfrac{1}{2}(\pi - x).$$

Prove similarly that

$$\sum_{r=1}^\infty \frac{1}{r} \cos rx = \log (\tfrac{1}{2} \operatorname{cosec} \tfrac{1}{2}x).$$

63. (i) If $F(x) = (R) \int_a^x f(t) \, dt$ and $G(x) = (R) \int_a^x g(t) \, dt$, prove

$$\int_a^b f(x)G(x) \, dx + \int_a^b g(x)F(x) \, dx = F(b)G(b).$$

(ii) If $g(x) \geqslant 0$ and G is defined as in (i), and f is integrable-R over $[0, G(b)]$, prove that

$$\int_0^{G(b)} f(y) \, dy = \int_a^b f\{G(y)\} \, g(y) \, dy.$$

64. Prove that $\operatorname{cosec} x - 1/x$ is integrable-R over $[0, 1]$ however the function is defined at $x = 0$. Starting from the formula

$$\int_0^\pi \frac{\sin (n + \tfrac{1}{2})t}{2 \sin \tfrac{1}{2}t} \, dt = \tfrac{1}{2}\pi \quad (n = 0, 1, 2, \ldots),$$

prove that

$$\int_0^\infty \frac{\sin x}{x}\, dx = \tfrac{1}{2}\pi.$$

Find $\displaystyle\lim_{n\to\infty} \int_0^1 \frac{\sin nt}{e^t - e^{-t}}\, dt.$

65. If S is any set in R_n and $|S| > 0$, prove that S contains a set S_1 such that $|S - S_1| = 0$ and every interval which intersects S_1 does so in a set having positive exterior measure.

66. If C is the set of all numbers of the form $\sum_{r=1}^{\infty} a_r 10^{-r}$ where a_r can be any integer from 0 to 9 inclusive with the exception of 5, prove that C is closed and null. Show that every real number can be expressed as $mx + ny$ where m and n are integers and x, y are in C.

67. Define a set of complex numbers of measure zero which is such that every complex number is the difference between two numbers in the set.

68. k is a positive integer and S_k is the set of all numbers x in $(0, 1)$ of the form

$$x = \sum_{r=1}^{\infty} \frac{x_r}{r!}$$

where each x_r is a non-negative integer less than k. By first considering those x which have only a finite number of non-zero x_r, prove that $|S_k| = 0$. Deduce that the numbers $\sum_{r=1}^{\infty} b_r/r!$ where $\{b_r\}$ is an arbitrary bounded sequence of non-negative integers form a set of measure zero.

69. If E is measurable in R_n, prove that there are null sets Z such that $E + Z$ is the intersection of a sequence of open sets.

If E is a measurable subset of $[0, 1]$ and k is any positive integer, prove that there is a function f which is continuous on $[0, 1]$ and, apart from a set whose measure is less than 2^{-k}, equal to 1 if $x \in E$ and 0 if x is not in E. Hence or otherwise show that there is a sequence of polynomials, uniformly bounded in $[0, 1]$, which converges for almost all x to 1 if $x \in E$ and to zero if x is not in E.

70. If F is measurable in $[0, 1]$, prove that there is a sequence of polynomials which converges almost everywhere to $F(x)$.

71. If $f(P)$ is continuous at all points of a closed bounded set K in R_n, show that for every positive number ϵ there is a number $\delta > 0$ such that, for all P and Q in K with dist $(P, Q) < \delta$, $|f(P - f(Q)| < \epsilon$. Show that if f is continuous throughout R_n, then the set of points $(P, f(P))$ of R_{n+1} is of Lebesgue measure zero.

72. C is a closed subset of $(0, 1)$; it contains no intervals and $mC > 0$. $f(x)$ is linear in each of the intervals of $(0, 1)$ contiguous to C, having the value zero at the lower end and the value 1 at the upper end of each such interval. Elsewhere, $f(x) = x$. Find the plane measure of the graph of f (i.e. the set of $(x, f(x))$ with $0 \leqslant x \leqslant 1$) and the plane measure of the closure of this graph.

73. If $S_1, S_2, \ldots$ are bounded subsets of R_n and $S_r \supset S_{r+1}$ for $r = 1, 2, \ldots$, prove that

$$m_* \prod_{r=1}^{\infty} S_r = \lim_{r \to \infty} m_* S_r.$$

74. Prove the inequality $|A + B| + |AB| \leqslant |A| + |B|$, (i) when A is measurable, and (ii) when A is non-measurable in R_n.

75. If I is an interval in R_1 and Z is a null subset of I, prove that if $\{\lambda_n\}$ is any sequence of real numbers tending to zero then for almost all ξ in I the relation $(\xi + \lambda_n) \in I - Z$ holds for all large n.

76. Prove that every set E in R_n is covered by a measurable set S such that $m_*(S - E) = 0$. Show that for every measurable set H, $|HE| = |HS|$.

77. F is the set of all numbers $\sum_{r=1}^{\infty} x_r 4^{-r}$ where each x_r is 0 or 1. Prove that F is perfect. If y is any real number and S_y denotes the set of all numbers $x + 2y$ as x ranges through F, prove that if y_1 and y_2 are distinct elements of F then S_{y_1} and S_{y_2} are in general disjoint. Which pairs y_1 and y_2 are exceptional? Show that the interval $(0, 1)$ can be decomposed into disjoint non-enumerable null sets.

78. If E is a countable set of complex numbers, prove that there exist real numbers a such that for every z in E and for every non-zero rational number r the number $z + ar$ belongs to the complement of E.

A non-negative real number $\mu(S)$ is assigned to every bounded set S of complex numbers so that (i) $\mu(A)+\mu(B) = \mu(A+B)$ if A and B are disjoint, and (ii) if the elements of any set S are all increased by the same real number a then the transformed set S_a satisfies $\mu(S_a) = \mu(S)$. Prove that $\mu(S) = 0$ whenever S is bounded and enumerable.

79. G denotes the set of numbers $m3^n$ where m and n are integers. S is a subset of the interval $(0, 1)$ such that every real number x has a unique decomposition $x = \sigma+\gamma$ with σ in S and γ in G. Prove that the complement of S intersects every set in R_1 with positive interior measure. Does it intersect every set in R_1 having positive exterior measure?

80. E is the set of all complex numbers $x+iy$ with x and y both rational; S is a set of complex numbers z with $|z| < 1$ and such that every complex number can be represented in exactly one way as z_s+z_e with z_s in S and z_e in E. Prove that S is not measurable considered as a set in R_2.

Show by repeated bisection that there is at least one radius of the circle $|z| \leqslant 1$ which has the property that every sector of the circle bisected by this radius intersects S in a non-measurable set.

81. $f(x)$ is measurable in R_1 and E is an enumerable set whose closure is R_1; for each ξ in $E, f(x+\xi) = f(x)$ for almost all x. Prove that if the set of x with $f(x) \geqslant \theta$ has positive measure then $f(x) \geqslant \theta$ p.p. Hence show that there is a number c such that $f(x) = c$ p.p.

82. $f(x)$ is integrable-R over $[0, 1]$ and E is the set of numbers η with the property that the set of x with $f(x) = \eta$ is not measurable-J. Prove that E is finite or enumerable.

83. If I is an interval in R_1 prove that I contains an open set $F(I)$ which has measure $\frac{1}{2}|I|$ and which has points in every sub-interval of I. By applying the operator F to the subintervals of $F(I)$ repeatedly, show that I contains a null set E such that $I-E$ is the union of a sequence of sets S_r each of which is nowhere dense (i.e. the closure of S_r does not contain any interval).

84. If $S \subset R_2$ and $0 < |S| < \infty$, prove that for every sufficiently large integer q there is at least one rational square K of side 2^{-q} such that $|SK| > \frac{1}{2}|K|$. If it is also given that $m_* S > 0$, and E is the set of all (x, y) which cannot be expressed as (s_1+h, s_2+k) where s_1, s_2 are in S and h, k are rational, prove that $|E| = 0$.

85. E is a bounded set in R_n. E_1 is the set of those P in E for which there is a sequence of closed cubes $K_1, K_2,...$ such that $P = \prod_{n=1}^{\infty} K_n$ and $\lim_{n\to\infty} |EK_n|/|K_n| < 1$. Prove by Vitali's theorem that $|E_1| = 0$.

86. If $U_1, U_2,..., U_q$ are disjoint (open) spheres in an interval I of R_n, prove that there is a sphere Ω in $I-(U_1+...+U_q)$ such that every sphere in I with centre in $I-(U_1+...+U_q)$ and radius bigger than that of Ω intersects $U_1+U_2+...+U_q$. Hence prove that I contains a sequence of disjoint spheres whose sum differs from I by a null set. Deduce that any one-one transformation of R_n which transforms every sphere into a sphere of equal radius leaves exterior measure invariant.

87. A real function $f(x)$ is defined so that for all a and b in $[-1, 1]$, $f\{\frac{1}{2}(a+b)\} \leqslant \frac{1}{2}\{f(a)+f(b)\}$; furthermore, $f(0) = 0$ and f is discontinuous at 0. Prove that f is unbounded above in every interval centred at 0. Deduce that for every positive number N the set of points x of $[-1, 1]$ with $f(x) > N$ has exterior measure not less than 1; hence show that f is not measurable in $[-1, 1]$.

88. If $x = (x_1,..., x_n)$ and $y = (y_1,..., y_n)$ are points of R_n then $x+y$ denotes the point $(x_1+y_1,..., x_n+y_n)$. If $E \subset R_n$ prove that E contains a bounded subset E_1 such that every x in E can be expressed in exactly one way as $\xi+r$ with ξ in E_1 and r a rational point. If $|E| > 0$, prove that E_1 is non-measurable.

89. N is a non-measurable set in $(0, 1)$. $f(x)$ is defined as $x+1$ if $x \in N$ and as x otherwise. Prove that f transforms null sets into null sets, but transforms some measurable sets into non-measurable sets.

90. f is a continuous transformation of R_n, i.e. to every point P in R_n is a assigned a point $f(P)$ of R_n so that if $\{P_r\}$ converges to L then $\{f(P_r)\}$ converges to $f(L)$. If $|f(S)| = 0$ whenever $|S| = 0$ prove that $f(S)$ is measurable whenever S is measurable. Prove also that any transformation F of R_n which is such that $F(S)$ is measurable whenever S is, must transform null sets into null sets.

Give an example of a continuous function of one variable which transforms certain measurable sets into non-measurable sets.

91. ϕ and ψ are both measurable in B and $f(P)$ is the greater of

$\phi(P)$ and $\psi(P)$ (or their common value when they are equal); prove that f is measurable in B.

92. Suppose f and f' are bounded in $(-\infty, \infty)$ and f' is always positive. If $f(E)$ is the set of values assumed by f in the range E, prove that $f(E)$ is open if E is open and deduce that $f(E)$ is measurable if E is measurable.

93. A function f is defined on E, a bounded set of real numbers, so that for every θ in E there is, for every positive number ϵ, a positive number $\delta(\theta, \epsilon)$ with the property $|f(x)-f(\theta)| \leqslant |x-\theta|\epsilon$ for all x in E with $|x-\theta| \leqslant \delta$. By considering for every positive integer n the set of those θ for which $\delta(\theta, \epsilon) > 1/n$, prove that $|f(E)| = 0$.

94. $f_1(x), f_2(x),\ldots$ are functions measurable in a set E and the sequence converges to a function $f(x)$ in E. If ϵ is any chosen positive number, prove that there is a number $N(\epsilon)$ such that the set of x in E for which $|f_n(x)-f(x)| > \epsilon$ for some n greater than N has measure less than ϵ. Deduce (Egoroff's theorem) that for every positive number δ there is a subset F of E in which the sequence $\{f_n(x)\}$ converges uniformly and $m(E-F) < \delta$.

95. $f(P), f_1(P), f_2(P),\ldots$ are defined in R_n, and for every positive integer r there is an integer N_r such that the set of P at which $|f_n(P)-f(P)| > 2^{-r}$ has measure less than 2^{-r} provided $n \geqslant N_r$. Prove that there is a sequence $n_1 < n_2 < \ldots$ such that $f_{n_1}(P)$, $f_{n_2}(P),\ldots$ converges to $f(P)$ for almost all P in B.

96. $\{P_n\}$ is a sequence of all the rational points of R_2, and U_r is the interior of the circle of radius 2^{-r} centred on P_r. If K is the complement of $U_1+U_2+\ldots$ and $f(x, y)$ is the distance from (x, y) to K, show that (i) f is everywhere continuous, and (ii) the set of (x, y) with $f(x, y) = 0$ has infinite measure but no interior points.

97. C is a closed bounded set in R_n and U is an open set covering C so that $m(U-C) < mC$. If d is the least value of the distances between points of C and points of the complement of U, prove that for every $x = (x_1,\ldots, x_n)$ with $x_1^2+x_2^2+\ldots+x_n^2 < d^2$ there are points $y = (y_1,\ldots, y_n)$ and $z = (z_1,\ldots, z_n)$ in C such that $x_r = y_r-z_r$ $(r = 1, 2,\ldots, n)$. (Steinhaus theorem on 'distances'.)

98. E is a subset of $(0, 1)$ with $|E| > \frac{3}{4}$ and S is a measurable subset of $(0, \frac{1}{2})$ with $mS > \frac{1}{4}$. Prove that if θ is any number in

$[0, \frac{1}{2}]$ then there are points in E and S respectively whose distance apart is θ.

99.   Suppose (i) $S \subset R_1$ and $mS > 0$, and (ii) $E \subset R_1$, E is enumerable and the closure of E is R_1. Prove that almost all x in R_1 can be written as $x = \sigma + \rho$ with σ in S and ρ in E. Hence prove that if $B \subset R_1$ and $|B| > 0$, then the set of numbers $\sigma - \beta$ with σ in S and β in B contains an interval.

100. f is a real function satisfying $f(x+y) = f(x)+f(y)$ for all real x and y. Prove that $f(x) = xf(1)$ for all rational x. If f is bounded on a set S with $m_* S > 0$, show by using Steinhaus theorem that f is bounded on some interval $|x| < \delta$ and deduce that $f(x) = xf(1)$ for all real x.

101.   Find a continuous function f which satisfies $f(z+w) = f(z)+f(w)$ for all complex numbers z and w and also $f(1-i) = 1+i, f(1+i) = i$.

102.   If $f(x)$ is real for all real x and $f(a+b) = f(a)f(b) \neq 0$ for all real a and b, and f is bounded on a set with positive measure, prove that $f(x) = \{f(1)\}^x$ for all real x.

103. C is a closed bounded set in R_1 and $mC > 0$. U_q is defined to be the union of all intervals of R_1 which have length $2/q$ and their centre in C. If $n_1 < n_2 < \ldots$ are chosen so that $\sum_{r=1}^{\infty} |U_{n_r} - C| < |C|$, and $\{\theta_r\}$ is any sequence of numbers with $|\theta_r| < n_r^{-1}$ $(r = 1, 2, \ldots)$ show that the numbers ξ in C which have the property $(\xi + \theta_r) \in C$ for all r form a closed set with positive measure.

104.   If f is the function defined in Exercise 14, show that f is unbounded on every set with positive interior measure. Is it unbounded on every set having positive exterior measure?

105. $\mathscr{B}$ is a basis of the real numbers over the rationals (see Exercise 14) and $m\mathscr{B} = 0$. A number x is said to have weight k if its expression in terms of numbers in $\mathscr{B}$ includes k such numbers. If X_ν is the set of all numbers with weight 2^ν or less, prove that every interval of R_1 includes points of every X_ν. If $D(S)$ denotes the set of non-zero numbers expressible as $x-y$ with x and y in S, prove that $X_{\nu+1} = D(X_\nu)$ $(\nu = 1, 2, \ldots)$, and deduce that, for some ν, X_ν is measurable while $D(X_\nu)$ is not.

106. Show that the function $\lim\limits_{m \to \infty} \lim\limits_{n \to \infty} \dfrac{1}{1 + n \sin (m! \, \pi x)}$ is summable but not integrable-R over $[0, 1]$.

107. $\{(a_n, b_n)\}$ is a sequence of disjoint intervals of $(0, 1)$ and

$$f(x) = \begin{cases} (x - a_n)/(b_n - a_n) & \text{if} \quad a_n < x < \tfrac{1}{2}(a_n + b_n) \\ (x - b_n)/(b_n - a_n) & \text{if} \quad \tfrac{1}{2}(a_n + b_n) < x < b_n, \end{cases}$$

and $f(x) = 0$ for all other x. Prove that $f(x)$ is summable but not necessarily integrable-R over $[0, 1]$. Prove that $|f(x)|^{-\frac{1}{2}}$ is not always summable over $(0, 1)$ and that if $f(x)/x$ is summable over $(0, 1)$ then $b_n/a_n \to 1$ as $n \to \infty$.

108. An even function $f(x)$ is continuous for all x and its value is $x^3 \sin (x^{-\frac{5}{2}})$ when $x > 0$. Prove that $|f'(x)|$ is summable but not integrable-R over $[-1, 1]$. Discuss the summability of the square and of the square root of $|f'(x)|$.

109. If $f(x)$ is the least value of $|x - t|$ when t ranges over numbers of the form $\sum\limits_{r=1}^{\infty} a_r 3^{-r}$ where each a_r is 0 or 2, prove that the value of the integral of $f(x)$ over $(0, 1)$ is $1/28$. Show that $\{f(x)\}^{-\frac{1}{3}}$ is summable over $(0, 1)$.

110. If F is measurable in B and S_n is the set of P in B with $n - 1 \leqslant |F(P)| < n$, show that if $|S_n| = \mu_n > 0$ for $n = 1, 2, \ldots$ then the function $G(P)$ equal to $(n^2 \mu_n)^{-1}$ in S_n is summable over B while $F(P)G(P)$ is not.

111. A sequence of functions $\{f_n\}$ which are continuous for all real x converges to a function $F(x)$ for all x. Prove that there is an interval (a, b) such that

$$\int_a^b F(x) \, dx = \lim_{n \to \infty} \int_a^b f_n(x) \, dx.$$

112. If $f(x)$ is non-negative and summable over $(0, 1)$ and $\int_0^1 \{f(x)\}^n \, dx$ has the same value for all positive integers n, prove that $f(x) = 1$ for all x in some measurable set and that $f(x)$ is zero almost everywhere else.

113. $f(P)$ is positive and measurable in E. Prove that as $n \to \infty$ the integral of $\{f(P)\}^n$ over B tends either to infinity or to a limit l

satisfying $0 \leqslant l \leqslant mE$. Discuss the cases which occur when (i) $f(x) = \exp(-1/x)$ and $E = (0, 1)$, and (ii) $f(x) = x^4 \exp(-x^2)$ and $E = (0, \infty)$. Prove that if f is summable over E, then the integral of $\{f(P)\}^{1/n}$ tends to mE as $n \to \infty$.

114. If $f(P)$ is summable over R_n and $\phi(y)$ is the measure of the set of P with $|f(P)| > y$, prove that $\sum\limits_{n=1}^{\infty} \phi(n) < \infty$.

115. If $f(P)$ and $g(P)$ are measurable in B and $\{f(P)\}^k$, $\{g(P)\}^k$ are both summable over B, prove that $\{f(P)+g(P)\}^k$ (if defined) is summable over B (k is any positive constant).

116. If $f(P)$ is positive and summable over B and $mB < \infty$, prove that $\{f(P)\}^k$ is summable over B for every positive constant k less than 1.

117. By finding the least value of $x^p/p - bx$ for $x > 0$, where b and p are positive constants, $p > 1$, prove that $a^p/p + b^q/q \geqslant ab$ for all positive a and b, where q is given by $1/p + 1/q = 1$. Show that equality occurs if and only if $a^p = b^q$. Deduce that if $|f|$ and $|g|$ are measurable in B and $|f(P)|^p$ and $|g(P)|^q$ have integrals over B both equal to 1, then

$$\int\limits_B |f(P)g(P)| \, dP \leqslant 1.$$

118. If $f(P)$ is positive and summable over B and $mB = \infty$, prove that $1/f(P)$ is not summable over B.

119. If $\{p_n\}$ is an increasing sequence of numbers tending to infinity, prove that the sum of the series

$$\sum\limits_{r=1}^{\infty} |p_r \exp(-p_r x) - p_{r+1} \exp(-x p_{r+1})|$$

is not summable over $(0, \infty)$.

120. Find an example of a sequence of functions $\{f_n\}$ such that $\int\limits_0^1 |f_n(x)| \, dx = 1$ for all n and $\int\limits_0^1 |f_n(x) - f_m(x)| \, dx = 2$ whenever $m \neq n$.

121. A sequence $\{f_n\}$ is defined as follows. If $2^m \leqslant n < 2^{m+1}$, $f_n(x)$ is unity in $[n2^{-m}, (n+1)2^{-m})$ and is zero elsewhere. Show that for $1 < x < 2$ the sequence $f_1(x), f_2(x), \ldots$ does not converge but that $\int\limits_1^2 \{f_n(x) - f_m(x)\}^2 \, dx \to 0$ as m and n tend to infinity.

122. Prove from the definition of measurability that if $\{\phi_n\}$ is a sequence of functions continuous throughout R_q which converges to a function ϕ, then ϕ is measurable in R_q.

S is a bounded set in R_n and $f_r(P)$ is defined in R_n as having the value 1 if there is a point of S whose distance from P is less than $1/r$ and as zero otherwise. Prove that f is summable over R_n. Show that the integral of $f_r(P)$ over R_n tends to $|S|$ as $r \to \infty$ if and only if the set of those limit points of S which do not belong to S has zero interior measure.

123. A sequence $\{f_n\}$ has the following properties in the range $0 \leqslant x \leqslant 1$: (i) each $f_n(x)$ is continuous and non-decreasing, and (ii) $r^2-1 \leqslant f_r(x) \leqslant r^2$. Assuming that each $f_r(x)$ is differentiable for almost all x, show that $\sum_{r=2}^{\infty} f_r'(x)/f_r(x)$ converges for almost all x in $(0, 1)$ to a function whose integral from 0 to 1 is at most $\log 2$.

124. If $f_1(x), f_2(x),\ldots$ are summable over $(0, 1)$ is it true that

$$\int_0^1 \lim_{n\to\infty} \cos\{f_n(x)\}\,dx \leqslant \lim_{n\to\infty} \int_0^1 \cos\{f_n(x)\}\,dx?$$

If $f_n(x) = e^{-2x}-ne^{-nx}$, find

$$\int_0^\infty \lim_{n\to\infty} f_n(x)\,dx \quad \text{and} \quad \lim_{n\to\infty} \int_0^\infty f_n(x)\,dx.$$

Comment on the connection with Fatou's lemma.

125. $f_1(x), f_2(x),\ldots$ are defined as follows in the range $[0, 1]$. If r is a non-negative integer and $n = 2^r+s$, where $0 \leqslant s < 2^r$, then $f_n(x) = 2^r$ if $s2^{-r} \leqslant x \leqslant (s+1)2^{-r}$ and $f_n(x) = 0$ otherwise. Find

$$\int_0^1 f_n(x)\,dx, \qquad \int_0^1 \lim_{n\to\infty}\left\{\frac{f_n(x)}{n}\right\}dx \qquad \int_0^1 \overline{\lim_{n\to\infty}}\left\{\frac{f_n(x)}{n}\right\}dx.$$

126. Prove that

$$\int_0^1 (\log x)^2(1+x^2)^{-1}\,dx = 2\sum_{n=0}^{\infty}\frac{(-1)^n}{(2n+1)^3}.$$

Assuming the bounded convergence of $\sum_{n=1}^{\infty}(\sin nx)/n$ to $\frac{1}{2}(\pi-x)$ in the range $0 < x < 2\pi$, show that

$$\sum_{n=0}^{\infty} \frac{\sin(2n+1)x}{2n+1} = \tfrac{1}{4}\pi \quad \text{if} \quad 0 < x < \pi;$$

hence or otherwise prove

$$\int_0^1 (\log x)^2(1+x^2)^{-1}\, dx = \pi^3/16.$$

127. If $0 < \theta < 1$, prove that $\lim_{n\to\infty} n \int_0^{\theta} (1-w)^n \cos nw\, dw = \tfrac{1}{2}$.

128. If $t > 1$ and $x > 0$, prove that $(1+x/t)^t > 1+x$. Prove that

$$\lim_{t\to\infty} t^{\frac{1}{2}} \int_0^{\infty} (1+y^2)^{-t}\, dy$$

exists and is finite.

129. Prove that $e^x \geqslant 1+x$ for all real x and deduce that, for all positive t, $(1+x/t)^t \leqslant e^x$ provided $x+t > 0$. By considering the arithmetic and geometric means of $n+1$ numbers, n of which are equal to $1+x/n$, prove that if $n+x > 0$ then $(1+x/n)^n < (1+x/(n+1))^{n+1}$. Show that if $\phi(x)$ is positive and measurable in $(0, \infty)$, then

$$\int_0^{\infty} \phi(x)e^{-x}\, dx = \lim_{n\to\infty} n \int_0^1 \phi(nx)(1-x)^n\, dx.$$

Show that the right-hand side of the equation is in general different from $\int_0^1 \lim_{n\to\infty} n\phi(nx)(1-x)^n\, dx$ assuming this exists.

130. Prove that

$$\lim_{r\to\infty} \lim_{n\to\infty} \left\{ n \int_0^1 (1-x)^n(1-x^2)^{n^2}...(1-x^r)^{n^r}\, dx \right\} = \int_0^1 \exp\left(\frac{y}{y-1}\right) dy.$$

131. Justify the equation

$$\int_0^{\infty} e^{-t} \log t\, dt = \lim_{n\to\infty} \int_0^n (1-t/n)^n \log t\, dt.$$

Deduce that when $x = 1$

$$\frac{d}{dx} \int_0^\infty e^{-t} t^{x-1}\, dt = \lim_{n \to \infty} \left\{ \log n - \sum_{r=1}^n \frac{1}{r} \right\}.$$

132. Prove that the function $\theta \sum_n n^{-2}$, where the summation is over all positive integers n exceeding θ, is bounded for $\theta > 0$ and tends to 1 as $\theta \to \infty$.

If $f(x)$ is non-negative and measurable in $(0, \infty)$, prove that

$$\lim_{T \to +0} \frac{1}{T} \int_0^T x \sum_{n=1}^\infty f(nx)\, dx = \int_0^\infty f(x)\, dx.$$

133. If $f(X)$ and $\int_0^X f(t)\, dt$ are bounded functions of X for $-\infty < X < \infty$, show that

$$\lim_{\lambda - \infty} \int_a^b f(\lambda t)\, dt = 0 \quad \text{if} \quad -\infty < a < b < \infty,$$

and deduce that

$$\lim_{\lambda \to \infty} \int_S f(\lambda t)\, dt = 0 \quad \text{whenever} \quad mS < \infty.$$

Hence prove that for every ϕ which is summable over $(-\infty, \infty)$

$$\lim_{\lambda \to \infty} \int_{-\infty}^\infty \phi(x) f(\lambda x)\, dx = 0.$$

Find

$$\lim_{n \to \infty} \int_{-\infty}^\infty (-1)^{[nx]} \phi(x)\, dx.$$

134. If S is a measurable set of real numbers and $mS < \infty$ prove that for every positive number ϵ there are sets A and B with $mA < \epsilon$ and $mB < \epsilon$ such that $(S+A)-B$ consists of a finite number of disjoint intervals. If $\{\theta_n\}$ is a sequence of constants prove that

$$\lim_{n \to \infty} \int_S |\cos(nx + \theta_n)|\, dx = \frac{2}{\pi} mS.$$

135. If $f(x) = \sum_{n=1}^\infty 2^{-n} \sin(\pi x\, 2^{2^n})$ and $k = \tfrac{1}{2} r\, 2^{-2^m}$, where m is a positive integer and $r = \pm 1, \pm 2,...$, prove that

$$\left| \frac{f(x+k)-f(x)}{k} - \frac{1}{r} \sin \left(\tfrac{1}{4}\pi r\right) 2^{2^m+2-m} \cos \left(\pi x\, 2^{2^m} + \tfrac{1}{4}\pi r\right) \right|$$
$$< \tfrac{1}{2}\pi(m-1)2^{2^{m-1}}.$$

Deduce that for every real x the ratio $\{f(x+h)-f(x)\}/h$ has values, both positive and negative, of arbitrarily large magnitude.

136. Z is an arbitrary null set in $[0, 1]$ and $U_1, U_2,...$ are open sets, each covering Z, and $mU_r < 2^{-r}$. For each n, $q_n(x)$ denotes the number of integers r which verify $x \in U_r$ and $1 \leqslant r \leqslant n$. $Z(x)$ is defined as

$$\lim_{n \to \infty} \int_0^x q_n(t)\, dt.$$

Prove that $Z(x)$ is monotonic and absolutely continuous in $[0, 1]$ and $Z'(x) = \infty$ for all x in Z.

137. Prove that for every real number θ there is a continuous and strictly increasing function $f(x)$ defined on $[0, 1]$ so that $f'(x) = x$ p.p. and $f(1)-f(0) = \theta$.

138. Prove that the continuous function $x^2 \sin (1/x)$ has bounded variation in $[0, 1]$ and that its variation in a subinterval $[a, b]$ cannot exceed $(b-a)(1+a+b)$. Define a function f with bounded variation in $[0, 1]$ which is such that for infinitely many numbers k the equation $f(x) = k$ has infinitely many solutions.

139. Find an example of a function which is continuous and of unbounded variation in $[0, 1]$ and has a zero derivative almost everywhere in $[0, 1]$.

140. If $f_n(x) = x \sin^2 (1/x)$ for $\frac{1}{n\pi} \leqslant x \leqslant 1$ and $f_n(x) = 0$ elsewhere, show that $f_n(x)$ is absolutely continuous in $[0, 1]$ for $n = 1, 2,...$ but that $\lim_{n \to \infty} f_n(x)$ is not.

141. If $f(x)$ is continuous and of bounded variation in $[a, b]$ and $f(x)$ is absolutely continuous in every $[\alpha, \beta]$ with $a < \alpha < \beta < b$, prove that $f(x)$ is absolutely continuous in $[a, b]$.

142. If f is summable over $[0, 1]$ and $k(x)$ has bounded variation on [0, 2], prove that

$$\int_0^1 f(t)k(x+t)\, dt$$

is an absolutely continuous function of x in [0, 1].

143. $f(x)$ is real for $0 \leqslant x \leqslant 1$ and is such that $f(I)$ is measurable for every interval I in [0, 1]. Prove that if $I_1, I_2,..., I_q$ are disjoint intervals in $(0, 1)$, then $|f(I_1)|+...+|f(I_2)|$ is the integral over $(-\infty, \infty)$ of the function $\phi(y)$ where $\phi(y)$ is the number of I_r with $y \in f(I_r)$.

$\{N_r\}$ is a sequence of nets over [0, 1] with $N_1 \subset N_2 \subset ...$. If the cells of N_r are $\delta_1^{(r)},..., \delta_{n_r}^{(r)}$ and $\lim_{r\to\infty} \max_s |\delta_s^{(r)}| = 0$, prove that

$$\lim_{r\to\infty} \sum_{s=1}^{n_r} |f(\delta_s^{(r)})| = \int_{-\infty}^{\infty} \mathcal{N}(y)\, dy$$

where $\mathcal{N}(y)$ is the number of distinct x in [0, 1] with $f(x) = y$, if this is finite, and $\mathcal{N}(y) = \infty$ otherwise. Prove that the integral of $\mathcal{N}(y)$ over $(-\infty, \infty)$ is (i) finite if f has bounded variation in [0, 1], and (ii) equal to the total variation of f in [0, 1] if f is continuous.

144. If f and g are real and measurable in B and f^2 and g^2 are both summable over B, denote by $(f|g)$ the integral of fg over B and by $\|f\|$ the number $(f|f)^{\frac{1}{2}}$. By first restricting f and g to have $\|f\| = \|g\| = 1$, show, by considering $\|f-\lambda g\|^2$, that $|(f|g)| = \|f\|\|g\|$ if and only if there is a constant λ with $f(P) = \lambda g(P)$ p.p. in B. Show also that if $\|f\|\|g\| \neq 0$, then $\|f+g\| = \|f\|+\|g\|$ if and only if there is a positive constant λ with $f(P) = \lambda g(P)$ p.p. in B and that in all other cases $\|f+g\| < \|f\|+\|g\|$.

145. With the notation of Exercise 144, f and g are called orthogonal (in B) if $(f|g) = 0$. Show that if $\phi_1,..., \phi_q$ are mutually orthogonal, then $\|\phi_1+\phi_2+...+\phi_q\|^2 = \|\phi_1\|^2+...+\|\phi_q\|^2$. If in addition $\|\phi_1\| = ... = \|\phi_q\| = 1$, show that

$$f - \sum_{r=1}^{q} (f|\phi_r)\phi_r$$

is orthogonal to each of the ϕ_r; deduce that for any sequence of such ϕ_r,

$$\sum_{r=1}^{\infty} (f|\phi_r)^2 \leqslant \|f\|^2.$$

146.   If $\|f\|$ denotes $\left(\int\limits_B |f(P)|^2 \, dP \right)^{1/2}$, where B is a set with finite measure, prove that if $f_1, f_2,\ldots$ are measurable in B and $\|f_r - f_{r+1}\| < 2^{-r}$ $(r = 1, 2,\ldots)$ and $\|f_1\| < \infty$, then for almost all P in B the sequence $\{f_n(P)\}$ converges, say to $f(P)$, and $\|f - f_n\| \to 0$ as $n \to \infty \cdot$ If g is measurable in B and g^2 has a finite integral over B, prove that

$$\int\limits_B f(P)g(P)\,dP = \lim_{n \to \infty} \int\limits_B f_n(P)g(P)\,dP.$$

147. α is an aggregate of functions $f(x)$ which are continuous for $0 \leqslant x \leqslant 1$ and are such that

$$\int\limits_0^1 \{f(x)\}^2 \, dx = 1, \qquad \int\limits_0^1 f(x)g(x)\,dx = 0$$

for every pair of distinct elements f and g of α. Assuming that every member of α is the limit of a uniformly convergent sequence of polynomials with rational coefficients, prove that α is finite or enumerable.

148.   If $f(x_1, x_2,\ldots, x_n) = (x_1 + x_2, x_2, x_3,\ldots, x_n)$ prove that, for every interval I, $|f(I)| = |I|$. If M is the matrix of any non-singular linear transformation of R_n, and $f(x) = Mx$ (x being a column vector), prove by expressing M as a product of elementary matrices and a diagonal matrix that $|f(I)| = |\det M||I|$. Show that this remains valid when I is replaced by an arbitrary set in R_n. Deduce that if ϕ is non-negative and measurable in R_n then

$$\int\limits_{R_n} \phi(x)\,dx = |\det M| \int\limits_{R_n} \phi(My)\,dy.$$

149.   If $0 < a < b$, prove that

$$\int\limits_0^\infty \frac{e^{-ax} - e^{-bx}}{x}\,dx = \log \frac{b}{a}.$$

Evaluate

$$\int\limits_0^\infty \frac{\tan^{-1} ax - \tan^{-1} bx}{x}\,dx.$$

150.   Starting from the formula

$$\int_0^\infty e^{-t^2 w^2}\, dw = \frac{\sqrt{\pi}}{2t},$$

prove that

$$\int_0^\infty \sin(t^2)\, dt = \frac{1}{\sqrt{\pi}} \int_0^\infty dw \int_0^\infty e^{-\theta w^2} \sin\theta\, d\theta = \tfrac{1}{2}(\pi/2)^{\frac{1}{2}}.$$

If $0 \leqslant a_1 < a_2 < \infty$ and $f_n(t) = \int_0^n \cos y\, e^{-ty}\, dy$, prove that

$$\int_{a_1}^{a_2} dt \int_0^\infty \cos y\, e^{-ty}\, dy = \lim_{n\to\infty} \int_{a_1}^{a_2} f_n(t)\, dt.$$

Hence prove that

$$\int_0^\infty \frac{\cos x}{x} \{e^{-a_1 x} - e^{-a_2 x}\}\, dx = \tfrac{1}{2} \log\left(\frac{1+a_2^2}{1+a_1^2}\right).$$

151.   If $t > 1$ prove that

$$0 < \int_0^\pi \frac{1 - \cos tx}{2 \sin \tfrac{1}{2} x}\, dx \leqslant \tfrac{1}{2}\pi \int_0^\pi \frac{1 - \cos tx}{x}\, dx < \tfrac{1}{2}\pi(\tfrac{1}{4}\pi^2 + 2 \log t).$$

152.   A plane set E is non-enumerable and has the property that every subset of E with plane measure zero is finite or enumerable. Assuming Fubini's theorem, prove that (i) every non-enumerable subset S of E satisfies $0 = m_* S < |S|$, and (ii) the complement of E intersects every perfect set in the plane.

153.   If $f(u)$ is summable over $[0, X]$ and a and b are positive, prove that $(X-t)^{a-1}\ (t-u)^{b-1} f(u)$ is summable over the square where $0 < u < X,\ 0 < t < X$. Prove that

$$\int_0^X (X-t)^{a-1} \left\{ \int_0^t (t-u)^{b-1} f(u)\, du \right\} dt = \frac{\Gamma(a)\Gamma(b)}{\Gamma(a+b)} \int_0^X f(u)(X-u)^{a+b-1}\, du.$$

154.   If $X = (x_1, \ldots, x_p)$ and $Y = (y_1, \ldots, y_q)$, then (X, Y) denotes the point $(x_1, \ldots, x_p, y_1, \ldots, y_q)$ of R_{p+q}. If $S \subset R_{p+q}$ and $X \in R_p$, denote by $S(X)$ the set of all Y in R_q with $(X, Y) \in S$. Prove that (i) $|\Omega_0(S(X); R_p)| \leqslant |S|$ for all S, (ii) if $S \in \mathcal{L}$, then $S(X)$ is, for almost all X in R_p, a measurable subset of R_q and

$$mS = \int_{R_p} mS(X)\, dX.$$

Deduce that if $f(X, Y)$ is non-negative and measurable in R_{p+q} then

$$\int_{R_{p+q}} f(X, Y)\, d(X, Y) = \int_{R_p} dX \int_{R_q} f(X, Y)\, dY.$$

155. Prove by induction that the measure of a sphere of unit radius in R_n is $\{\Gamma(\tfrac{1}{2})\}^n/\Gamma(1+\tfrac{1}{2}n)$. What is the limit of this as $n \to \infty$?

156. If v_n is the measure of the set of all $(x_1, x_2,..., x_n)$ with all $x_r > 0$ and $x_1+x_2+...+x_n < 1$, prove that $v_n = v_{n-1}/n$. Deduce that

$$\int_0^\infty dx_1 \int_0^\infty dx_2... \int_0^\infty \exp\{-(x_1+x_2+...+x_n)^2\}\, dx_n = \Gamma(1+\tfrac{1}{2}n)/n!$$

157. S is an infinite set of real numbers such that every subset of S has at least one isolated point. By considering the family of intervals whose intersection with S is finite or enumerable, prove that S is enumerable.

158. A function $f(x)$ is defined for $0 \leqslant x \leqslant 1$ and is such that every perfect set K in $[0, 1]$ includes at least one point ξ at which f is continuous relative to K. A positive number ϵ is chosen and an aggregate of intervals (a, b) in $(0, 1)$ defined as follows: $(a, b) \in \alpha$ if and only if there is a sequence of polynomials which converges for all x in (a, b) to a limit differing from $f(x)$ by not more than ϵ. Prove that α satisfies the conditions of Romanovski's lemma.

159. A function $f(x)$ is continuous and of bounded variation in $[a, b]$, and the points x at which $|f(x+h)-f(x)|/h$ is unbounded are finite or enumerable. By applying Romanovski's lemma to the family of intervals in which f is absolutely continuous, prove that f is absolutely continuous in $[a, b]$.

160. Find a trigonometric series which converges to $\cos \lambda x$ for $|x| \leqslant \pi$. If λ is not an integer, show that

$$\pi\lambda \operatorname{cosec} \pi\lambda = 1 + 2\lambda^2 \sum_{n=1}^{\infty} \frac{(-1)^n}{\lambda^2 - n^2},$$

$$\pi\lambda \cot \pi\lambda = 1 + 2\lambda^2 \sum_{n=1}^{\infty} \frac{1}{\lambda^2 - n^2}.$$

Deduce that

$$\sin \pi\theta = \pi\theta \prod_{n=1}^{\infty} \left(1 - \frac{\theta^2}{n^2}\right) \text{ for all real } \theta.$$

161. If $f(x) = e^{x\lambda}$ for $|x| < \pi$ and f has period 2π, find the Fourier series of f and its sum when x is an integral multiple of π. Sum the series

$$\sum_{n=1}^{\infty} \frac{1}{(\lambda^2 + n^2)^2} \quad \text{and} \quad \sum_{n=1}^{\infty} \frac{n^2}{(\lambda^2 + n^2)^2}.$$

162. Justify the assertion that each of the three series

$$\sum_{n=1}^{\infty} \frac{\sin 2nx}{n}, \qquad \sum_{n=1}^{\infty} \frac{\sin 2^n x}{2^n}, \qquad \sum_{n=2}^{\infty} \frac{\sin nx}{\log n}$$

converges for $|x| < \pi$ and that the sum of the third series is not summable over $(-\pi, \pi)$. If $f(x)$ and $g(x)$ are the sums of the first and second series, prove that

$$\int_{-\pi}^{\pi} f(x)g(x)dx = 2\pi/3.$$

163. Prove that

$$|\sin x| = \frac{4}{\pi} \sum_{n=1}^{\infty} \frac{1 \cos 2nx}{4n^2 - 1}, \quad (-\infty < x < \infty).$$

Use this to prove that

$$\frac{1}{\log p} \int_{0}^{p} \frac{|\sin px|}{\sin x} dx$$

tends to a positive limit as $p \to \infty$ through integer values.

164. If $f(t) = \log \left|\frac{\pi}{t}\right|$ when $0 < |t| < \pi$ and f has period 2π, prove that

$$f(t) = \tfrac{1}{2}a_0 + \sum_{n=1}^{\infty} a_n \cos nt \quad \text{if } t/2\pi \text{ is not an integer,}$$

and show that $na_n \to 1$ as $n \to \infty$.

165. S is the set of all real numbers x for which $\cos (n!x)$ tends to a non-zero limit as $n \to \infty$. Using the Riemann-Lebesgue theorem, or otherwise, prove that $|S| = 0$. By first proving that if $\cos(n!x)$ tends to a limit as $n \to \infty$ then so does $\cos(n!2x)$, prove that for almost all x the sequence $\{\cos(n!x)\}$ oscillates.

166. If a trigonometric series converges absolutely at x_1 and at x_2, prove that it converges absolutely at $2x_1 - x_2$. Use Steinhaus's theorem on distances to show that if the series converges absolutely in a set with positive measure then it converges absolutely for all x. Show that the closure of the set of x for which $\sum_n \sin(2^n x)/n$ converges absolutely is R_1. Prove that the set itself is null.

167. U is an open set which includes all numbers πt where t is rational. $f(x) = 1$ if $x \in U$ and $f(x) = 0$ otherwise, and f has period 2π. By considering an expression for

$$\sum_{s=-k}^{k-1} f(2\pi s/k),$$

prove that if k is any positive integer then

$$a_k + a_{2k} + \ldots + a_{rk} + \ldots = 1 - \frac{1}{2\pi}\,|U(-\pi, \pi)|,$$

the a_n being the Fourier cosine coefficients of f.

168. f is an even function which is of period 2π, and of bounded variation in $[-\pi, \pi]$. Show that for every real number h

$$\int_{-\pi}^{\pi} \{f(x+h) - f(x)\}^2\,dx = 4\pi \sum_{n=1}^{\infty} \sin^2(\tfrac{1}{2}nh)a_n^2,$$

the a_n being the Fourier coefficients of f. Find $\sum_{n=1}^{\infty} n^2 a_n^2$ if $f(x) = e^x$ for $0 \leqslant x \leqslant \pi$.

169. Determine which of the following functions are (i) bounded, (ii) of summable square over $(0, 2\pi)$:

(a) $\sum_{n=1}^{\infty} \left\{ \frac{1}{\sqrt{n}} - \frac{1}{\sqrt{(n+1)}} \right\} \cos nx;$ (b) $\sum_{n=1}^{\infty} \left(1 - \sqrt{\frac{n}{n+1}}\right) \cos nx.$

170. If $\{\theta_n\}$ is a sequence of non-negative real numbers and $\sum_n \theta_n < \infty$, prove that there exists a continuous function f such that

$$\int_0^{2\pi} f(x) \sin nx\,dx = \theta_n \quad \text{for} \quad n = 1, 2, \ldots .$$

Prove that there is a continuous function $h(x)$ such that

$$\int_0^{2\pi} h(x) \sin nx\, dx = \frac{1}{\log n}$$

for infinitely many values of n. Show that for every function $h(x)$ which is summable over $(0, 2\pi)$ this equation is false for infinitely many positive integers n.

171. If $0 < k < 1$, prove that

$$\sum_{n=1}^{\infty} n^{-k} \sin nx = \sum_{n=1}^{\infty} \left\{ \frac{1}{(n+1)^k} - \frac{1}{n^k} \right\} \left\{ \frac{\cos (n+\frac{1}{2})x - \cos \frac{1}{2}x}{2 \sin \frac{1}{2}x} \right\}.$$

Using Exercise 151, deduce that $\sum_{n=1}^{\infty} n^{-k} \sin nx$ is the Fourier series of its sum $S(x)$. If N is any positive integer exceeding 2, prove that

$$S\left(\frac{1}{N}\right) > -1 + \frac{1}{2\pi^2 N} \sum_{n=1}^{N} \frac{(n+\frac{1}{2})^2}{(n+1)^{3/2}}.$$

Show that although the series for $S(x)$ converges uniformly in any closed subinterval of $(0, \pi)$, the series is not boundedly convergent in $(0, \pi)$.

172. f is an even function which is summable over $(0, \pi)$ and

$$\sigma_n = \frac{1}{\pi} \int_0^{\pi} f(x) \left(\frac{\sin \frac{1}{2}nx}{\sin \frac{1}{2}x} \right)^2 dx.$$

Prove that (i) if $\lim_{x\to 0} f(x) = 0$ then $\frac{1}{n}\sigma_n \to 0$ as $n \to \infty$, and (ii) if $f(x) = g(x) \log x$ and $g(x)$ is bounded in $(0, \pi)$ then $\sigma_n/(n \log n)$ is bounded.

173. A function f is defined in $[0, 1]$ as follows. If $x = \sum_{r=1}^{\infty} x_r 3^{-r}$ where every x_r is 0 or 2, then $f(x) = \sum_{r=1}^{\infty} x_r 2^{-r}$; for all other x, $f(x) = x$. Prove that f is continuous p.p. in $[0, 1]$. Show that the integral of $x\, df(x)$ over $[0, 1]$ is $3/2$.

174. If n is an odd positive integer and $e(y)$ is the measure of the set of x in $(-\pi, \pi)$ for which $\cos nx < y$, prove that

$$\int_{-1}^{1} e(y) y^n\, dy = \frac{2\pi}{n+1}\left\{ 1 - \frac{(n+1)!}{2^{n+1}(\{\frac{1}{2}(n+1)\}!)^2} \right\}.$$

175. If $F(x)$ is absolutely continuous in $[0, 1]$ and C is a closed set in $(0, 1)$, and $X(x) = 1$ if $x \in C$ and $X(x) = 0$ otherwise, prove that

$$\int_0^1 F(x) \, dX(x) = 0.$$

176. Prove that

$$\int_{-p}^{p} x \, d[e^x] = \log([e^p]!)$$

if p is a positive integer.

177. If $f(x) = 2x(1+[x])$ and $g(x) = \int_x^\infty e^{-t^2} \, dt$, prove that

$$\lim_{n \to \infty} \int_0^n g(x) \, df(x) = \sum_{r=0}^\infty e^{-r^2}.$$

178. If $g(x)$ has bounded variation in $[0, \omega]$ for every positive real number ω, and $\lim_{x \to \infty} g(x) = 0$, prove that $\int_0^\omega e^{-xy} \, dg(x)$ converges as $\omega \to \infty$, if $y > 0$. Prove that the limit tends to $-g(0)$ as y tends to zero through positive values.

179. A function ϕ is defined so that $\phi(x) = 0$ except when x is of the form $(2r+1)/2^n$ for some positive integer n in which case its value is 4^{-n}. Show that $\int_0^1 f \, d\phi = 0$ for all f continuous on $[0, 1]$.

180. A function $\theta(x)$ is defined as follows. If x is rational, $\theta(x)$ is the least positive integer n which makes nx an integer; if x is irrational, $\theta(x) = 0$. Is it true that $\int_0^1 f \, d\theta = 0$ for all f continuous on $[0, 1]$?

181. If $\phi(x)$ is integrable-R over $[a, b]$, prove $I(k) = \int_a^b \sin kx \, d\phi(x)$ exists for every real k and that $I(k)/k \to 0$ as $k \to \infty$.

182. If f and ϕ are real and bounded in $[a, b]$ and are never simultaneously discontinuous, and ϕ is monotonic increasing, prove (the analogue of Darboux's theorem) that as $g(N) \to 0$, $L(f; \phi; N)$ tends to the upper bound of all possible $L(f; \phi; N)$.

183.   If $g(x) = 0$ for all x in Cantor's set and $g(x) = 1$ otherwise, prove that $g(x)$ is integrable-R over $[0, 1]$ but is not integrable df where f is the monotonic function defined in Exercise 39.

184.   To every real function $f(x)$ summable over $[a, b]$ is assigned a real number $\Omega(f)$ so that (i) $\Omega(\lambda f + \mu g) = \lambda\Omega(f) + \mu\Omega(g)$ for all constants λ and μ, and (ii) $\Omega(f) \to 0$ as $\int_a^b |f|\, dx \to 0$. For every number α in (a, b) we define $X_\alpha(x)$ to be 1 in (a, α) and 0 elsewhere, and write $\Phi(\alpha)$ for $\Omega(X_\alpha)$; prove that there is a function ϕ which is bounded in $[a, b]$ and equal almost everywhere to $\Phi'(x)$. Show that

$$\Omega(f) = \int_a^b f(x)\phi(x)\, dx$$

(i) for every step function f, and (ii) for all f summable over $[a, b]$. Is there more than one function ϕ with this property?

BIBLIOGRAPHY

CARATHÉODORY, C. *Vorlesungen über reelle Funktionen*. Leipzig–Berlin, ed. 2, 1927.

FRAENKEL, A. *Einleitung in die Mengenlehre*. Berlin, ed. 3, 1928.

HARDY, G. H. *A Course of Pure Mathematics*.† Cambridge, ed. 5, 1928.

HOBSON, E. W. *The Theory of Functions of a Real Variable*. Cambridge, ed. 3, 1927. (Dover reprint)

LEBESGUE, H. *Leçons sur l'intégration et la recherche des fonctions primitives*. Paris, ed. 2, 1928.

RUSSELL, B. *Introduction to Mathematical Philosophy*. London, ed. 2, 1930.

SAKS, S. *Théorie de l'intégrale*. Warsaw, 1933.

SIERPIŃSKI, W. *Leçons sur les nombres transfinis*. Paris, 1928.

TITCHMARSH, E. C. *The Theory of Functions*. Oxford, 1932.

VALLÉE-POUSSIN, CH. J. DE LA. *Cours d'analyse infinitésimale*. Louvain–Paris, ed. 3, 1914.

ZYGMUND, A. *Trigonometrical Series*. Warsaw, 1935. (Dover reprint)

ROSENTHAL–FRÉCHET–MONTEL–ZORETTI. 'Neuere Untersuchungen über Funktionen reeller Veränderlichen', *Enzyklopädie der Mathematischen. Wissenschaften*, ii. 3, 1924, Leipzig.

† Referred to in the text as *Hardy*.

INDEX OF DEFINITIONS AND SYMBOLS

∞, ϵ, δ, x, and y as real numbers. 2.

1. $P \in \alpha$, $P \,\overline{\in}\, \alpha$. 3.
2. $(x_1, x_2, ..., x_n)$, (P, x_n), R_n. 3.
3. & and 'implies'. 3.
4. $\mathscr{S}(P; P$ satisfies $C)$. 4.
5. (a, b), $[a, b]$. 5.
6. $A \subset B$, $A \supset B$, $A = B$. 6.
7. AB, $\prod_r A_r$. 6.
8. $A \dotplus B$, $A + B$, $\sum_r^* A_r$, $\sum_r A_r$. 6.
9. $A - B$, $\bar{A}$. 7.
10. $\alpha \sim \beta$. 9.
11. Section of integers. 9.
12. Infinite aggregate. 9.
13. Enumerability. 9.
14. $\{a_n\}$. 10.
15. dist(P, Q). 13.
16. Sphere. 14.
17. S^o. 16.
18. Open set. 16.
19. Limiting point. 17.
20. S', S^c. 18.
21. Closed set. 18.
22. Contiguous intervals. 20.
23. $P = \lim_{n \to \infty} P_n$. 21.
24. Covering aggregate. 26.
25. Point of condensation. 27.
26. $f(P)$. 30.
27. $M(f; S)$, $m(f; S)$, $\omega(f; S)$. 30.
28. $M(f; P)$, $m(f; P)$, $\omega(f; P)$. 30.
29. $f(P)$ continuous. 31.
30. $g(N)$. 32.
31. cI, $|I|$. 32.
32. $L(f; N)$, $U(f; N)$. 32.
33. $\overline{\int} f(x)\, dx$, $\underline{\int} f(x)\, dx$, $(R) \int_a^b f(x)\, dx$. 33.
34. p.p. 36.
35. $\lim_{g(N) \to 0} \phi(N)$. 40.
36. Primitive. 46.

37. Uniform convergence. 52.

37.1. $(CR) \int_a^b f(x)\, dx$. 54.

38. $\Omega_0(f; S)$ S linear. 55.

39. $\bar{c}S, \underline{c}S, cS$, measurable-$J$. 56.

40. m^*S. 67.

41. $|S|$. 69.

42. $S \in \mathscr{L}, mS$. 71.

43. Half-space. 75.

44. m_*S. 81.

45. $F(P), f(S)$ (transformation). 87.

46. Restricted transformation. 87.

47. Inverse transformation. 87.

48. $\Omega_0(f; B), \Omega_1(f; B), \Omega(f; B)$. 92.

49. $\mathscr{C}(h; B)$. 94.

50. Measurable function. 97.

51. $\overline{\lim}_{n\to\infty} f_n(P), \underline{\lim}_{n\to\infty} f_n(P)$. 100.

52. $\int_B f(P)\, dP, f(P) \geqslant 0$. 114.

53. $\int_a^b f(x)\, dx$. 114.

54. $f_+(P), f_-(P)$. 128.

55. $\int_B f(P)\, dP, f(P)$ real. 128.

56. $f(P) \sim g(P)$ in B. 139.

57. Equivalance to summable function. 140.

58. Bounded convergence. 147.

59. $\int_B f(P)\, dP, f(P)$ complex. 157.

60. $D^+f(x), \overline{D}f(x)$. 172.

61. $T_+(f; J), T_-(f; J), T(f; J)$. 185.

62. Absolute continuity. 188.

63. S_α. 214.

64. Point of non-summability. 215.

65. $(H) \int_a^b f(x)\, dx$. 215.

66. $V(F; I\bar{S})$. 218.

67. $(D) \int_a^b f(x)\, dx$. 218.

68. $s_n(f; x), \mathfrak{S}(f; x)$. 229.

69. $D_n(x)$. 233.

70. $\psi_x(f; t)$. 235.

71. $(C, 1)$. 240.

72. $\sigma_N(f; \phi), \sigma_N*(f; \phi), \int_a^b f\,d\phi$.

GENERAL INDEX

The numbers refer to pages.

Absolute continuity, 188.

absolute continuity and bounded variation, 189.

absolute continuity of integral, 154, 189.

absolute continuity of $F\{\phi(x)\}$, 193.

accumulation, 17.

aggregate, 3, 8, 28.

almost all, 36.

almost everywhere, 36.

Baire, 25.

Banach, vi, 86.

base, 94.

belongs, 3.

Bendixson, 28.

Bessel's inequality, 246.

Borel, 26.

bottom of cylinder, 94.

bounded convergence, 147.

bounded set, 15.

bounded variation, 185, 187.

bounded variation and monotone functions, 185, 187.

Cantor, 24, 28, 84.

Carathéodory, v.

Cauchy-Riemann integral, 54, 116, 135.

Cauchy-Lebesgue integral, 213.

cell, 32.

centre of interval, 5.

centre of sphere, 14.

closed envelope, 18, 19, 20.

closed interval, 5.

closed set, 18.

Cohen, L. W., 109.

complement, 8.

complex function, 156.

condensation, 27.

contained, 6.

content, 32, 57.

contiguous, 20.

continuous, 31.

continuous function measurable, 105.

contour integral, 263.

convergence tests for Fourier series, 236, 237, 238.

convergent sequence, 21.

coordinates, 3.

corresponding point function, 30.

cover, 26.

covering theorems, 26, 85.

cube, 5.

cylinder, 94.

Darboux, 40.

Darboux-Stieltjes integral, 250.

Denjoy integral, 218.

Denjoy and Lebesgue integrals, 220, 223.

dense in itself, 18.

derivate, 172.

derivative of monotone function, 176, 201.

derivative of function of bounded variation, 188.

derived set, 18.

difference of sets, 7.

differentiation of integral, 45, 46, 173.

differentiation under integral sign, 170.

differentiation of series of monotone functions, 176.

dimension, 3.

Dini, 237.

Dirichlet's kernel, 233.

discontinuities of monotone function, 163.

discontinuities of function integrable-R, 37.

distance, 14.

double integral, 203.

Element of set, 3.

empty set, 4.

end-points, 5.

enumerable, 9.

envelope, 18.

equal aggregates, 6.

equivalent aggregates, 9.

equivalent functions, 139.

equivalent to a summable function, 140.

Estermann, vi, 101, 158.

exterior Jordan content, 56.

exterior Lebesgue measure, 67.

exterior measure of union, 69, 78.

Fatou, 124.

Fejér, 240.

finite aggregate, 9.

Fourier coefficients, 229.

Fourier series, 229.

Fraenkel, 3, 28.

Fubini, 176, 203.
function of P, 30.

Gamma function, 117, 159, 211.
gauge, 32.
Gauss, 159.
general principle of convergence, 29, 249.
greatest set of ordinates, 92.

Half-space, 75.
Heine, 26.
Hölder-Lebesgue integral, 215.
Hölder-Lebesgue and Denjoy integrals, 220.

Implies, 4.
indefinite D-integral, 219.
infinite aggregate, 9.
infinity as real number, 1.
integrable-CR, 54.
integrable-D, 219.
integrable-H, 215.
integrable-R, 33, 36.
integral absolutely continuous, 153, 189.
integral continuous, 162.
integration by parts, 162, 208, 255, 263.
integration by substitution, 192.
integration of derivatives, 46, 174, 178, 180, 183, 224, 226.
integration of Fourier series, 241.
integration of series, 53, 123, 144, 146, 149, 241.
integration of limit functions, 50, 65, 66, 120, 124, 125, 126, 136, 137, 138, 167.
interior, 16.
interior Jordan content, 56.
interior Lebesgue measure, 81.
intersection of closed sets, 20, 24.
intersection of sets, 6.
interval, 5.
inverse transformation, 88.

Jordan, 56, 238.
Jordan content, 56, 62, 67, 113.

Least set of ordinates, 92.
Lebesgue and Cauchy-Riemann integrals, 116, 135.
Lebesgue and Denjoy integrals, 220, 223.
Lebesgue and Jordan measures, 68, 69, 82.
Lebesgue and Riemann integrals, 115, 130, 262.
Lebesgue and Stieltjes integrals, 262.
Lebesgue exterior measure, 71.

Lebesgue integral, 114, 128, 140, 157.
Lebesgue interior measure, 81.
Lebesgue measure, 71.
limit of sequence, 21.
limiting point, 17.
Lindelöf, 26.
linear functional, 265.
linear set, 4.
linear transformation, 87.
lower limit, 100.
lower sum, 33.
lower Riemann integral, 33.
Lusin, 111.

Maximum, 30.
measurability of limit functions, 102.
measurability of open set, 77.
measurability of union and product, 74, 75.
measurable and continuous functions, 109.
measurable and open sets, 80.
measurable function, 97.
measurable function as limit of bounded functions, 108.
measurable-J, 57.
measurable set, 71.
measure, 71.
measure additive, 73.
minimum, 30.
monotone function measurable, 106.
mutually exclusive, 6.

Negative variation, 185.
net, 32.
non-enumerable sets, 27, 28.
non-measurable set, 89.
non-summability, 215.
null, 36.

Open, 16.
ordinate sets, 92, 114, 128.
origin, 3.
oscillation, 30, 31, 249.

Parseval, 245.
perfect set, 18, 25, 84.
plane set, 4.
point function, 30.
point of non-summability, 215.
point of R_n, 3.
positive variation, 185.
primitive, 46.

Rational interval, 5, 13.
rational point, 3, 13.
real numbers, 1.

regular points, 214.
repeated and double integrals, 205, 208.
restricted linear transformation, 87.
Riemann and Lebesgue integrals, 115, 130.
Riemann integral, 33.
Riemann integral and Jordan content, 55, 62.
Riemann-Lebesgue theorem, 299.
Riemann-Stieltjes integral, 248.
Riesz, F., 199, 265.
Riesz-Fischer, 244.
Romanovski, v, 217, 218.

Saks, v.
Schwarz, 152.
second mean-value theorem, 165, 262.
section, 9.
selection axiom, 28, 90.
sequence, 10.
set, 4.
Sierpiński, 28.
singular points, 214.
space R_n, 3.
special half-space, 75.
sphere, 14.
Stieltjes sum, 249.

sub-aggregate, 6.
sub-sequence, 10.
subset, 6.
substitution formula for integrals, 161, 192.
sum of sets, 6.
summability $(C, 1)$, 240.
summability of derivatives, 174.
summability of modulus, 129, 157.
summability of product, 147, 149, 152.
summable function, 114, 119, 129, 131.

Top of cylinder, 94.
total variation, 185.
transformation, 87.
triangle theorem in R_n, 14.
trigonometric series, 228.

Uniform convergence, 52.
union of sets, 6.
upper limit, 100.
upper Riemann integral, 33.
upper sum, 33.

Vitali, 85.

Weierstrass, 24.

Zygmund, vi, 181, 232.

INDEX TO THE EXERCISES

The numbers refer to exercise numbers.

Apollonius' theorem, **20.**

Basis, **14.**
Bernstein polynomial, **45.**
Bessel's inequality, **145.**

Cantor-Bernstein theorem, **19.**
Cantor's set, **39.**
Cantor's theorem, **18.**
Connected open set, **29.**
Continuous function extension, **47.**

Density theorem, **85.**
Distances in a set, **97, 105.**

Egoroff's theorem, **94.**

Fubini's theorem, **154.**

Hölder's inequality, **117.**

Mean-square convergence, **121, 146.**

Non-differentiable continuous function, **135.**
Non-measurable set, **80, 88, 89, 90, 105.**
Normal expansion, **9.**

Orthogonal functions, **145.**

Riemann-Lebesgue theorem, **62, 133.**

Scalar product in R_n, **22.**
Scalar product of functions, **144.**
Steinhaus theorem, **97, 100.**